On Cue 1

Canadian Cataloguing in Publication Data
Main entry under title:

On cue 1

ISBN   0-7747-1368-2

1. Canadian drama (English) – 20th century.*
2. American drama – 20th century.   3. Canadian drama (English) –
20th century – Problems, exercises, etc.*   4. American drama –
20th century – Problems, exercises, etc.   I. Eaton, Diane F.

PS8307.06 1990   C812'.5408   C90-093257-0
PR9196.3.06 1990

Illustration: Andrea Lawson and Kathryn Adams
Cover Illustration: Frank Viva

Printed in Canada

  2   3   4   5   JDC   94   93   92

On Cue 1

Diane F. Eaton

HBJ HARCOURT BRACE JOVANOVICH, CANADA
TORONTO • ORLANDO • SAN DIEGO • LONDON • SYDNEY

Acknowledgments

The author and publisher gratefully acknowledge the consultants listed for their contribution to the development of this project:

Bil Chinn
Consultant, Personnel Staffing Services
Edmonton Public Schools
Edmonton, Alberta

Kevin Fatkin
English Department Head
D. W. Poppy Secondary School
Langley District School Board
Langley, British Columbia

Graham Foster
Language Arts Supervisor
Calgary Separate School Board
Calgary, Alberta

Bruce Reevely
Assistant Department Head
Humberside Collegiate
Toronto Board of Education
Toronto, Ontario

G. John Terpstra
English Department Head
City Adult Learning Centre
Toronto Board of Education
Toronto, Ontario

Table of Contents

To the Reader

"Perhaps theatre is a very simple activity in which a group
of people get together to focus on what is best about
themselves."
John Gray

rama comes from life. It is about people, what they
say and do, and how they change.

A young man scrawls "I LOVE YOU, BEAUTIFUL
ELANA" in enormous letters across the back of a
warehouse. His message to Elana could give us the
starting point for writing a play. Without knowing
anything, we can guess that he feels as if his life has
taken a new turn since he fell in love. What might
happen between him and Elana? Does he really love
her? How does she feel about him? Could they "live
happily ever after"? Of course we can't know what will happen
to them or how they'll change as a result. We can only know
that they *will* change.

We all have to live with change, in our own lives and in the
world around us. We cope by looking for meaning. We want to
know who we are and where we are going. We also want to
know what other people are really like inside, what motivates
them, and how they are changing. We want to know why things
happen.

A playwright is another person searching for answers, who uses
writing as a process for discovering patterns of meaning in human
experience. When the words of the play are written, the playwright's work is done, but the play is just beginning. The words
aren't meant just to be read and understood. They are meant to
become voices, expressions, movements—patterns of light and
sound and human activity. A play is an experiment waiting to
happen, waiting for a team of creators to take the playwright's
words off the page and give them life.

This book contains twelve plays selected from three different
media—radio, television, and the stage. They take place in

different parts of Canada as well as other parts of the world. Some recreate the past, many dramatize the present, and one envisions the future. The situations, attitudes, and ideas brought to life in these plays are as different as the playwrights who wrote them, yet they all provide reflections of the world you live in.

The activities before and after each play will help you explore the world of that dramatization, and find its meanings. Sometimes you will be thinking and writing on your own, developing your responses to a play in a personal journal. The entries you make in this book should be considered as private reflections unless you choose to share them with classmates. At other times you may be working with a partner or a group, sharing your ideas, broadening your insights through critical discussions, and engaging in creative activities such as roleplaying to extend and deepen your initial experience of the drama. You will come to see how drama works, as well as how dramas in different media are alike in some ways and different in others.

As you read the plays and respond to the activities, you will identify with some of the characters in the plays. Hopefully you will come to see yourself more clearly, to understand other people a little better, and to develop a richer sense of the world that lies around you.

▼ ▼ ▼   *INTRODUCTION TO:*

Esso

Linda Svendsen

"I'm trying to write a story told its best and only possible
way . . ."
Linda Svendsen

inda Svendsen was born in 1954 and grew up in and
around Vancouver. She studied creative writing at
the University of British Columbia and then enrolled
at the Columbia School for the Arts. Her short stories
have appeared in numerous magazines and short
story collections, and in 1980 she won first prize in
the *Atlantic Monthly*'s American Short Story Contest.

She now lives in New York City where she writes
film scripts and fiction. Svendsen typically uses something that she or someone else has experienced as a
starting point for making up her own stories. Even though her
writing is only loosely based on real experiences, Svendsen says
that she likes to believe she tells "an emotional kind of truth."

Svendsen adapted this play from one of her short stories. It is
about a fourteen-year-old girl who finds comfort working at her
uncle's gas station. *Esso* is part of Atlantis Television Interna-
tional's award-winning series of family dramas.

GETTING STARTED

1. Is there a special person or place you go to when you need to
work out your feelings about something? In a brief paragraph,
describe the person or place and how you feel when you are
there. You might share your paragraph with one or two
classmates.

2. In a group, brainstorm a list of the three most common subjects
on which adults give teenagers advice. Choose one subject,

summarize what adults usually say, and suggest what kinds of advice might be more useful to teenagers. Share your ideas with another group.

3. In a personal journal, make an entry about what thoughts and feelings the phrase "leaving home" brings to mind.

▼ ▼ ▼   *TELEPLAY*

Esso

Linda Svendsen

CHARACTERS

VAL—*a teenage girl who works at her uncle's gas station*
SYD—*Val's uncle, owner of Watson's Esso*
MUM—*Val's mother, who sells cosmetics door to door*
GREG—*a teenage boy who works at Watson's Esso*
GORDY—*a regular customer of Watson's Esso*
NICK—*a mechanic employed by Syd*
A CUSTOMER OF WATSON'S ESSO
LADIES—*friends of Val's family*
MOURNERS, MINISTER

1. EXT. PUMPS. DAY.
(Opening titles and music over ECU and CU details of a gas pump: the floating ball, a tiger beaming, a sign advertising a 60s gas price, the Esso insignia.)
VAL: *(VO)* Will it be a fill?
(The gas cap is whipped off, the nozzle enters the tank, the price gauge climbs and dings. We see bits and pieces of a young dynamo in Esso cap and overalls, a tiger tail hanging from her back pocket.)
(ANOTHER ANGLE
The girl dashes in front of the car and throws open the hood.
ANOTHER ANGLE
The dipstick goes in, comes out, is wiped with a rag.)
VAL: *(VO)* Down a quart!
(ANOTHER ANGLE
The spout crunches into the quart of oil.
ANOTHER ANGLE
The quart pouring into the tank. Cap screwed on. Hood banged shut.

ANOTHER ANGLE

A Lady *in a pink Lincoln touches up her lipstick as* Val *wipes the windshield clear with a squeegee. We see* Val's *face for the first time. She's fourteen — pretty, perky, sensitive. She flashes a quick grin to the* Lady.

ANOTHER ANGLE

Val *bounds back to the pumps, hangs up the hose, and returns to the* Lady.)

VAL: That's five on the nose. *(Takes bills)* Would you like the glasses or a tiger tail?

(The phone rings and Valerie *looks over at the office.)*

LADY: Do you still have those moose glasses? With that moose family?

VAL: Ran out. We have Canada geese now.

SYD: *(VO)* Valerie!

(Val looks back at the office, the phone still rings, Lady *starts car.)*

LADY: With gold rims?

VAL: Yup.

LADY: Just give me the geese.

(Val quickly hands over the box, and bolts toward the office. The car pulls away. Val *remembers something at the last minute.)*

VAL: Happy motoring!

2. INT. OFFICE. DAY. MOMENTS LATER.

(Val runs in and picks up the phone. The office is homey: coffeepot, pop machine, calendar, cash register, and Val's *homework.)*

VAL: Watson's Esso. Satisfying service. *(Beat)* Oh, hi Mum.

  (Val travels with the receiver and pours a half-cup of coffee. She adds sugar, stirs.)

  Uh huh. *(Beat)* Want me to get him?

(Val puts down the receiver and takes the coffee to Syd.)

3. INT. GARAGE. DAY.

(Val walks into the garage, passing Nick *working on a hoisted car, and stops by the jacked-up car in the other bay. Legs in overalls shift on concrete.* Val *squats down by them and puts the coffee within reach of her uncle. A greasy hand reaches out.)*

SYD: *(VO)* Half-inch.

(Val chooses a wrench, lies down on her front, and hands it under. Her legs, from knees down, criss-cross in the air.)

VAL: Guess who's on the phone Uncle Syd?

SYD: Will I win anything?

VAL: Trip to Hawaii.

SYD: It's got to be your grandmother then.
(Syd *slides out on his dolly, sits up, takes a gulp of coffee.*)
Crack of dawn she woke me today. Drove her down to that
Surprise Sale, and I was still in my damn pajamas. Where
does she want to be picked up?

VAL: It's not Gramma. Guess again.
(Syd *gets to his feet. He's a hard worker, 40s, medium build.
He gives* Val *a "not-her-again" look and heads for the phone.
Val* tags his heels.*)
Just tell her you need me until we close. *(Beat)* Tell her Nick
hurt his arm again bowling.

4. INT. OFFICE. DAY.
(Syd *picks up.*)

SYD: (To Mum) Hi, sis. Sorry to keep you waiting.
(*During this chat* Val *watches* Syd *intently, and vice-versa.*)
I know. *(Beat)* Well, she's got her homework right here,
Lorraine.
(Syd *gestures to the textbook;* Val *quickly picks up a book,
flips it open, and points.*)
Working on, uh, the early explorers. *(Beat)* I don't know.

VAL: Champlain.

SYD: Some guy Champlain. *(Beat)* Well, Nick's busted up again.
(Beat) Bowling. *(Beat)* Until eight, O.K.?
(*The bell rings.* Syd *gives* Val *a winner's wink; she grins and
makes the A-OK and runs to serve the customer.*)

5. INT. VAL'S KITCHEN. NIGHT. LATER THAT SAME DAY.
(Val *tackles her dessert: Jello. She's dressed in overalls, big shirt,
and cap. Avon cosmetics clutter the table and she and* Mum *are
in the middle of a discussion.*)

MUM: Not my good Hoover, Valerie!
(Val *looks up at her mother.*)
You're not taking my good vacuum to that house of grime.

VAL: It's only Saturdays. I can't wash cars without doing
interiors.

MUM: That's not the point. Who knows what it could pick up in
perfect strangers' cars.

VAL: So you want me to whisk broom people's cars?

MUM: I don't want you do anything in anybody's car.

VAL: Dream on, Mum.

(Mum *collects herself. She sits down by her daughter and they share a fond gaze.*)

MUM: Do you think you could try and make me understand why you spend so much time at the Esso?

(Val *thinks about this.*)

VAL: Something's always going on.

MUM: Like?

VAL: Guys drop in and tell Uncle Syd about car accidents. People who are lost come in and ask directions.

MUM: And that's fun?

VAL: Yup. (*Beat*) And Uncle Syd's teaching me alignment and balance.

(Mum *considers this.*)

MUM: Summer's over, Val. I could see helping Uncle Syd during the holidays, but now you're in high school. You'll be wanting to get into the swing of things, maybe try out for the band . . .

(Val *idly picks up a lipstick and plays with it. This is a hard topic for her and she avoids* Mum's *probing gaze.*)

VAL: There's too many people in band. I won't know anybody.

MUM: That's a nice color. Brings out the red in your hair.

VAL: I don't have any red in my hair. Do I?

MUM: Of course you do. You'd see it if you ever took off your cap.

(Mum *picks up another lipstick and reaches for* Val's *wrist.*)
Try this one. Come on . . . live dangerously.

(Val *smiles, holds out her arm, and* Mum *puts lipstick on her wrist.*)
This is one of my new fall colors. What do you think?

VAL: Too pink.

(Val *and* Mum *hold a gaze for a beat.*)

MUM: I know it's tough starting out high school. Once you get to know people, it won't be so bad.

VAL: Easy for you to say.

MUM: You think it was easy my first day selling Avon? Ringing perfect strangers' doorbells?

VAL: No, but you're different . . .

MUM: That Esso's become your whole world, Val. (*Beat*) You don't want to be like Uncle Syd hiding under the hood of a car all your life. Do you?

(Val *withdraws her arm.*)

VAL: What do you mean hiding?

(Mum *stands and starts putting products back in the case.*)

MUM: Well, it's just the longer anyone hides from things, the harder it gets.

6. EXT. ESSO. DAY. A FEW DAYS LATER.

(Val *bikes by the pumps en route from school.* Greg, *a nice-looking boy, sixteen, serves a* Customer.)

GREG: (*To* Customer) Would you like the glasses or the tiger tail?

(Val *stares so hard she almost coasts into a tire tree.*)

7. INT. OFFICE. DAY.

(Syd *and his regular customer,* Gordy, *are talking. We see* Val *kick her bike stand into place by the window.*

Val *bursts in.* Gordy *waves hi.* Val's *got ants-in-her-pants about the new boy.*)

VAL: Who's that working the pumps, Uncle Syd?

(Val *grabs her overalls off the hook, goes into the back room, and changes.*)

Uncle Syd?

(Greg *runs in with bills.* Val *comes out and represses her questions; she watches him while she finishes buttoning and puts on her cap.* Syd *oversees* Greg *at the cash register.* Greg *makes change.*

Greg *dashes out.* Val *tries to watch him inconspicuously out the window.*)

GORDY: I should be moseying along.

SYD: Key's in the ignition.

(Val *turns to* Syd *as* Gordy *salutes and ambles into the garage.* Nick *works on a car in the BG.*)

VAL: Who's that guy? Did you hire him?

(Syd *nods. We hear* Gordy's *car start up.*)

Why?

SYD: Well, you know I've always talked about taking Gramma to Hawaii. (*Beat*) I figured if I went I'll be needing extra help —

(Outside, Mum *pulls up and hurriedly gets out of the car.*)

VAL: Was this Mum's idea?

SYD: Speak of the devil —

(Mum *rushes through the office door.*)

MUM: Syd, Mother collapsed in town. They've taken her to St. Mary's.

(*This stuns* Syd *for a second, then he hurries out.* Mum *turns to* Val.)

Do you want to come?

VAL: I'll stay here.

MUM: (*Hugs* Val) I'll call.

SYD: (*Yells to* Greg) Greg! I'll be back later.

(Mum's *car pulls out.* Greg *and* Val *look at each other awkwardly.* Val *looks away.* Greg *looks away, then turns back.*)

GREG: My name's Greg, by the way.

VAL: I heard.

GREG: Big ears, eh?

8. INT. VAL'S KITCHEN. DAY. TWO DAYS LATER.

(Mum's *on the phone finishing up an Avon order.*)

MUM: So one Field Flowers bubble and one Charisma. (*Beat*) Well, Mum's a fighter . . .

(Val *walks by and whisks away a spray cologne.* Mum *notes this.*)

But she's no spring chicken.

9. INT. VAL'S BEDROOM. DAY. MOMENTS LATER.

(*A girlish room with stuffed-animal snake, teddy, MAD magazines, a George Harrison shrine, Esso paraphernalia.* Val, *prepping for the Esso, sprays cologne behind her ears. A knock at the door.*)

MUM: (*VO*) Maid service.

(Mum *enters with a small basket of folded laundry. She smells the cologne.*)

That also comes in hand lotion. I'll give you a good discount.

VAL: Oh. Thanks.

(Val *puts the cologne on her dresser and starts putting away laundry.* Mum *picks it up and spritzes herself.*)

MUM: How's the new boy working out?

VAL: Drinks a ton of Orange Crush.

(Mum *sits on the bed and puts her feet up. She picks up the snake.*)

MUM: Are you coming with me to see Gramma?

VAL: I sent her a card.

MUM: A card's not you. She'd like to see you in person.

VAL: It's going to be busy today.

MUM: This is your grandmother. It would be nice of you to pay your respects.

VAL: She doesn't care if she sees me, Mum.

MUM: Not true.

VAL: Yes it is. All she ever says is I could look like a Lennon Sister if I fixed my hair.

(Mum *tugs* Val *down beside her on the bed.*)

MUM: Valerie, Lord knows your Gramma's not perfect, but she loves you. And she's very, very sick.

VAL: That's not what Uncle Syd says.

MUM: What does he say?

VAL: He says she'll be back home with him any day now. She's flirting with the doctors.

MUM: That's Syd for you. He's always had a hard time facing up to things, Val. *(Beat)* I think you should go see her.

(This gets through.)

VAL: I'll go next week after school.

MUM: Thanks.

(Mum *gets up. She lifts* Val's *cap, pecks her head, and puts it back.)*

10. EXT. PUMPS. LATER THAT SAME DAY.

(A car circles the pumps. Val *grins behind the wheel,* Syd *coaches her.)*

11. INT. CAR. DAY.

*(Syd *adjusts* Val's *grip on the wheel. A FOR SALE sign rests on the dash. The car idles.)*

SYD: Good. Now pretend I'm holding a cup of hot coffee. Got it?

VAL: A cup of hot coffee.

SYD: When you brake . . . you have to brake so that not one drop lands in my lap.

VAL: Not one drop in your lap.

SYD: O.K.

(Val *puts her foot on the gas and the car moves forward.)*
Look out for that deer!

(Val *brakes abruptly. She and* Syd *look at each other.)*

VAL: No cigar, eh?

SYD: Other than my cleaning bill and a deer with a cane, not bad. But you're doing better than the wife when she learned in this old car.

(Val *hits the gas again.* Nick *rolls a tire into the garage in the BG.)*

So are you ready to drive me to the hospital?

VAL: I would if I could.

SYD: You haven't been up to see her yet, have you?

VAL: Next week. Word of honour.

SYD: Next week? She'll be out practicing her hula by then.

(Val *glances at him. This is miles from what* Mum *has implied.*)

12. GARAGE. NIGHT. LATER THAT SAME DAY.

(Val *lounges in the* FOR SALE *car's back seat. She holds an Orange Crush; "Monster Mash" plays on the radio.*)

GREG: *(VO)* Checking the brake lines.

(*A noise, and then* Val *goes up the hoist. She looks out the window for* Greg, *who disappears under the car.*)

They look O.K., but you never know until you see the drums.

VAL: This used to be my Aunt Lucy's car. Uncle Syd's wife.

GREG: *(VO)* Syd's married?

VAL: He was, but she left. She and Gramma didn't exactly get along. *(Beat)* Know what was sad? Uncle Syd ran over Aunt Lucy's poodle in this car. He was going out for cigarettes after dinner and it was sleeping right behind the tire.

(Greg *bangs and* Val *talks more to herself, involved in the memory.*)

Aunt Lucy was crying, and Gramma kept saying it was a blessing in disguise because the dog didn't have to suffer the miseries of old age. Then Aunt Lucy said she hoped Gramma wouldn't suffer the miseries of old age either, and Uncle Syd just yelled, "Shut up or else." *(Beat)* Nobody could figure out who he was yelling at.

(Greg *walks out from under the car. He hasn't been spellbound.*)

GREG: Is that right? Brakes look O.K . . . *(Beat)* Boy, when I get a car . . .

VAL: When you get a car what?

GREG: Vamoose. To the States.

VAL: Where? The Falls?

(Greg *checks the tires.*)

GREG: Are you kidding? Niagara Falls is nowhere, Val. *(Beat)* Detroit.

VAL: Oh yeah?

GREG: It's *the* place. You can take the Chrysler tour, and the Ford tour, and the GM. They give you Coke and a hardhat. It's something.

(Greg *hits the controls and the car comes down.* Val *watches him.*)

It's Motown. Means Motortown, you know.

(Greg *opens the door, takes his Crush and chugs, hands it back to* Val, *walks to the hood and throws it open.* Val *looks at the bottle and quickly sips. She follows* Greg's *path and sits on a stack of tires near him. He tinkers.*)

VAL: You miss school?

GREG: Nope. Couldn't hack it.

VAL: My mother wants me to play xylophone in the band. She thinks it will build my personality.

GREG: What's wrong with it? Your personality?

VAL: She thinks I don't have one.

GREG: You're just different. For a girl.

VAL: What do you mean different?

GREG: You're sort of like an import.

VAL: An import?

GREG: Yeah. Something you don't see on the road every day. (*Beat*) Like a Fiat.

(Val *doesn't quite know what to make of this.*)

13. INT. GARAGE. DAY. NEXT DAY.

(Syd *whistles and works on a car.* Val, *at his beck and call, catches a glimpse of herself in a mirror. She looks different to herself. She is different—a boy likes her back—and her awareness of this has made her dress sharper, fuss with her hair.*)

VAL: Like a Fiat.

SYD: What?

VAL: Ever own a Fiat?

SYD: Could you see me driving Gramma around town in a fancy sportscar?

VAL: Pretty keen car, eh?

SYD: Sure. I'd venture to say quite keen.

(Val *realizes she's in seventh heaven. We hear a honk outside the garage.*)

GREG: *(VO)* Val! Come here!

(Val *jumps.*)

VAL: I think I hear Greg.

14. EXT. ESSO. DAY.

(Greg *is at the wheel of the FOR SALE car. He watches* Val *skip to the passenger door, then holds the keys up—a tiger tail*

attached to the ring.)
GREG: Hop in.
VAL: It's yours?
GREG: Put a down payment on it.
(Val, suddenly nervous and shy, gets in. It's hard to know who's more hyper: her or Greg. Throughout Greg's speech, Val fidgets with the visor, glove compartment, cigarette lighter. Greg keeps glancing at Val, then looking away.)
Syd gave me a great deal. It's got whitewalls. The mileage is incredibly low. And Syd says he cracked ninety once on the 401. *(Beat)* Might get new seat covers. I've got this buddy at Simpson's who gets things marked down. *(Beat)* That takes a sec to get hot.
(Greg turns on the radio, then grips the wheel tight.)
It's more than a good deal, it's a steal. God, Val, this is great.
(He turns to Val. They lean towards each other and shyly kiss. They gaze into each other's eyes for the first, long time, and it's frightening, adult.)
You want to learn? *(Beat)* I'll teach you to drive.
VAL: *(Beat)* You drive.

15. INT. OFFICE. NEXT DAY.
(Val, beyond seventh heaven, drifts in and deposits coins for a Crush. She's wearing a fresh blouse, pink pants, a locket. We see Greg through the window polishing his new car. Syd, at the desk, works on his budget.)
VAL: Hi.
(Val takes her pop and sits on the desk by him.)
Do you see any red in my hair, Uncle Syd?
SYD: Will I win anything?
(The phone rings. Val goes to answer, but Syd picks up.)
Watson's Esso, Syd here.
(Val takes her pop and watches Greg out the window. She stands on one foot, then the other. The fan blows her hair wildly. Syd's voice is low.)
When? *(Beat)* I'll be right there. *(Hangs up)* That was your mother. Gramma's left us.
(Val turns around; she doesn't understand what she's heard.)
Her heart just stopped.
(Val looks at Syd for two beats. Then she goes and hugs him. He leans against her, then manages to pull himself together.)

I'm going over now.
(Val nods.)

16. EXT. ESSO. DAY.
(Val follows Syd to his car. He gets in, she closes the door, he starts and pulls out.)

17. INT. VAL'S LIVING ROOM. LATE AFTERNOON. TWO DAYS LATER.
(Mourners are seated, standing, murmuring, snacking. Val weaves through the Mourners carrying a big plate of baked goods. She sees Mum saying good-bye to a Mourner in a coat.)
MUM: Thanks for coming. It's too bad we only seem to see each other at times like this.
(Val sees the Minister trying to engage Syd in conversation at the other end of the living room.)
ELDERLY LADY: It was a good turn-out, wasn't it?
VAL: Yes it was.
ELDERLY LADY: You're Lillian's granddaughter, aren't you?
VAL: Yes.
ELDERLY LADY: I remember when you were just this high. At your Dad's funeral. (Beat) Do you still want to be an airline stewardess?
VAL: No, you have to learn French.
ELDERLY LADY: What a shame. The sky's a fine place for a girl these days.
(Val smiles politely and moves toward Mum. The Neighbour Lady taps Val.)
NEIGHBOUR LADY: Valerie, I'm sorry about your Gramma. She was so proud of how you helped Syd out at the Esso.
(The Neighbour Lady and Val both turn to watch Syd put on a record at the stereo. Sad Hawaiian music plays. There's an uneasy moment as Syd sits back down. Mum comes up, takes Val's plate, and gives her a crystal glass. The Neighbour Lady watches Syd and shakes her head.)
MUM: Take this over to him.
(They exchange worried looks.)
Go on.
(Val walks over to Syd, hands him the glass, and stands there.)
VAL: Here you go, Uncle Syd.
(Syd takes it, nods thanks, puts it down, and picks up the Polaroid.)
SYD: Did you see this? I took it today. Look at the flowers by

the coffin, Val. The arrangements.

VAL: They're pretty.

(Val *bows her head and* Syd *grips the hem of her tartan skirt.*)

SYD: Used to take my mother for rides, Val. Used to go right by that graveyard in my old Ford.

(Val *can't meet his eyes.* Mum *comes over, takes* Syd's *hand from* Val's *skirt, and holds it.*)

MUM: It was a beautiful eulogy, wasn't it Syd? You know, when he said paradise, I couldn't help thinking she might get there after all. Some sort of paradise where Mother could reach up and pick an orchid off a tree. That's what heaven would be for her.

SYD: I always wanted to take her to Hawaii. And now it's too late.

(Syd *hides his face.* Mum, *tears in her eyes, looks at* Val. Val *can't be around this sadness one second longer. She slips out.*)

18. INT. GARAGE. NIGHT. TEN MINUTES LATER.

(Greg *adjusts the idle on a car and races the engine.* Val *watches him from the back—in his T-shirt, arms busy—with all the fondness in the world. She talks when she can trust her voice.*)

VAL: Hi.

GREG: Hi. There's some jujubes on the dash.

(Val *walks over and lets herself rest against him. He holds his arms away from her.*)

I can't touch you. I'm filthy.

VAL: I don't care.

GREG: How was today?

VAL: It went all right.

(Val *looks around the garage. It reminds her of* Syd.)

Let's go for a ride.

GREG: A ride?

(Val *nods.*)

Where?

VAL: I don't know. Someplace.

GREG: We could grab a bite after I close. I'm starved.

VAL: Let's close now.

GREG: Are you nuts? There's two hours to go. Syd would kill us if we closed early.

(Greg *heads for the office.*)

Want a Crush?

(Val *waits a beat, then follows.*)

19. INT. OFFICE. NIGHT.

(Greg *downs his Crush.* Val *walks into the office determined to make him take her out of here.*)

VAL: Greg?

GREG: What?

VAL: I don't want to be here right now.

(*The bell rings and* Greg, *saved by it, makes for the door.*)
Do this one, then let's go, O.K.?

GREG: Will I win anything?

(*He heads out and* Val *looks after him—*Syd's *phrase ringing in her mind.*)

GREG: (VO *to customers in Edsel*) What can I do for you?

(Val *looks around the office and quickly grabs* Greg's *tiger tail car keys.*)

20. EXT. ESSO. NIGHT.

(A *nip in the air. The Esso sign shines over* Greg's *car as* Val *runs up, fumbles with the key, opens the door, tumbles in. She sees* Greg *hanging up the hose. She adjusts the seat. The bell rings as the customer pulls out.*)

GREG: (VO) Happy motoring!

(Val *locks the door just before* Greg *knocks on it.*)
What do you think you're doing?

VAL: I'm not talking to you.

(Val *locks another door, just before* Greg *tries it.*)

GREG: You're in my car and you're not talking?

(Greg *runs to the other side, and* Val *locks it in the nick of time.*)

VAL: Right.

(Val *locks the passenger door.*)

GREG: You're in my car, you should talk to me.

VAL: It's not your car yet.

(Val *turns the ignition key. The dash lights shine. She pulls dials—headlights, high beams.* Greg *runs through the headlights back to* Val's *side.*)

GREG: You're killing my battery!

(Val *tries to start up and the car makes a terrible sound. So does* Greg.)
You're flooding it, stupid! (*Beat*) Valerie, I can tell you've had a bad day. Just open the door, slide over, and I'll take you wherever you want to go.

VAL: I'll take myself!

(The car finally kicks in and Val *revs it. It roars beneath her touch. She turns on the radio to drown out* Greg.)

GREG: I don't believe this. Val, you can't even drive! Valerie, open the damn door!

(Val leans back in the seat. She positions her hands on the wheel at 10 to 2, grips firmly, and looks ahead. Greg, seeing he's getting nowhere, strides back into the office and stares at her through the office window. She's on her own.)

Fade out.

AFTERWORD

1. Val is sorry that she was too tied up with Greg to visit her grandmother. Write a journal entry about a time when you or someone you know neglected someone else. How do you (or how do you think that person might) feel about that incident now?

2. Val's mum says to Val, "You don't want to become like Uncle Syd, hiding under the hood of a car all your life. Do you?" What do you think she means? With a partner, roleplay a conversation between Val's mum and a close friend in which Val's mum talks about what is happening to Val. Present your roleplay to another group.

3. How do Syd and Val feel about each other? In a group, discuss their relationship, and then choose one scene or perhaps one line that captures the essence of the relationship. Decide what kinds of expressions, gestures, and movements could combine with the text to suggest how the characters feel about each other. Present your ideas to the class, and, together, decide what advice the director should give the actors who play these roles.

4. a) Imagine you are Val, and ten years have gone by since you worked at the Esso station. Write a diary entry in which you look back on those final moments in Greg's car. What do they mean to you now?

    b) In your journal, describe an incident from your past that is still important to you today.

5. Your group is responsible for promoting the television première of *Esso*. First, create a script for a thirty-second television commercial. It should present the viewer with essential information, such as title and viewing time, and it should also capture his or her interest. Your script should specify not only the content of each shot, but also how long it will last and what kind of shot it is. (See the Glossary, page 380, for information about scripting.) You might wish to make a tape of your commercial, or create a poster to accompany your promotional package.

6. Linda Svendsen once wrote, "Young writers—older ones, too—rarely hear from readers. . . . How pleasant and encour-

CAMERA CUES AND CONTENT	VOICEOVER
1. (3 sec.) Medium Shot	
	New this fall on CTN. Thursday night at nine . . .
2. (1 sec.) Medium Shot	
	Code Green
3. (3 sec.) Close-up	
	Carrie Wright . . . a new kind of journalist for a changing world.
4. (3 sec.) Close-up	
	Her beat is the environment.
5. (3 sec.) High Angle Long Shot	
	She's out to uncover the deadliest stories of all.

6. (9 sec.) Medium Shot	
	"Those storage tanks are forty years old and leaking toxic waste into the ground-water. Mr. Ames, your greed is endangering an entire community!"
7. (3 sec.) Medium Shot	
	"Hey, I don't mind being threatened occasionally. It just means I'm on to something big."
8. (2 sec.) Long Shot	
	Code Green, with Jennifer Wilson as Carrie Wright.
9. (3 sec.) Medium Shot	
CODE GREEN THURSDAYS AT 9:00 PM	Thursday night at nine, brace yourself for an hour of adventure on CTN.

aging it would be for these writers to receive a letter from 'out there', to know that they have made contact, to know that their work has been received." If you could talk with the play-wright, what would you say about your responses to the play? In a letter to Linda Svendsen, tell her how you feel about *Esso*.

7. In a group, choose a section of the play to prepare for the class. Present it as a reader's theatre (see Glossary, page 380), as a stage play using minimal props and costumes, or as a videotape (see Glossary, page 382). After your performance, ask your audience for the major strengths of your presentation and sugestions for improving it.

▼ ▼ ▼ *INTRODUCTION TO:*

Words on a Page

Transcript by Keith Leckie
Based on a short story idea by Daniel Moses

"And there was the beaver and the loon and the hawk circling
above the treetops. And below the trout and the sturgeon
slipped silently through the black water. Creatures as powerful
as the great moose, as small as a minnow. She and her father
took their place among them."
from Lenore's short story in Words on a Page

his teleplay is an episode from the "Spirit Bay" television series. Filmed on location on the Rocky Bay
Reserve in northern Ontario, the series dramatizes
the lives of the people of Spirit Bay, a small fictional
Ojibway community on the shore of Lake Nipigon
in the Canadian Shield. The people of Spirit Bay live
close to nature and maintain their traditional values.
Yet because of radio, television, English schools, and
the occasional tourist, the community is also in daily
contact with contemporary values.

Words on a Page is about Lenore Greene, a sixteen-year-old who
dreams of becoming a writer. The story idea came from Daniel
Moses, a native Canadian writer. The script was written by Keith
Leckie, a television writer and director who has a number of
teleplays to his credit. Leckie won several awards for *Words on
a Page*, including a Blue Ribbon in the New York Film Festival.

GETTING STARTED

1. a) Recall a dream that you remember vividly. Why do you
think the dream stayed with you? Share the dream with
some classmates: do any of them see a message in the dream?
Discuss whether or not a dream contains a message. If so,
what is the purpose of the message?

b) What role do you think dreams play in your life?

2. How hard is it for some people to retain the culture of their parents or grandparents if it is different from the predominant culture around them? In a group, think of one or two problems they might face; then explain your group's ideas to the class.

3. Under what conditions do you think a teenager should take a major step, such as changing schools, quitting school, taking a job, or leaving home, even if a parent strongly disapproves? Share your ideas in a group, and then roleplay one such disagreement between a teenager and a parent.

4. In your journal, describe a real or imagined place that represents perfect peace and happiness to you.

▼ ▼ ▼ *TELEPLAY*

Words on a Page

Transcript by Keith Leckie
Based on a story idea by Daniel Moses

CHARACTERS

LENORE GREEN—*an Ojibway teenager*

PETE GREEN—*Lenore's father, a fisherman and trapper*

CONNIE GREEN—*Lenore's mother*

SADIE GREEN—*Lenore's younger sister*

MISS WALKER—*Lenore's grade ten teacher*

THE PRINCIPAL OF LENORE'S HIGH SCHOOL

VARIOUS STUDENTS

DRIVER

MAN

ACT ONE

1. INT. CLASSROOM. DAY.
(It is a sunny fall afternoon in Lenore's *grade ten English class. Sunrays through dust particles in the air. There are a dozen classmates, a mixture of white and native, listening as* Lenore *reads a story she has written.)*

LENORE: . . . So on that morning before she left, they went by canoe one last time to those favourite places. It was at first light, when the water is a mirror and the trees are still, as if nature is holding her breath.

(A variety of young faces listen, all enthralled with her story. Camera moves slowly, panning across the classroom holding on different faces.)

And there was the beaver and the loon and the hawk circling above the treetops. And below the trout and the sturgeon slipped silently through the black water.

(Camera stops on one Girl, *listening intently, then moves again. Camera holds on two* Boys *slouching close together,*

almost touching, but their eyes and attention are on Lenore *at the front of the class.*)

Creatures as powerful as the great moose, as small as a minnow. She and her father took their place among them.

(*Camera cuts to* Miss Walker, *the native teacher. She sits to one side of* Lenore *listening as intently as the rest. She is very impressed. Camera pans and pulls focus to hold finally on* Lenore *as she finishes the story. She has memorized most of it and hardly has to look at the page. She speaks very well with skilled emphasis and a personal passion for her words.*)

And in this world there was a peace and harmony that she knew no matter how far she travelled, she would never find again. She understood now why her father had brought her here. She felt the morning sun on her face and the gentle rocking of the canoe and smiled because she knew that here would always be her home.

(Lenore *stops speaking, holds the few pages against her chest with both arms and looks at* Miss Walker *a little anxiously. There is a hushed silence for a moment.*)

MISS WALKER: (*Quietly*) Lenore, that was beautiful!

(Lenore *gives a shy, tentative smile.*)

What did you think, class?

(*The class gives a collective chatter of positive response, then . . .*)

GIRL #1: It was real sad.

BOY #1: It reminded me of . . . like around Shadow River.

GIRL #2: It was just like a book.

(*There is a silent moment after this pronouncement.* Lenore *looks at the other students trying to suppress her excitement.*

The bell rings signaling the end of class and the students quickly exit the classroom. When the wave of students has passed, Lenore *is left still standing there.* Miss Walker *puts a hand on her shoulder.*)

MISS WALKER: I'm really very impressed, Lenore. Leave your story on my desk. There are some people I'd like to show it to.

(Miss Walker *then exits, leaving* Lenore *alone. She takes a deep breath then allows herself a beaming smile as she hugs her story against herself.*)

2A. EXT. STREAM. AFTERNOON.

(*The prow of a cedar canoe cuts through the calm water.* Lenore *and her father* Pete, *in the stern, are canoeing their way*

up a quiet stream. It is late in the afternoon. The shadows are lengthening, and the sunlight retains the shimmering intensity of this time of day as it filters through the autumn foliage.)

PETE: Good here for beaver. Heavy willow growth. Lots of food.

(Lenore notices a beaver swimming. She points.)

LENORE: Look, Baba.

(Shot of beaver swimming. He suddenly slaps his tail loudly and dives—stock shot.)

He's warning his friends about us.

PETE: *(Seriously)* You know that a long time ago the beaver only had a little skinny tail.

LENORE: Oh yeah?

(Lenore looks back smiling expectantly. She knows this is the opening to one of her father's crazy stories.)

PETE: *(Storytelling tone)* You see, one day Nanabozho was out paddling his big canoe. He's pretty lazy so he decided if he gave the beaver a big paddle tail, he could tie them on the back and they would push his canoe. But once he had given the beaver a paddle tail, the beaver was too quick to catch. So he didn't get a chance to try it.

LENORE: *(Only half serious)* D'you think it would work?

PETE: Cheemo and I tried it once.

LENORE: Really?

PETE: Sure! Roped a couple 70 pound beavers on the back of his canoe.

LENORE: What happened?

PETE: Well, they chewed a hole in the canoe and we all sank and they got away!

(Lenore laughs at this image and turns to look back at her father.)

LENORE: Serves you right.

(Pete laughs too. They continue paddling slowly, quietly.)

2B. EXT. BEAVER POND. DAY.

(They canoe near a bubbling beaver dam with more beaver houses visible.)

PETE: You said you had a dream to tell.

LENORE: Yes. *(She turns around in canoe, facing him.)* It's pretty simple, I guess. I'm standing in the woods. There's a raven flying just above my head. It hovers there. It has something to tell me. *(Pause, thinking)* It wants to land . . . but it can't. It only hovers there. It never lands.

(Pete thinks about the dream very seriously for a moment.)
PETE: Sounds like a good dream. Can't tell you what it means.
Maybe it isn't finished with you yet. *(Lenore smiles. Pause)*
You know Cheemo had the same dream for five nights in a
row. He dreamed he was swimming underwater.
LENORE: Yeah?
PETE: Every night, same thing. Swimming underwater!
LENORE: Yeah?
PETE: On the sixth day, he couldn't stand it anymore. He
jumped in the lake! And no more dream.
(They both laugh again.)
We'll go upstream to the next pond and . . .
LENORE: *(Hesitant)* Baba, I . . .
PETE: What?
LENORE: *(Feeling badly)* I've got all kinds of homework to do.
We've got a lot of tests coming up . . .
PETE: Isn't it enough they have you all day at that school?
LENORE: I'm sorry, Baba.
PETE: *(Gruffly)* Never mind.
*(Pete quickly backpaddles to turn the canoe around and they
head back the way they came. Lenore looks unhappy.)*

3. *EXT. SCHOOLYARD. DAY.*
*(It is lunch break at school. A number of students are sitting
around on the grass and walls eating lunch. Some play volley-
ball nearby. Lenore is sitting on a bench reading some poetry to
a Classmate. Sadie, Lenore's sister, is listening in. Lenore reads
with feeling from the book.)*
LENORE:
"Up on the hill against the sky,
A fir tree rocking its lullaby,
Swings, swings
Its emerald wings,
Swelling the song that my paddle sings."
CLASSMATE #1: That's neat!
LENORE: Yeah. Pauline Johnson. She's a native poet who travelled
all around these lakes almost 100 years ago. Musta been hard
to get gas for her outboard then, eh?
*(They laugh. Miss Walker comes up behind them with a letter
in her hand. She crouches behind them.)*
MISS WALKER: *(Excited, smiling)* Lenore? I've got some news for
you. I sent your story into the District Writing Competitions.

You've been accepted as a finalist!
(She shows Lenore *the letter.* Lenore *and* Sadie *read it together.* Lenore *is both excited and disbelieving.)*
Next week you go down to Thunder Bay to read your story to the judges!
*(*Lenore *and* Sadie *look at each other in amazement.)*
This is wonderful! If you do well there, they could send you to a special high school in the south. Then maybe to study English at university!

LENORE: *(Mixed emotions)* University!

MISS WALKER: Well, let's see how Thunder Bay goes. We just need a letter of permission from your parents and we're all set!
*(*Lenore *looks at the letter again, confused and excited.* Miss Walker *smiles at her, then leans forward and gives her a little hug.)*
I'm proud of you.
*(*Miss Walker *gets up and leaves them. Again* Sadie *and* Lenore *look at each other.)*

SADIE: Nice going!

LENORE: *(Grinning)* Yeah! I can't believe it! *(Frowning)* I just wonder what Baba's going to say.

4. INT. KITCHEN (LENORE'S HOME). EVENING.
*(*Lenore, Sadie, *their mother* Connie, *and* Pete *are having fish dinner.* Pete *eats his food hungrily.* Lenore *looks up at him once, then again. Then she notices* Sadie *staring at her impatiently.* Lenore *glares at* Sadie *and they both resume eating.)*

PETE: *(To all)* Good trout, eh? We caught them way north of Mulligan Bay. Cold and deep.
(He takes another huge mouthful.)

CONNIE: We should have enough in the freezer to last until Christmas.

PETE: The King of France never ate better than this.
(There is a moment of silence. Sadie *can wait no longer.)*

SADIE: Baba, Lenore has something to ask you.
*(*Pete *and* Connie *look up.* Lenore *glares at* Sadie.*)*

PETE: Uh huh?
*(*Lenore *bolsters her courage.)*

LENORE: Well . . . I've been doing some work at school . . .

PETE: Yeah. So?

LENORE: You know . . . like writing.
*(*Pete *takes another large bite of fish, only vaguely interested.)*

Anyway . . . the new teacher, Miss Walker, said I've been doing real well . . . and there was a story I wrote . . .

PETE: A what?

LENORE: (*Hesitating*) Well, a story . . . and they, ah . . .

SADIE: (*Interrupting*) The story won a contest and now she has to go to Thunder Bay to read it and then they'll send her away to university!

(Lenore 'looks daggers' at Sadie. *Both* Pete *and* Connie *look at* Lenore *in surprise.*)

LENORE: Can't you shut up!

PETE: University!

(Lenore *passes* Pete *the letter.*)

LENORE: Well no! It's only if I win, but . . .

(Pete *glances at the letter then pushes it away.*)

PETE: That's crazy! You're only a young girl! You can forget about going to Thunder Bay.

LENORE: But I have to! I'm representing the school!

PETE: They can find someone else.

LENORE: But they want my story!

PETE: Then send the story to Thunder Bay.

LENORE: (*Approaching tears*) But I want to go!!

PETE: "Want" and "Can" are not always the same thing.

(Pete *goes back to his dinner.*)

LENORE: You never..!

(Lenore *is about to continue her argument but her mother is signalling her not to continue along these lines.* Lenore *stands up and quickly exits the kitchen.*)

ACT TWO

5. INT. CLASSROOM. DAY.

(*The classroom is empty except for* Lenore *standing at the front and* Miss Walker *sitting in a desk several rows back.* Lenore *is practising reading her story with a compelling intensity.*)

LENORE: She found her father out behind the shed laying the steaming cedar strips across the frame of a new canoe, his strong hands molding the soft wood. "Baba," she said, "Why can't I visit Aunt Doreen for the summer? I'm not a child anymore. I want to ride a subway, Baba! I want to climb to the top of a skyscraper, and see a museum and go to a play. I want to see the world!" But her father turned away and would not look at her.

(Lenore *stops and thinks about her father for a moment.*)
MISS WALKER: *(Quietly)* Yes. Go on.
(*Suddenly all of* Lenore's *momentum is gone. She appears weary.*)
LENORE: Can we stop now?
MISS WALKER: Sure. Sure, that's fine. It's coming along really well, Lenore. Parents' Night will be a good rehearsal for the finals. *(Pause, looking at* Lenore *who appears distracted)* Is everything alright?
LENORE: Yes. I'm just tired.
MISS WALKER: Good. You get a good sleep. I'll see you tomorrow.
(Lenore *gives her a half-hearted smile and leaves the classroom.* Miss Walker *looks after her, wondering if there is anything wrong.*)

6. INT. KITCHEN (LENORE'S HOUSE). DAY.
(Lenore *comes into the kitchen, tosses down her books and flops down at the table. Her mother is making bannock bread. They are alone. Her mother notices her unhappiness.*)
CONNIE: How was school?
LENORE: Okay. *(Pause)* Actually it was lousy. *(Sudden anger)* I just don't understand! Why won't he let me go?!
(Connie *stops work and sits down across from her.*)
CONNIE: *(After a moment)* He is afraid of what will happen to you.
LENORE: He wants to trap me!
CONNIE: It might seem like that, but he believes he's protecting you.
LENORE: *(Deflated)* What am I going to do, Mum?
CONNIE: He's stubborn. The harder you push, the more he digs in his heels. *(Pause)* D'you remember the story of the Sun and the Wind, how they had a contest to see who could get the coat off a passing man? The Wind blew as hard as he could, but the man held the coat on tightly. When the Sun had his turn, he shone warm and bright and the man just took off his coat.
LENORE: I should be the sun?
(Connie *nods.*)
CONNIE: Maybe you can read your story to him.
LENORE: I have to read it on Parents' Night. But he'll never come.
CONNIE: Maybe this time, if you ask, he will.
(Lenore *looks suddenly hopeful.*)

LENORE: You think so?
CONNIE: *(Smiling)* Maybe.
(Lenore smiles happily.)

7. EXT. WOODS. DAY.
(A small cedar tree crashes to the ground near the banks of a stream. Pete *stands beside the stump, axe in hand. He wipes a sleeve across his sweating forehead, then quickly begins to trim the branches.*

With a smaller axe Lenore *competently trims the branches of another downed cedar in the foreground. In the background we see a sturdy lean-to three-quarters completed, large enough to sleep two or three people with provisions — side walls, open front, firepit.* Lenore *lifts her ten-foot cedar pole, takes it to the structure and fits it in place, resting on the centre beam nailed between two trees.*

Pete *is suddenly beside her and places his pole beside hers which almost completes the superstructure of the roof. He smiles at her.)*
PETE: Now the tarp, a good layer of cedar boughs and one snowfall will make it warm and dry. Ron and I'll live here a week for trapping. *(Looking at her)* What d'you think? You want to come?
LENORE: Where?
PETE: Out on the new trapline in November with Ron and me?
LENORE: *(Excited)* Yeah! *(Then subdued)* But I've got school.
(Pete turns away to adjust the poles on the crosspiece.)
(Hopefully) But maybe I can get off for a couple of days.
PETE: *(Not looking at her)* You think about it.

8. EXT. ROCKY STREAM BED. DAY.
(Lenore kneels down on a flat rock. Holding her hair back she drinks from the surface of the black, bubbling stream. Camera at stream level. She looks up, satisfied, her face wet. She watches her father who puts his face right down in the water and shakes his head, splashing and blowing bubbles. He looks up at her and they both laugh, water dripping off their faces.

Pete *cups some water in his hand and brings it to his lips to drink.* Lenore *watches him a moment.)*
LENORE: Sometimes I wish I could be a son for you, Baba.
(Pete looks up at her curiously at this statement out of the blue.)

PETE: A son?

LENORE: Yes. I know every father wants a son.

(Pete *considers this as he fills a canteen with water.*)

PETE: I would like a son. Maybe someday . . . *(Pause)* but the first time I saw you and you smiled at me, I wouldn't have traded you for ten sons!

(Lenore *smiles at this, watching him fill the canteen.*)

LENORE: Baba?

PETE: Hummm?

LENORE: Parents' Night is on Wednesday.

PETE: *(Distastefully)* Parents' Night?!

LENORE: Yeah. I'm going to read something. Be real nice if you were there.

PETE: I don't have anything to say to those teachers.

LENORE: You don't have to say anything.

PETE: *(Resisting)* And we're fishing the next day. We'll be outfitting the boat.

LENORE: Just for a little while? Maybe? *(Pause)* Please?

PETE: Okay. I'm not promising but I'll try.

(Lenore *smiles, her eyes sparkling.*)

9. EXT. OPEN SKY (DREAM). DAY.

(*In slow motion against a blue sky background a single bird comes into frame. Shot in slightly slow motion. It hovers above the camera. After a moment it is joined by other birds . . . two, three, four, all hovering in frame above the camera. It is not a threatening image. The motion is beautiful to watch. The sound of the wings becomes steadily louder.*)

10A. INT. LENORE'S BEDROOM. NIGHT.

(Lenore, *with a little gasp, suddenly sits up in bed, staring out in front of her. Her tense body relaxes. She thinks for a moment about the images of the dream. She lays down again and rolls over, her face toward camera. She smiles with excitement and anticipation.*)

10B. EXT. SPIRIT BAY DOCKS. LATE DAY.

(A *pick-up truck stops beside the docks.* Pete *is waiting. The* Driver *gets out and opens the tailgate.*)

DRIVER: Got your new nets, Pete.

(Pete *inspects the three bundles of nets as the* Driver *drops them on the ground.*)

PETE: Hey, they don't have floats!
(The Driver *hands him the bill.)*
DRIVER: See? Nothing about floats.
(Pete looks at the bill. The Driver *looks at him, then turns the bill right side up for him to read.* Pete *glances at it and stuffs it into his pocket.)*
PETE: Gonna take me all night to sew floats on these nets.
DRIVER: You want 'em or not?
(Pete nods. The Driver *drops the last net on the ground, gets back in the truck and drives off. As the truck drives away,* Pete *checks his watch, looks unhappy, then carries the first bundle toward the boat.)*

11. INT. SCHOOL AUDITORIUM. EVENING.
(It's Parents' Night in the small auditorium. There are about two dozen parents present, native and white. Tables display artwork of various kinds and highly graded tests and essays. There is a coffee and pastry table where parents stand in small groups talking with four or five teachers.
There is a podium at the front of the auditorium. Lenore *stands near it anxiously watching the doorway, holding the pages of her story.)*
SADIE: Betcha he doesn't come.
LENORE: He'll come.
(Miss Walker approaches them.)
MISS WALKER: Hi Lenore. Are you ready?
LENORE: *(Anxious)* I think so.
MISS WALKER: You'll do great! Are your parents here yet? I was looking forward to meeting them.
LENORE: *(Eyeing the doorway)* They'll be here any minute.
(The Principal *moves behind the podium to address those present. Conversation dwindles.)*
PRINCIPAL: Good evening, and welcome to the first Parents' Night of the year at Nipigon District Junior High School. Glad you could come out. In a moment I'll ask one of our students to come up and read a prize-winning story she's written . . .
(Principal's talk continues over dialogue between Lenore *and* Miss Walker, *below.)*
But first I would like to say a few words about the challenges facing us in the coming year. Never before has there been such an abundance of information and communication in our world . . .

(Lenore whispers anxiously to Miss Walker.*)*

LENORE: Wait! I can't do it yet!

MISS WALKER: Don't worry. I'll stall him if necessary. *(Smiling)* Mr. Crankhurst goes on forever, anyway.

(Lenore tries to smile. She looks at the Principal.*)*

PRINCIPAL: It is almost overwhelming when you consider it. In the face of this, a sound education has never been more important. And so, our goal will remain a high standard of academic achievement and individual excellence in all our endeavours. We are deeply aware of our responsibility here at Beardmore to mould the bright minds of young men and women who will in a few short years forge the destiny of our world!

(Connie comes through the door into the auditorium. She is alone. Lenore *watches her.* Connie *stops, looks around the room and sees* Lenore. *She looks at her and shakes her head sadly.* Pete *is not coming.* Lenore *appears as if she's about to cry.* Sadie *takes this all in.)*

So now let me introduce one of those bright young minds, to read her story that has been selected for the finals of the District Writing Competition . . . Lenore Green.

(There is polite applause. Lenore *turns to* Miss Walker *in anger and frustration.)*

LENORE: I'm not going to do it.

MISS WALKER: *(Sudden alarm)* What!?

LENORE: Why bother!

(The applause dies out. The Principal *and all others are looking expectantly at* Lenore. *With story in hand,* Lenore *turns and exits the auditorium. There are whispered comments in the audience of parents.* Miss Walker *quickly follows* Lenore.*)*

12. INT. HALLWAY (SCHOOL). EVENING.

(The hallway is deserted. Lenore *walks determinedly away from the auditorium.* Miss Walker *comes out the door and calls after her.)*

MISS WALKER: Lenore! Lenore!

(Lenore stops and turns back. Miss Walker *comes up to her.)* What's wrong!? I don't understand.

LENORE: I don't want to read my story. And I don't want to go to Thunder Bay!

MISS WALKER: But Lenore! This is a great opportunity! This is the first big step in your career.

LENORE: What career?!

MISS WALKER: You could do anything—go to university, become a journalist or an English professor or a playwright. You've been given a talent. You can't turn your back on it!

LENORE: It's only a stupid story. I'm sorry I even wrote it.

(Lenore *throws the story down on the floor, turns and walks away. After a beat* Miss Walker *reaches down and picks up the spilled pages. She looks at them, then watches* Lenore *walking away from her.*)

ACT THREE

13A. INT. CLASSROOM. MORNING.

(Miss Walker *is sitting at her desk marking tests in the empty classroom. She works quickly for a moment, but then her momentum slows, her eyes leave her work and brows knitted she begins to think again about Lenore. She can't figure it out.*

Sadie *and* Connie *enter the room behind her.* Connie *is intimidated by a woman of her own generation with a university education. She looks uncomfortably around the room.*)

SADIE: Miss Walker?

MISS WALKER: *(Turns around and stands)* Hi Sadie . . . and Mrs. Green. How are you?

(Connie *nods shyly. It takes a moment to find the words, but she speaks them with determination.*)

CONNIE: There is something you should know. Lenore loves to write more than anything. And she wants to go to Thunder Bay. But my husband . . . *(A little ashamed)* he won't let her.

SADIE: Baba doesn't believe in schools and books and stuff.

MISS WALKER: *(Reflectively)* I see. Please sit.

(Miss Walker *gestures to a chair for* Connie *and another for* Sadie.)

14. EXT. SPIRIT BAY DOCKS. AFTERNOON.

(Pete *is unloading his catch after a good day's fishing. He is on the dock. A* Crewman *hands him a tub full of ice and fish from the deck on the boat. There are several tubs on the dock.*)

PETE: *(Feigning pain)* Uhhh! The only trouble with a good catch is it's bad for my back!

(The Crewman *laughs.*

Pete *lifts the tub of fish and walks a few steps to the other tubs when he notices* Lenore. Lenore *stands — with school books — at the far end of the dock watching* Pete *from a distance. Other students pass by behind her on their way home.* Lenore *and* Pete *look at each other a moment.* Pete *puts the tub down with the others and wiping his hands with a rag takes a step toward her.* Lenore *turns and quickly walks away.* Pete *stops and watches her, feeling badly.)*

13B. INT. CLASSROOM. AFTERNOON.
*(*Connie *and* Sadie *are talking to* Miss Walker. Connie *is more relaxed now. She is reflective.)*

CONNIE: When I was Lenore's age, I was real good at school too. Top of my class. I might have gone on to university, even! But I couldn't decide . . . and then I met Pete . . . *(Pause, then with conviction)* I want this for Lenore!

MISS WALKER: So do I.

CONNIE: We're having a roast Sunday. Why don't you come by? *(*Connie *and* Miss Walker *and* Sadie *share a conspiratorial smile.)*

MISS WALKER: Good! I will.

15. EXT. LENORE'S HOUSE. DAY.
(Establishing shot/time passage. A car and a pickup truck are parked outside.)

16. INT. KITCHEN (LENORE'S HOUSE). DAY.
(The table is nicely laid out with flowers and a bright, plastic tablecloth and a variety of food — fish, slices of moose, potatoes and other vegetables, and bannock bread. Miss Walker *sits at one end of the table,* Pete *at the other.* Sadie *and* Connie *sit on one side,* Lenore *on the other.*

Lenore *is very quiet. She is angry at her father and embarrassed by* Miss Walker *being there. She is uncomfortable to be at the table with both of them.* Miss Walker *takes a platter of meat from* Lenore.*)*

MISS WALKER: Thanks Lenore.

*(*Pete *is eating his food hungrily, eyes on his plate.* Miss Walker *is talking mostly to* Connie, *though she watches* Pete *for any response.)*

. . . and we're getting in a new portable classroom and adding to the library . . .

*(*Pete *without looking up grunts his disfavour over this.)*

And what I'm hoping for by the end of the year is a computer terminal for the students to use . . .

PETE: *(Grunts again)* Pass the moose.

(Miss Walker finds the platter of moose beside her and passes it.

Pete *piles moose meat on his plate.* Miss Walker *looks at him, is about to say something to him, then thinks better of it.)*

MISS WALKER: One thing I'm excited about *(She looks at* Pete) . . . and Mr. Crankhurst seems open to it . . . is an Ojibway Studies course.

(Pete looks up at this.)

PETE: *(With disdain)* Ojibway Studies?

MISS WALKER: Yes. The language and customs and history . . .

PETE: Like one of them dead civilizations in a museum.

MISS WALKER: No! Not at all. In fact, you trap and fish. Maybe you'd come in and give demonstrations of your expertise?

PETE: Expertise! If you get paid by the word, that's a ten dollar one for sure!

(Sadie giggles at this. Miss Walker *is angry. The gloves are off.)*

MISS WALKER: I can see you don't think much of education, but it can give all kinds of things to a girl like Lenore.

PETE: You mean like a one-way ticket out of here.

(Miss Walker takes out the folded pages of Lenore's *story and unfolds them.)*

MISS WALKER: Have you read this?

PETE: No.

(Connie looks worried.)

MISS WALKER: Well I think you should read it!

PETE: *(Suddenly awkward)* I will . . . later.

MISS WALKER: Read it now! Just the first page.

(She stands up, reaches over and puts the manuscript down in front of him. Pete *moves it away.* Miss Walker *stays standing.)*

PETE: No.

MISS WALKER: Well if you don't care enough to even read . . .

(Pete stands up angrily.)

PETE: You saying I don't care about my daughter?!

MISS WALKER: She has talent and imagination and desire! You can't imprison her here!

PETE: Prison!!

MISS WALKER: There's a whole world waiting for her out there!

(Lenore sits there becoming angry and frustrated listening to this.)

PETE: In that world she'll be an outsider! She'll be alone and unhappy and forget who she is!

(Lenore *stands up and looks at* Pete.)

LENORE: You don't know who I am! *(Then at* Miss Walker*)* Neither of you! No one even cares what *I* want!

(Lenore *turns away and exits the house.* Pete *and* Miss Walker *look at each other, now sorry that they have been so insensitive.)*

17. EXT. END OF DOCK (SUNSET LODGE). DAY.

(Lenore *crouches on the end of the dock. She looks down at her reflection in the black water. She holds out a pebble and lets it drop into the reflection. When it clears a moment later, her father's reflection can be seen behind. He stands there a moment.)*

LENORE: *(Residual anger)* Why won't you read my story?

(Pete *crouches down beside her and looks out at the water a moment. He doesn't look at her as he speaks.)*

PETE: Because . . . I can't.

(Lenore *looks at him in surprise.)*

I never learned to read so good. You never knew, eh?

(Lenore *shakes her head, pause, then bitterly)*

When I went to school there was a teacher . . . If I didn't learn my lessons or talked Indian, he'd beat me with a switch and call me names. One day I took the switch away from him and never went back. Never been in a school since.

(Lenore *watches her father, her expression softening.)*

LENORE: Come for a walk?

(Pete *looks up at her for the first time, smiles and nods.)*

18A. EXT. SPIRIT BAY FIELD. DAY.

(A telephoto lens shows Pete *and* Lenore *walking side by side toward camera. The background shows the picturesque village of Spirit Bay on the edge of the lake. They walk in silence for a moment.)*

PETE: I'm afraid. *(Pause)* Afraid that you'll go away and become a stranger to us.

LENORE: How could I do that?!

PETE: If you go south to school. It's very different there.

18B. EXT. SPIRIT BAY ROAD. DAY.

(Pete *and* Lenore *walk toward camera, telephoto lens.)*

LENORE: I'll always be Nishnabe, Baba. And Spirit Bay is my home.

PETE: Others have said that and not come back.

LENORE: I'll come back! I want to learn to write better so I can live here and tell about our people! That's why I want to write!

(Pete *thinks about this hard as they walk along. They fall silent again.*)

19. EXT. DREAMER'S ROCK. AFTERNOON.

(Pete *and* Lenore *sit atop Dreamer's Rock facing the lake that stretches out before them to the horizon. The village can be seen below, and distant islands in the lake.*)

LENORE: I've been waiting to tell you the last of the dreams. The dreams of the bird that wants to land.

PETE: *(Very interested)* Yes! Is it finished?

LENORE: It's finished.

PETE: How did it end?

LENORE: Remember I told you the bird was hovering and trying to land? *(Pete nods)* Well then each night there were more birds—a few and then dozens . . . then hundreds of birds! *(Pause, remembering)* And there was a wide open field of snow! And there they began to land, black against the white snow.

(Pete *is listening intently.*)

PETE: They all landed?

LENORE: Yes! And as each bird landed it became a letter. And the snow was like a page. And the bird-letters formed words. And the words sentences. (Looking at him) They were my words, Baba! They were the words I wrote!

(Lenore *stops, thinking about the images.* Pete *smiles at her, excited by the dream but saddened by its meaning.*)

PETE: Sounds like you are meant to be a writer. I won't stop you.

(Lenore *is not satisfied.*)

LENORE: But I need more, Baba. I don't know if I can do it alone. I need your help.

PETE: *My* help? I can't even read!

LENORE: Not that kind. I need your . . . *(Pause, finding right word)* courage. Will you come to Thunder Bay and hear me read my story?

PETE: *(Unhappily)* At the university?!

(Lenore nods. Pete hesitates, then answers.)
I'll come.
(Lenore takes his hand and smiles at him happily.)

20A. EXT. LAKEHEAD UNIVERSITY. DAY.
(Establishing shot of the university with an identifying sign.)

20B. INT. UNIVERSITY HALLWAY. DAY.
(Pete, Lenore, Sadie, Connie and Miss Walker *approach a* Man *in a suit outside the lecture room doors.* Pete *looks around uncomfortably.)*
MISS WALKER: *(To* Man*)* Is this the District Writing Finals?
MAN #1: *(Officious)* Yes. They're about to begin.
(Lenore is excited and scared. She hesitates at the door.)
LENORE: I . . . I don't think . . .
(Pete puts a hand on her shoulder. She looks up at him.)
PETE: *(Smiling)* Read it to me. Just to me.
(Lenore takes heart in these instructions. She smiles and goes quickly inside followed by the others.)

21. INT. LECTURE HALL. DAY.
(The lecture hall is quite full of people. A panel of six judges sits at a table at the front listening as Lenore *reads her story.)*
LENORE: So on that morning before she left, they went by canoe one last time to those favourite places. It was at first light, when the water is a mirror and the trees are still, as if nature is holding her breath.
(Near the front rows sit Miss Walker, Pete, Connie *and* Sadie *listening.* Lenore *reads directly to her father inspired by his presence.* Pete *listens intently.)*
And there was the beaver and the loon and the hawk circling above the treetops. And below, the trout and the sturgeon slipped silently through the black water.
   Creatures as powerful as the great moose, as small as the minnow. She and her father took their place among them.
(Pete, in his solemn features, reveals amazement at his daughter's ability and the touching sentiments of the story.)
And in this world there was a peace and harmony that she knew no matter how far she travelled, she would never find again.
   She understood now why her father had brought her here. She felt the morning sun on her face and the gentle rocking

of the canoe and smiled because she knew that here would always be her home.

(When Lenore *finishes, the hall is silent.* Pete, *very moved by his daughter's story, rises immediately to his feet. He begins to applaud loudly—the only one in the hall. The* Judges *look at him with disfavour. But then* Sadie *applauds and stands and* Connie *and* Miss Walker *stand applauding and then others and finally the whole hall is on its feet applauding. Even two of the* Judges *give polite applause.* Connie, Miss Walker *and* Sadie *smile at* Pete. Pete *looks only at* Lenore.)

Pete *and* Lenore, *with tears in her eyes, look at each other and smile meaningfully at one another.)*

AFTERWORD

1. a) Describe the relationship between Lenore and her father. Find one or two lines in the play that support your view of their relationship, and share your ideas with a group. How is their relationship like some father-daughter relationships you know? How is it different?

b) What would Pete say to his daughter after hearing her story? Roleplay the conversation they might have on their next canoe trip.

2. Using what you know about Lenore from this play, create a brief character sketch of her. Ask a classmate to read your sketch and comment on how well you captured Lenore's personality.

3. In Scene 16, Pete says he is afraid that if Lenore goes south she'll be alone and unhappy and forget who she is. What other concerns do parents usually have about their children? With a partner, roleplay

• a conversation that two parents might have about their teenagers;

• a conversation between a teenager and a parent or guardian.

4. Illustrate one of the nature scenes described in *Words on a Page*. Choose a line from the teleplay for a caption. On the back of your illustration, write a brief explanation of the mood you want to convey, and tell how the scene contributes to the meaning of the play.

5. A reporter from a local television station wants to interview Lenore after the contest. What would people want to know about Lenore? What questions would the reporter ask? How would Lenore likely respond? With a partner, roleplay the interview for your class, or videotape it.

6. Lenore's dream is to become a writer so that she can record the lives and stories of the Ojibway Indians. How realistic do you think her dream is? What might she do to achieve it? In your journal, write about your dreams for the future and what you will need to do to achieve them.

7. A storyboard is an illustrated plan of a film or television program (see drawing). Each frame of the storyboard shows what one shot will look like: the camera angle, camera distance, and

STORYBOARD FOR WORDS ON A PAGE – SCENE 3	
PICTURE	WORDS
Shot 1: CU (close up)	
	Lenore: Upon the hill against the sky. A fir tree rocking its lullaby . . . Classmate: That's neat
Shot 2: LS (long shot)	
	Miss Walker: Lenore I've got some news for you. Lenore: University!
Shot 3: MCU (medium close-up)	
	Miss Walker: I'm proud of you. Sadie: Nice going.
Shot 4: CU (close up)	
	Lenore: Yeah! I can't believe it! I just wonder what Baba's going to say.

positioning of actors, props, and background. The illustrations are not just a series of cartoon-like sketches; their purpose is to give the director, crew, and cast a general sense of what each shot will look like.

With a group, select one scene from *Words on a Page* that you find interesting, and create a storyboard for it. Begin by reading through the scene and considering where the actors will be positioned and what they will be doing during the scene. Decide how many shots you will use and where each shot will begin and end. (The script tells you about some, but not all, of the shots. You'll have to create the rest.) For each shot, specify what camera angle and camera distance you want. You might watch a few television programs carefully to observe what kinds of camera techniques are used.

You don't have to include dialogue in your storyboard, but each frame should have a caption referring to the appropriate part of the script. When your storyboard is finished, compare it with another group's. How are the storyboards similar? different?

INTRODUCTION TO:

The Tender Branch

David French

avid French first achieved recognition as an important playwright with his very successful play *Leaving Home*. It was a play that he felt he had to write: "I knew the things I wrote best were the things I knew best and felt deeply, the things that *had* to come out of me or I was in trouble," he says. "At the time I still had a lot of unresolved conflicts inside me about my family and I knew I would always be in a turmoil unless I could come to terms with all that."

The whole idea of becoming a writer had come to him unexpectedly when he was fifteen. Up to that time, French had no interest in books. He spent most of his time playing soccer, baseball, and hockey for his school and relaxing with his friends. But all that changed two days before he graduated from grade eight. He was in class wasting time as usual. The teacher told him to stop talking, take a book from the bookcase, sit down and read it. He did, and his world changed. This is French's description of what happened: "The book was *Tom Sawyer* and as soon as I finished it I knew I was hooked: I wanted to be a writer". He wanted to be a writer. After leaving high school, he worked at a variety of jobs and trained to be an actor. After he sold his first playscript, he gave up acting to write full time.

His teleplay *The Tender Branch* was written for CBC Television. French was living in a tiny rented cottage on Prince Edward Island in the summer of 1981 when he came across an ad in the "personals" column of a Charlottetown newspaper. That ad became the inspiration for this play.

G E T T I N G   S T A R T E D

1. *"Retired widower wants a wife between the ages of 50–65. Protestant. Reply by letter. John Whalen, Hammerhead Bay. P.E.I."*

Using this ad as a springboard, imagine a character who could be the main focus of a play. Write a brief character sketch, including a physical description, a short personal history, and a brief list of the character's main personality traits.

2. In a group, think of five ways in which a television drama filmed "on location" is different from a stage drama presented live in a theatre. Share your ideas with another group.

3. You are a writer and have decided to develop a magazine article about some of the frustrations senior citizens experience. You begin your research by listing three or four things that you think healthy seniors might find frustrating in their lives. Show your list to a partner, and explain why you think each item is important.

▼ ▼ ▼   *TELEPLAY*

The Tender Branch

David French

CHARACTERS

JOHN WHALEN—*a vigorous man of seventy, a widower who lives in rural Prince Edward Island with his son*

HARRY WHALEN—*his middle-aged son*

BERNICE WHALEN—*his daughter-in-law, married to Harry*

JENNY WHALEN—*his seven-year-old granddaughter*

PHYLIS ARLINGTON—*an attractive woman of sixty-three, a widow who lives in Summerside, Prince Edward Island*

VIOLA ARLINGTON—*Phylis's middle-aged daughter*

PERCY—*owner of the local general store*

ED
JACK } *customers at Percy's store*

HUGHIE PINE—*John's friend*

IDA MACKENZIE—*a friend of John and his deceased wife*

THE MINISTER OF THE VILLAGE CHURCH

ACT ONE
Fade in on: Scene 1.

1. EXT. HIGHWAY. DAY.
(A long shot of two figures on the bleak winter landscape.)
Cut to: Scene 2.

2. EXT. HIGHWAY. DAY.
(John Whalen and Jenny, his grand-daughter, standing on the side of the highway waiting for the yellow schoolbus that approaches. John is a handsome man of seventy, tall and slim and straight as a ramrod. The child is seven.)
JENNY: I'm cold, grandpa.
JOHN: You are? *(Kneeling)* Here.

(He lifts her scarf around her mouth and nose)
How's that, darling?
(The little girl nods.)
(Touching her head gently) I used to stand on this very spot years ago and put your father on the schoolbus. Did you know that?
(She shakes her head negatively)
Wasn't long ago, either. And it won't be long before you'll be doing the same with yours. That's the way life is.
(Just then the bus brakes to a stop and the door comes open. John gives the child a hug and lifts her into the bus. As the door closes, he waves. The bus pulls away leaving the old man standing on the highway looking after it.)
Cut to: Scene 3.

3. *INT. PORCH. DAY.*
(John sits rocking in his Boston rocker, staring out the window at the softly falling snow.

Harry, *his son, entering the porch from the hallway. Harry is a large man in his mid-forties, with curly hair and thick glasses. The kind of man you expect to see slinging a side of beef over the bloodied shoulder of a white coat. He leans, unnoticed, against the door jamb and sips his breakfast coffee from a large mug. He watches his father ruminatively.*

John *glancing at his watch. Then he stands, steps to the window, pushes his face close to the frosty glass and peers out.)*
HARRY: *(Flatly)* Kind of early for the mail.
(John stiffens, startled at the fact that he is not alone. He backs into the rocker and sits. Then slowly he turns and stares at his son.)
JOHN: *(Crustily)* And what makes you think I'm waiting for the mail?
HARRY: *(A little uneasy under the directness of his father's stare)* No reason. Just thought you were, Dad.
(A slight pause.)
JOHN: *(Rocking gently — to the window)* I suppose some of those that hang around your service station think it's a fine joke.
HARRY: What's that, Dad?
JOHN: *(Taking out his tobacco and papers from his shirt pocket under his cardigan)* You know what. My ad in *The Guardian.*
HARRY: I wouldn't know, Dad. I don't talk about it. It's none of their business.

JOHN: What about you, Harry? What do *you* think? Am I an old fool?

HARRY: *(Putting down his coffee mug)* It's none of my business, either. Well, I'll see you later. I'm late.

(Harry *buttons up his coat and goes out the porch door.* John *shakes the tobacco pack above the cigarette paper but only a few shreds of tobacco fall out. He crumples the pack in anger and throws it to the floor.)*

Cut to: Scene 4.

4. EXT. HIGHWAY. DAY.

(John *walks briskly along the snowy highway, like a man used to walking daily. Suddenly his feet go out from under him and down he goes. Sitting on the highway, he grimaces with pain, and then the indignity of it hits him and he scrambles as quickly as possible to his feet and angrily brushes himself off.)*

Cut to: Scene 5.

5. INT. GENERAL STORE. DAY.

(Three men are in the store. Ed *leans casually against the counter, smoking.* Jack *has a newspaper spread on the counter and is turning the pages. And* Percy, *the owner, has a leg on the windowsill, looking out at the highway.)*

PERCY: *(A beat)* Here comes old John Whalen. That man could walk me to death, and I'm twenty years his junior. *(To* Jack) His ad still in the paper?

JACK: Let's see. Yep. 'Retired widower wants a wife between the age of 50–65. Protestant. Reply by letter. John Whalen, Hammerhead Bay. P.E.I.'

ED: Snow on the roof but fire in the furnace.

(In the middle of chuckling over Ed's little joke, the door opens and in steps John Whalen. The laughter dies away. John closes the door. Percy moves behind counter.)

PERCY: Morning, John. What can I do for you?

JOHN: *(Crossing to counter)* I'll have a pack of tobacco, Perce.

(As Percy *takes the tobacco down from the shelf,* John *glances at* Jack *busy with his newspaper.)*

Mail been by yet, Jack?

JACK: Not yet, John.

PERCY: Here you are. Anything else?

JOHN: No, that's all. *(He pays)* Thanks, Perce. Give my regards to the wife.

(As John *starts for the door—)*
ED: Any of those lonesome widows you don't want, Mr.
   Whalen, be sure to send 'em my way.
*(John hesitates just a moment. There is silence in the store.
Then he opens the door and exits, without turning.)*
Cut to: Scene 6.

6. INT. PORCH. DAY.
*(John sits rocking in his chair, staring out at the highway.
Suddenly he springs from his chair and puts his nose to the
window.*
   *From his POV we see the green pickup stop in front of his
roadside mailbox, the mailman put something in his box and
drive off.* John *is visibly excited.)*
BERNICE: *(Off.)* Well, aren't you going to get the mail?
(Pull back to reveal Bernice, *his daughter-in-law. She is in her
mid-forties. She treats the subject of the ad with amused
tolerance.)*
JOHN: You know one of the things I resent about getting old?
   The way people sneak up on you. And as for the mail—I'll
   get it in my own good time. *(With that he sits)*
BERNICE: Do you want me to get it?
JOHN: *(Indignantly)* No, I do not.
   (He stands up and hitches up his trousers, a habit of his)
   I may be seventy years of age but I'm not incapacitated. Not
   yet anyway.
BERNICE: Suit yourself, Dad.
(As soon as Bernice *exits the porch,* John *breaks into a grin and
reaches for his galoshes and coat.)*
Cut to: Scene 7.

7. EXT. HIGHWAY. DAY.
*(John crosses the highway, opens the front of the corrugated
aluminum mailbox and removes a letter. He is excited. He removes his gloves and slips on his reading glasses. Finally he
manages to rip open the envelope. He should react throughout
the letter to its contents.)*
JOHN: *(Reading aloud)* 'Dear Mr. Whalen, you must be a very
   direct and unorthodox man. At least your methods are. Or
   perhaps you are realistic enough to admit how little time is
   left for people like ourselves.'
Cut to: Scene 8.

8. INT. JOHN'S BEDROOM. DAY.
(John sits on the edge of his bed reading the letter.)
JOHN: 'At any rate I would be pleased to meet you. I would rather not go into detail about myself in this letter, except to say that I am a widow. If you are interested, please contact. I am home most days. Best regards. Mrs. Viola Arlington. 14 Elm Drive, Summerside.'
(He removes his reading glasses and sets the letter down on the bed. A pause. He picks up the brown-tinted silver-framed wedding photo resting on his bedtable. From his POV we see a young John Whalen and bride, circa 1921.)
(Softly) Dorothy.
(He sets the photo back on the table and looks curiously at his hands. Then rising, he crosses to the bureau mirror and peers at himself up close. His hand moves across his face with wonder, with a sort of bewildered sorrow.)
Cut to: Scene 9.

9. EXT. SERVICE STATION AT A CROSSROADS. DAY.
(As John approaches, Harry is just finishing pumping gas. He screws on the gas-tank lid.)
JOHN: It's twelve o'clock. Go on home. Bernice's got a hot meal.
HARRY: You sure you don't mind spelling me, Dad? Hughie can do it.
JOHN: Mind? I like it. Go on. *(Then gesturing to the car)* He paid?
HARRY: *(As he climbs into his truck)* Three dollars. See you at one.
JOHN: Take your time.
(The man at the wheel rolls down the window and sticks out three dollars.)
(Beaming) Thank you, sir. Come again.
(The car pulls away and John starts for the office.)
Cut to: Scene 10.

10. INT. OFFICE OF SERVICE STATION. DAY.
(Hughie Pine leans against the Coke machine, chewing gum. He is the same age as John Whalen.
John *enters, closes the door.)*
JOHN: 'Lo, Hughie. Cold enough for you?
HUGHIE: The winter's are getting longer all the time, John. Longer and colder.
(John goes behind the cash register and rings up the sale.

Then he takes the broom and begins to sweep up, whistling to himself.)
(A beat) Want me to do that, John? I used to be a janitor, you know.
JOHN: No, no, I—*(John stops and considers. Then)* All right. If you want to.
HUGHIE: Thank you, John.
(The broom switches hands, and John *leans against the Coke machine while* Hughie *sweeps happily.)*
JOHN: *(A beat)* I got an answer in the mail today.
(Hughie stops sweeping, leans on his broom.)
HUGHIE: You didn't?
JOHN: I did. A widow from Summerside. Not a crackpot either. Sounds like a nice woman.
HUGHIE: John, I never said a word to you before, but it seems to me that a man like yourself don't need to advertise for a wife. There's plenty women in this village.
JOHN: Maybe, Hughie. Maybe.
HUGHIE: Why, take Ida Mackenzie. Now there's a fine attractive woman. She was a good wife to Gus for thirty-five years.
JOHN: That she was.
HUGHIE: And it's plain to see she's got a special fondness for you, John. Oh, I tell you, John, if it was me . .
JOHN: *(Looking out at the bleak winter landscape)* Hughie, I told myself long ago if I was ever to remarry it would be a complete stranger. I just wouldn't feel right about the women Dorothy knew. That's the way I want it, and that's the way it's going to be. Dorothy would understand. *(Pause—simply)* She was the love of my life, Hughie, and I miss her bad.
Cut to: Scene 11.

11. EXT. HIGHWAY. DAY.
(This is a stretch of highway looping a hill. The little United Church with its white pointed steeple and tiny cemetery sits atop the hill. The camera moves with John Whalen *as he walks, his breath coming heavily. Finally he stops, wipes his forehead. He has a single red rose in his hand.)*
JOHN: *(To himself, irritated)* Must be getting old.
Cut to: Scene 12.

12. EXT. CEMETERY. DAY.
(A long shot of John *moving among the headstones in the snow-covered graveyard.*

John *standing beside his wife's grave. The stone is capped with snow, too. He brushes the snow off the stone and then kneels, staring at the headstone.)*

JOHN: *(Softly)* I brought you a rose, Dorothy. *(Then intimately)* You know, it's strange. I always feel less lonely up here.

(He places the single red rose on the snowy grave, and the camera begins to pull back slowly, slowly until—)

Cut to: Scene 13.

13. INT. DINING ROOM OF JOHN'S HOUSE. NIGHT.

(The family are all seated around the table. The meal is well in progress.)

HARRY: *(A beat)* Bernice tells me you were shovelling snow again, Dad. You know that's too hard on your heart. You're not forty anymore, you know.

JOHN: I'm glad you told me, Harry.

JENNY: Grandpa, can I have your dessert?

JOHN: *(Smiling)* 'Course you can, darling.

(He passes her the dessert.)

BERNICE: *(To Jenny)* What do you say?

JENNY: Thank you, Grandpa.

HARRY: From now on wait'll I get home, will you? Or let Bernice do it.

JOHN: *(Insulted)* Bernice!

BERNICE: He's only thinking of your own good, Dad.

JOHN: Well, I appreciate that. But what am I supposed to do, curl up behind the furnace like an old dog? I'd die in no time flat. *(Disgusted)* Bernice!

(Bernice signals Harry. He nods.)

HARRY: *(A beat—then)* So you got a letter today . . . from that ad.

JOHN: I did. And that reminds me—Harry, I need your truck tomorrow. I'm driving to Summerside.

BERNICE: *(To Harry)* To see the lady.

JOHN: That's right.

HARRY: *(Fighting back his anger)* You asked me this morning what I thought of this whole business. Well, now I'll tell you. I think you're making a fool of yourself, Dad, and the whole family along with it.

(He throws down his napkin and gets up and walks angrily away from the table)

BERNICE: *(To John)* Excuse me. *(Calling)* Harry!

(She gets up and exits after her husband)

JENNY: What's wrong, grandpa? Why is daddy so mad?
JOHN: Well, I guess he wants me to start acting my age.
(The slightest of pauses) Whatever that means.
Fade out.

ACT TWO
Fade in: Scene 14.

14. INT. BATHROOM. THE NEXT DAY.
(John is lathering up his face, whistling to himself.)
Cut to: Scene 15.

15. INT. JOHN'S BEDROOM. DAY.
(John sits on the bed polishing his shoes. He holds up the toe to see if he can see himself in it. He nods with approval.)
Cut to: Scene 16.

16. INT. JOHN'S BEDROOM. DAY.
(John stands before his bureau mirror. He is dressed in his good blue suit, shirt and tie. He smooths down his white hair and steps back to survey himself.)
JOHN: *(Smiling with ironic self-approval)* Don't look a day over
  sixty-nine.
Cut to: Scene 17.

17. EXT. BACKYARD OF JOHN'S HOUSE. DAY.
(John climbs into the truck. He now wears his blue overcoat over his suit.)
Cut to: Scene 18.

18. EXT. HIGHWAY. DAY.
(John drives along.)
JOHN: *(A beat—aloud to himself a little nervously)* I don't know
  if I can live with another woman, after Dorothy. It'd be
  strange, for sure. Take a lot of getting used to. *(A slight
  pause)* That's if she consents. *(A slight pause)* A big if. *(A
  slight pause)* Why, she might take one good look at me and
  throw a fit of laughter. *(Nodding)* Harry's right. No fool like
  an old fool.
Cut to: Scene 19.

19. EXT. QUIET STREET IN SMALL TOWN. DAY.
(John pulls up in front of the house and shuts off the motor.

He glances at the house and has a last minute attack of nerves.)
JOHN: *(Aloud to himself)* I had a long and happy life with one
woman, already. That's more than most have. I should just
drive away. *(The slightest of pauses — indignantly)* And curl up
behind the furnace like an old dog? The hell I will!
*(He whips open the door and gets out of the truck. He slams
the door and walks around the front of the truck and up the
snowy walk to the small frame house. He hesitates a moment,
then knocks. Waits. The door opens and a middle-aged woman
answers. This is* Phylis, *Mrs. Arlington's daughter.)*
PHYLIS: *(Friendly)* Yes?
JOHN: I'm John Whalen. I've come to see Mrs. Viola Arlington.
PHYLIS: Oh. *(Giving him the furtive once-over)* Oh, come in,
please.
(John enters, and she closes the door.)
Cut to: Scene 20.

20. INT. HALL. DAY.
PHYLIS: *(Taking his coat)* I'm Phylis. *(Hanging it up)* Mother's up-
stairs. I'll go call her. The living room's on the left, Mr. . . .
JOHN: Whalen. John Whalen.
(Phylis starts up the stairs and John *enters the living room.)*
Cut to: Scene 21.

21. INT. LIVING ROOM. DAY.
*(John looks around him and sits in a comfortable armchair.
Silence. His stomach growls, so he folds his arms across it.
Silence. The sound of the clock on the mantle is loud in the
silence. He glances at the mantle, then rises and crosses to it.
He picks up a photo. From his POV we see that it is of an
elderly man, obviously Mr. Arlington. At that moment*
Mrs. Arlington *appears in the entrance to the living room.)*
VIOLA: That's my late husband. He was a dentist. We were mar-
ried twenty-six years. *(Then)* I'm Viola Arlington.
(A little embarrassed, John *sets the photo down on the mantle
and turns.)*
JOHN: I'm John Whalen.
(Mrs. Arlington crosses the room and shakes John's *hand.)*
VIOLA: I must tell you my daughter thinks you're a very hand-
some man.
JOHN: She does?
VIOLA: She's been trying to marry me off for three years now.

Oh, I don't blame her. She'd like to get me out from under-foot. *(A slight pause)* Won't you sit down?
(They both sit on the sofa.)
Would you like an ashtray?

JOHN: No, no, thank you.

VIOLA: I should offer you a drink.

JOHN: I'm not a drinking man, Mrs. Arlington.

VIOLA: Call me Vi. Neither am I, John. I never touched a drop of liquor in my life. Well, that's a lie. I did, once. At my wedding. *(A slight pause)* I'm sixty-three years of age.

JOHN: I'm seventy.

VIOLA: *(A slight pause)* Well.

JOHN: *(A slight pause)* Vi, I won't beat around the bush. I'm not much for small talk and such. Never was. Besides, we both know why I'm here, and we've both had a moment to look each other over. Personally, I like what I see.

VIOLA: Why, thank you.

JOHN: *(Stands, paces the room nervously)* And I think I should be frank. If we do marry, there are certain . . . conditions . . .

VIOLA: I'm listening.

JOHN: First—when I pass away, I'm to be buried alongside my late wife. I won't have it any other way. The plot is already paid for.

VIOLA: I understand, John.

JOHN: And if I go first, the house will be yours, but my other property—some thirty acres of farmland—will go to my son, Harry. And after you, the house is to revert to my son. That'll all be drawn up in a new will.

VIOLA: That seems fair, John.

JOHN: *(Relaxing, patting his forehead with a handkerchief—smiling)* Well, I guess that's all.

VIOLA: No, there's one other thing, John. *(A slight pause)* I'm Catholic.

JOHN: *(The smile fading)* Catholic? *(He sits)* Didn't I make myself clear in the ad? Catholic!

VIOLA: I suppose I thought if we met . . . I just took it for granted that we both are in the same boat, so to speak, or you wouldn't have advertised and I wouldn't have written.

JOHN: *(Confused)* You see, Vi, I come from a long line of die-hard Irish Protestants, and there's never been a Catholic inside our front door, let alone inside our family. Generation after generation of Orangemen.

(A pause — as if that's not enough of an explanation)
Why, just the mention of Rome was enough to raise my
father's blood pressure! (He stands) No, I'll have to think
about this, Vi.
VIOLA: Well, you do that, John. I'll be pleased to hear from you.
As I said before — I'm home most days.
Cut to: Scene 22.

22. *EXT. JOHN'S HOUSE. DAY.*
(The truck pulls up into the lane and John *climbs out and*
walks up to the front porch. His walk lacks its former bounce.
He looks dejected and lonely.)
Cut to: Scene 23.

23. *INT. DINING ROOM OF JOHN'S HOUSE. EVENING.*
(Silence. The camera pans slowly around the table: Jenny,
Harry, Bernice, *and stops on* John. *A beat.* John *looks up.)*
JOHN: *(Crustily)* Well? Doesn't anybody want to ask how it
went?
*(*Harry *and* Bernice *say nothing.)*
I've got good news for you, Harry. Mrs. Arlington's a Catholic.
JENNY: Grandpa, what's a Catholic? Is that bad? Is it, grandpa?
*(*John *looks at the child, struck by her questions. Hold on a*
close-up of John's *face. Then —)*
Cut to: Scene 24.

24. *INT. JOHN'S BEDROOM. NIGHT.*
*(*John *is lying in bed, reading his Bible. He closes it, tucking it*
under his chin.)
JOHN: *(Aloud softly, impressed with one of the verses)* 'Life is but
a shadow that passeth away.' *(Nods)* Yes.
(He removes his glasses and puts the glasses and the Bible on
the bedtable and clicks off the light. In the darkness the moon-
light breaks through the window and spotlights a corner of his
bed. The ticking of the clock is loud in the silence, in the dark-
ness. The camera moves in for a close-up of John. *He begins to*
softly hum a bar or two of a hymn, then he starts to sing it,
very softly, almost a whisper, and —)
Cut to: Scene 25.

25. *EXT. HIGHWAY. DAY.*
(The sun is shining. It is one of those gorgeous winter days just

*before spring, when you can almost feel green buds thrusting
under the snow.* John *is walking along, his Bible in one hand,*
Jenny *in the other. And the hymn that he had just begun to sing
in the previous scene is picked up now, being sung in BG by the
church choir, as if it were coming from a great distance away.*
*This is the stretch of highway, Scene 13, approaching the
church.* Ida Mackenzie, 60, *stands at the foot of her lane as*
John *and* Jenny *approach.)*

IDA: Morning, John.

JOHN: *(Nods)* Ida.

IDA: Going to church?

JOHN: I am, unless the devil waylays me.

IDA: I'll walk along with you.

JOHN: My pleasure.

(Ida takes his arm. The camera moves along with them.)

IDA: *(A beat)* I see your ad's still in *The Guardian.* Had a good
mind to write you myself, John Whalen.

JOHN: *(Smiling)* Don't say? Why, Ida Mackenzie, what would a
fine figure of a woman like yourself want with the likes of an
old reprobate like me?

IDA: Haven't lost a bit of your conceit, have you, John Whalen?
Nor your charm.

JOHN: Ida, you and I go back a long spell. Too far, I guess.
(Then) I loved Gus, like a brother.

IDA: And I thought the world of Dorothy. *(A slight pause)* Well,
I don't suppose there's much point in pursuing business on
the Sabbath. *(Another pause)* I must say I admire your delicate
footwork.

(As they continue to stroll along—)
Cut to: Scene 26.

26. *INT. CHURCH. DAY.*
*(It is very small inside, the kind of village church that hasn't
changed in almost a hundred years. The* Minister *is at the pul-
pit, just ending his sermon.* John *is seated with* Jenny *in the
family pew.)*

MINISTER: . . . And Job said: *(Reading from the Bible)* 'My days are
past, my purposes are broken off, even the thoughts of my
heart.'

*(John, listening to all this, the words imbued with special
meaning for him.)*

(Over) 'They change the night into day: the light is short

because of darkness. If I wait, the grave is mine house: I have made my bed in the darkness. And where is now my hope? As for my hope, who shall see it?'
(Minister, *closing the Bible*)
Let us pray.
(The congregation bows its head.)
Dear Heavenly Father, Grant that in the midst of our loneliness and despair we might remember another verse from Job. Chapter 14, Verse 7:
(John, *looking straight up at the* Minister.)
(Over) 'For there is hope of a tree, if it be cut down, that it will sprout again, and that the tender branch thereof will not cease.' Amen.
JOHN: *(Softly)* Amen.
Cut to: Scene 27.

27. EXT. CHURCH. DAY.
(The service is over, and the congregation files out and down the church steps, dispersing. John takes Jenny's hand and leads her around the side of the church.)
Cut to: Scene 28.

28. EXT. CEMETERY. DAY.
(John and Jenny approach Dorothy's grave.)
JENNY: Is this where grandma lives?
JOHN: *(Smiling)* That's right, darling. *(Kneeling)* You don't remember her, do you?
(He brushes away the snow until he finds the rose he left there the day before)
You were too little.
(He stands and puts the rose on the top of the gravestone.)
JENNY: Is grandma cold?
JOHN: No, I don't think so, darling.
JENNY: I am. How come grandma's not? Is it because she lives under the snow?
JOHN: Something like that, darling.
Cut to: Scene 29.

29. EXT. HIGHWAY. DAY.
(John and Jenny walking toward a stationary camera.)
JOHN: Jenny, would you like a new grandma? Someone who didn't live under the snow?

JENNY: Yes, grandpa. Can I have one? Can I?

JOHN: *(Smiling)* We'll see, darling. We'll see. *(Then)* Maybe tomorrow I'll take a little ride. Would you like to go into Summerside for a visit?

(They pass the camera.)

Cut to:

(John *and* Jenny *walking away from the camera down the winter highway. And as the credits roll, they gradually diminish in the distance.)*

Final fade-out.

AFTERWORD

1. You are a friend of John's, and he has asked you what he should do: remain single? marry his old friend, Ida Mackenzie? marry the woman who replied to his ad, Viola Arlington? Write a short monologue in which you tell him what you think he should do, and why. You might wish to read your monologue to a group of your classmates.

2. Imagine that David French is discussing *The Tender Branch* in a playwrighting course he is teaching. His students are thinking about ways to begin a teleplay. They ask:
   - Why did French start with a long shot of a "bleak winter landscape"?
   - What did French want the audience to know about John Whalen's life and character from the dialogue and actions included in the second scene?

   Write down the answers you think French might give, and then discuss your ideas with a group. You may want to modify your ideas as a result of the discussion.

3. In Scene 13, what do you think Harry means when he says, "I think you're making a fool of yourself, Dad, and the whole family with it"? With a partner, roleplay a short scene in which Harry tries to explain to Bernice why he thinks his father's behaviour is wrong. If you were the playwright, would you include this scene?

4. The camera can move in close to the actors, recording every small gesture and action. With a partner, choose a scene in which one of John's gestures or actions reveals something important to the story. Try out various ways in which an actor playing John might perform that gesture, and select the one that best captures the meaning of the scene. Dramatize part or all of the scene to demonstrate your idea, and discuss with another group how successfully you have conveyed the meaning you want to suggest.

5. a) In a group, discuss what you think John really needs or wants. Be sure to support your response with examples from the play. What things or people get in John's way as he tries to reach his objective? Again, support your response with examples. At what point do you think John's problem is resolved? Present a chart or report of your conclusions to your class.

b) As a short research project, prepare a similar chart for an episode of your favourite television sitcom. What does the main character seem to want or need? What keeps the character from achieving his or her objective? How is the conflict finally resolved? Share your chart with your group. Do the various sitcoms have similar or different patterns?

6. David French has said jokingly that good critics are those who like his work. In French's terms, would you be a good critic? Write your response to *The Tender Branch*, adding your ideas about what qualifies a person to be a good critic.

7. As the director of this play, you review Viola Arlington's letter to John in Scenes 7 and 8 and her dialogue and actions in Scene 21 to get a sense of her character. Consider the following questions:
   • How attractive and likeable a character is she?
   • What seem to be her major personal characteristics?
   • Do you think that she makes an appropriate match for John? Explain.
   Using your responses as a guide, what qualities do you decide that the actress who plays this role should emphasize? Discuss your ideas with classmates.

8. Look back at Scene 29 and compare it with Scenes 1 and 2. How is it like the opening two scenes? How is it different? How has John changed? If you could talk to David French, what would you say to him about the way he chose to open and close his play? In a group, share your reactions.

9. A "shooting script" like the one that follows records all the camera-work in the left-hand margin, opposite the dialogue and action to which it applies. (Look in the Glossary under "Camera angle," "Camera distance," "Camera movement" and "Film transitions" for a basic vocabulary of film terms.) Select a scene from *The Tender Branch* and prepare a shooting script for it.

   As you prepare your shooting script, keep these questions in mind: How many shots would you use to film the scene? Where would you change to new shots? What camera angles would you use? What camera movement, if any, is desirable?

   If video cameras are available, film the scene, using other class members as your actors.

Shooting script for a segment of the opening scenes of the motion picture adaptation of Henrik Ibsen's play *An Enemy of the People*. After last credit title fades out —

FADE IN:
1. INTERIOR. MEETING ROOM. Camera PANS around long directors' table, at which are seated a group of very austere Directors of the Baths, all facing toward the speaker at one end of the table. We hear the sonorous voice of the speaker during the pan. The camera reaches him — it is Peter Stockmann, Chairman of the Board and Burgomaster of the town. We hold on him for a few moments as he reads his report on the excellent condition of the Baths and the great benefits it has brought to the people of the town.

BURGOMASTER: I regret, gentlemen, that the medical officer of the Baths is not here to give us his regular report.

Suddenly the camera dollies fast away from the Burgomaster. His voice fades.

CUT TO:
2. INT. HOSPITAL ROOM. Camera dollies back from a bed, on which a patient is lying. We hear two voices whispering, and the camera rides between two men, including them in the scene. One is a doctor, the other Dr. Thomas Stockmann, medical officer of the Baths.

DOCTOR: *(Softly)* Yes, Dr. Stockmann, I'm certain that it's typhoid.

DR. STOCKMANN: *(Worried)* That's the fifth case within the past three weeks.

DOCTOR: And all those gastric attacks have us mystified, too. You know, one of our typhoid patients died this morning, Doctor.

CUT TO:
3. *MEDIUM SHOT along directors'
table toward the Burgomaster.
Camera slowly takes in beaming faces
of directors.*

> BURGOMASTER: —And we are proud of the health which the Baths have brought to countless visitors.

CUT TO:
4. *INT. HOSPITAL, MEDIUM CLOSE-UP
of Dr. Stockmann and Doctor.*

> DR. STOCKMANN: This is serious, Brandes. I must take some definite action to stop it.
> DOCTOR: But, do you have any idea as to the cause, Dr. Stockmann?
> DR. STOCKMANN: Yes—one idea. *(Making sure no one is near)* Have you failed to notice that every one of these cases has resulted after the patient used the health baths?

*Doctor Brandes puts his hand to his
mouth to stifle the exclamation.*

> DOCTOR: *(Whispering)* The Baths—!

Dr. Stockmann nods.

> DR. STOCKMANN: Not a word. I'm not sure, you know.

Dr. Stockmann leaves.

CUT TO:
5. *EXTERIOR OF THE HOSPITAL.
Evening. MEDIUM SHOT of two
young boys playing near the door.
They are Stockmann's sons: Morten,
10, and Eilif, 8. Dr. Stockmann exits
from the hospital, and the boys rush
up to him.*

> MORTEN: *(Breathlessly)* Where do we go now, father?
> DR. STOCKMANN: We'll walk up to the Bath house.
> MORTEN: *(Jokingly)* Fine! Eilif's neck is dirty. We'll give him a bath.
> EILIF: Hey, you!

Eilif runs around after Morton, who dodges behind his father.

DR. STOCKMANN: Here, here, Gentlemen! We have business to attend to.

Both boys straighten up, serious. They start up the street, one on each side of Dr. Stockmann, apparently "gentlemen." Slyly reaching around behind his unsuspecting father, Eilif slaps Morton on the back of his head. The latter whirls around, wondering where the blow came from.

WIPE OUT:
6. INT. OF WHAT LOOKS LIKE A SWIMMING POOL. There is a sign marked "HEALTH BATH." Camera pans down from sign, along water to edge, where a hand is holding a small bottle in the water. The hand pulls the filled bottle out, and the camera PANS to take in Dr. Stockmann wiping the bottle with his handkerchief. He puts the bottle into his pocket and leaves.

▼ ▼ ▼   *INTRODUCTION TO:*

Icetime
Carol Bolt

" . . . what I want to do is create, in contemporary terms, the
[heroic] character: the adventurer, the seeker, the idealist who
strives for heroic possibility."
Carol Bolt

arol Bolt is a prolific writer of both adult and children's plays. Her work has been produced by theatre
companies all over Canada. She has been called a
"social idealist" because her plays dramatize the stories of idealistic individuals who try to change the
world. Even though her plays are often based on actual people and events, Bolt does not think of them
as documentaries: "I would like to think that the
value of my plays lies in their theatricality and their
entertainment qualities. I think they're 'true,' but history is really only their starting point."

Icetime is based on a real person and real events. Justine Blainey,
a young girl from Toronto, made national headlines in the mid-
1980s because she wanted to play on a team in the MTHL—a
boys' hockey league.

Icetime received a Chalmer's Award as one of the best Canadian
plays of 1988–89.

GETTING STARTED

1. With a group, brainstorm a list of the sports in which a woman
has become a well-known competitor. Share your list with the
class.

2. Think of someone you admire for standing up for his or her
beliefs. Tell your group whom you chose, explaining how that
person earned your respect.

3. Justine Blainey wrote this open letter to the *Globe and Mail*:

Dear Sir or Madam:
I *can* play! But may I?
MTHL try-out time is here again, and I'm going to hear the same words again, "Yes, you're good enough. We wish we *could* use you. But you're a girl."
The Canadian Charter of Rights says I can't be discriminated against, but Ontario's Human Rights Code allows sexual discrimination in amateur sports. This means it bars girls from the top levels of amateur competition.
Is there an individual or group that can help me? Is there a lawyer willing to devote his or her time to fight this unfairness?
I want to be judged on my ability alone.
Justine Blainey
Hockey Player, age 12
May, 1985

After reading the letter, imagine what Justine might be like, and then create a brief character sketch for her. As you read *Icetime*, compare the character you imagined with the one Bolt dramatizes in her play.

▼   ▼   ▼   STAGE PLAY

Icetime

Carol Bolt

CHARACTERS

JUSTINE BLAINEY—*a young teenage girl who is an excellent hockey player*

DAVID BLAINEY—*her brother, slightly younger and also a hockey player*

BITSY—*Justine's friend, a figure skater who has a tendency to be scatterbrained*

JASON—*David's friend, who would like to be strong and manly*

The roles below are taken by the actors who play David, Bitsy, and Jason:

AN OFFICIAL FROM THE ONTARIO WOMEN'S HOCKEY LEAGUE (BITSY)

JUSTINE'S LAWYER (BITSY)

OPPOSING LAWYER (JASON)

JUDGE (DAVID)

SPORTS DOCTOR (JASON)

CWHO NEWS TEAM (BITSY AND JASON)

(Justine, David *and* Jason *are dressing for a hockey practice, while* Bitsy *is practicing figure skating.* Jason *might be a goalie.*)

JUSTINE: My name is Justine Blainey. I love hockey. And all I want to do is play hockey, the best hockey I can.

BITSY: Justine, hockey is sweaty.

JUSTINE: And compulsory figures are boring.

BITSY: But it's graceful, figure skating is graceful. (*She demonstrates ungracefully.*)

JUSTINE: I guess I don't care about graceful.

BITSY: Figure skating is what girls do, Justine.

(Jason *and* David *take shots on each other as* Justine *explains.*)

JASON: Come on, David. Try to deke me out.

JUSTINE: It all started when we were six years old. And my

brother David went off to play house league hockey every Saturday morning.

JASON: Hey, David . . .

DAVID: Hey, Jason . . .

JASON: Try to score on me. Come on.

DAVID: Okay.

(He scores. Easily. Jason *sprawls trying to block the puck. As he picks himself up)*

JASON: Hey, try it again. I wasn't ready.

JUSTINE: I went off to learn figure skating. There I was every Saturday morning, tracing compulsory figures, until I realized something.

(Bitsy has tired of figure eights and drifted over to where the boys are practicing.)

BITSY: Hey, David . . . Hey, Jason . . .

DAVID: Hey, Bitsy.

BITSY: I've come to watch your game, okay?

JUSTINE: Everyone else was watching hockey. I mean, my mother, my father. They didn't care about compulsory figures any more than I did.

(David scores on Jason *again.* Bitsy *cheers wildly.)*

BITSY: Give us a D. Give us an A. Give us a V. Give us an I. Give us a D.

JUSTINE: I think I decided I wanted some attention. So I told my mother that I wanted to play hockey.

DAVID: My dad says hockey is like life. You know, it's about winners and losers and getting out there and fighting. He says I like it because of the adrenalin. But why do I like the adrenalin?

JUSTINE: The coach says David thinks too much. It slows him down.

DAVID: I like the feeling you get skating out on new ice. I like the feeling you get just before the ref drops the puck. I like the feeling you get on a breakaway, when you know everything's right, it's going to work, when you're concentrating so hard that things that were colour go to black and white, and you can't even hear the crowd anymore.

JUSTINE: David wrote a poem about hockey once.

DAVID: It wasn't a poem.

JUSTINE: He was inspired by one of those big machines that clean the ice.

DAVID: It was an essay.

JUSTINE: A poetic essay. He called it *The Zamboni.*

DAVID: Forget about *The Zamboni*.

JUSTINE: *The Zamboni* by David Blainey.

DAVID: I was six years old at the time, so you can forget about my poetry.

JUSTINE: This is him. My brother. The poet.

DAVID: This is my sister. Justine. She thinks she's funny.

JUSTINE: *(To audience)* My brother and I both play minor peewee because we were born in the same year . . . But we aren't twins . . . Look, don't ask me to explain, okay?

JASON: Hey, David, how come you and Justine were born in the same year, but you're not twins?

JUSTINE: *(To audience)* . . . Because it's boring to explain.

DAVID: *(To* Jason*)* Because Justine was born in January and I was born in December.

JUSTINE: Because when people find out, all they say is "Boy, your mother must have been busy that year."

JASON: Boy, your mother must have been busy that year.

*(*Justine *moves in to score on* Jason *who tries for a save but sprawls on the "ice".)*

JUSTINE: She shoots. She scores. Sorry Jason.

JASON: Okay, once more. Go ahead. I'm ready this time.

(She does. And she scores again.)

JUSTINE: I like winning. I can't help it. Sometimes I think victory is winning a trophy in a contact sport.

JUSTINE and DAVID sing:

My dad says
Life is just like hockey
And I say "Hey, wouldn't that be great?"
I mean if Life were like playing a game
And if somebody told you the rules
You would know what to do
You could be on the team
You could go find some ice
And just skate.

I remember
One game
I was right on the point
And I deked out this guy
And I set up a shot
It can be such a high
When you know that you're hot.

I remember
That game
I was back of the net
And I came round the side
Took a shot at the goal
It can be such a high
It's as good as a win
When you try.

So when my dad says
Life is just like hockey
I say "Hey, wouldn't that be great?"
I mean if Life were like playing a game
And if somebody told you the rules
You would know just what to do
You could be on the team
You could go find some ice
And just skate.

(Bitsy *enters to join* Justine.)

BITSY: My mom says winning is a zero-sum situation.

JUSTINE: A what?

BITSY: For every winner, there's a loser, right? I mean, you can't
have winners without losers, right? Winners minus losers
equal zero. And zero plus zero is not exactly progress.

JUSTINE: But what if you're winning? And you keep winning?

BITSY: My mom says sports is just aggression.

JASON: What's wrong with that?

BITSY: She says we have sports and the stock market and the
nuclear arms race and it's all the same thing.

JASON: What's wrong with that?

BITSY: Did you show your father your report card, Jason?

(Jason *blocks one of* David's *shots. They congratulate each
other with high fives.*)

DAVID: Hey, Jason . . .

JASON: Hey, David . . .

BITSY: Jason's father thinks report cards are mucho serious. It's
as if they were NHL scores.

JASON: My father's going to kill me.

BITSY: I guess he's not the kind of guy to understand. How you
failed everything but cooking. But what I want to know is
how did you pass cooking?

JASON: Hey, anyone can cook, Bits. I've heard even girls can cook.

BITSY: Your dad *should* kill you, Jason. *I* should kill you, Jason. *(She goes after him. He uses* David *as a shield.)*

JASON: What are you and Justine going to do this winter, Bitsy? I mean, when David and I are playing hockey? You want my recipe for ginger snaps?

BITSY: Justine's playing hockey.

JASON: Justine's playing ringette or something. And David and I tried out for the Metropolitan Toronto Hockey League.

JUSTINE: You tried out for the East Enders. So did I.

JASON: Tell Justine she can't play MTHL, David.

DAVID: Why can't she?

JASON: Because MTHL is serious stuff. And Justine isn't serious.

BITSY: And Jason isn't real.

DAVID: Justine's serious.

JASON: My dad says that hockey is like life, David. And life is serious. You know my dad still plays hockey with guys he used to play with in the MTHL. And one of them is his bank manager and one of them is his accountant . . .

BITSY: Have I seen them? Do they have a beer commercial?

JASON: You know when my dad used to play in the MTHL, he knew a guy whose little cousin played with Gretzky. Now Gretzky is serious. Do you think Justine is Gretzky?

DAVID: Justine isn't. I'm not. Neither is your father.

JASON: Justine doesn't *care* about hockey.

DAVID: Sure she does.

JASON: She likes to play, that's all.

DAVID: So why can't she? If she's good enough? If she can make the team?

JASON: Oh sure.

DAVID: And she'll make the team, don't worry.

JASON: Oh sure.

BITSY: You're jealous, Jason.

JASON: Me?

BITSY: Aren't you?

JASON: Me? Jealous? It's called *Barbie Plays Hockey.*

JUSTINE: Get him out of here, David.

JASON: Me? Jealous? Of Miss Sweatpants of 1986?

JUSTINE: Does he want to live?

DAVID: Let's get out of here, Jay.

JASON: I guess the girls have got important stuff to do, like fix their hair or something.

JUSTINE: I warn you, Jason . . .

(Jason *hides behind* David.)

JASON: Help, David . . .

JUSTINE: You're dead meat.

JASON: It's *Barbie Goes Rambo.*

JUSTINE: Go and count your chest hair, Jason.

(The boys retreat. Bitsy does elaborate things with make-up.)

BITSY: Don't you think hockey is kind of, you know, jock?

JUSTINE: Jock?

BITSY: Don't you think guys will think you're kind of, you know, weird?

JUSTINE: I'm not weird.

BITSY: But what if people thought you were, Justine?

JUSTINE: Then they'd be wrong, Bitsy.

BITSY: Don't you ever, kind of, you know, worry? About what people think?

JUSTINE: Why should I?

BITSY: Because other people are important, Justine. You have to live with other people.

JUSTINE: Bitsy, why do people call you Bitsy?

BITSY: Beg your pardon?

JUSTINE: Don't you worry sometimes? Because everybody always calls you Bitsy? Don't you think that could mean people don't think you're serious?

BITSY: But I'm not serious.

JUSTINE: Bitsy . . .

BITSY: Why would I be serious?

JUSTINE: Okay. So you're thirteen years old. But say you were twenty years old. Say you wanted to be something. A brain surgeon.

BITSY: Hey, if I were a brain surgeon I could operate on you.

JUSTINE: Who ever heard of a brain surgeon named Bitsy.

(Bitsy *studies her hair.*)

BITSY: Should I dye this part? Green? Should I get a Mohawk?

JUSTINE: Cut it out.

BITSY: You ever hear of a brain surgeon with a Mohawk?

JUSTINE: Please stop acting like an airhead.

BITSY: But Justine, I am an airhead.

JUSTINE: We're supposed to be friends, aren't we?

BITSY: Sure. Except you're mucho serious. And you want me to be mucho serious. And get involved in sports and school politics and extracurricular activities. What you don't understand is I want to be an airhead. Because the last time I thought seriously about growing up, I thought how am I going to get to grow up, I mean without blowing up or glowing in the dark. So I thought, why bother? When all I want is a platinum credit card.

JUSTINE: I don't believe you.

BITSY: About what? About being blown up?

JUSTINE: I don't believe all you care about is money.

BITSY: And I don't believe all you want is more icetime. Justine, give me a break.

JUSTINE: It's not all I want. I tried out for the team, that's all. Because I thought I could make the team. And I want to play. Hockey. For as long as I can and as well as I can.

BITSY: You know, you should get a Mohawk.

JUSTINE: Bitsy . . .

BITSY: *(Sings)*
Girls all know that
Girls just want to have fun
They want to go to the Virgin Islands
Lie at the pool
Drinking Shirley Temples
When the sun
Goes down
They'll get down to the
Serious party

JUSTINE: *(Sings)*
I like cabanas
I like computers
Chocolate cookies
Tom Cruise's hair
And Sidney Sheldon
And Benetton sweaters
And I think I'd like to travel
Everywhere

BITSY: *(Sings)*
Girls all know that
Girls just want to have fun
They want to go to the Mall on Friday
Don't want to think what will happen Monday
When the sun goes down
They'll have fun
Coming up with something

JUSTINE: *(Sings)*

I like Nina
In *The Seagull*
Have you ever read that play?
My ambition is to travel
Want to see the world some day
My ambition is to travel
Everywhere!

They sing:
Girls all know that girls
Just want to have fun
(Jason *and* David *enter.*)

DAVID: Hey, Justine. The tryout's going to start.
(*A number which becomes faster and faster paced as* Justine,
David, *and* Jason *"try out" and* Bitsy *blows whistles, throws
pucks on the "ice", whatever.*)

They sing:
You try out for a lot of teams
It always works the same
They put you through a lot of drills
They want to see your shooting skills
And then they say "We've got your name
So don't call us. So we'll call you"
And so you know you're kind of through
Unless they ask you back
To their next tryout.

You try out for a lot of teams
It always works the same
They put you through a lot of drills
They want to see your shooting skills
They want to see how hard you try
How long you last before you die
And then they say "We've got your name
So don't call us. So we'll call you"
And so you know you're kind of through
Unless they ask you back
To their next tryout.

Can you deke and can you pass
Can you think about the game
Can you speedskate, are you fast
You try to cut it, you try to last

You try out for a lot of teams
It always works the same
They put you through a lot of drills
They want to see your shooting skills
They want to see how hard you try
How long you last before you die
And so they say "We only want the best
We'll see if we want you"
And so you know you're kind of through
Unless they ask you back to their last tryout.

(At the end of the tryout, Justine, David *and* Jason *collapse.* Bitsy *hands letters to* Justine *and* David.*)*

BITSY: Justine! David! You have letters from the MTHL.

*(*Justine *and* David *open the letters. And cheer.)*

DAVID: Justine! We made it!

JUSTINE: You made it! I made it!

(The kids congratulate each other until Bitsy *notices that* Jason *has wandered away from the group.)*

BITSY: Hey, guys . . . Jason didn't get a letter.

DAVID: I know how you feel, Jay.

JASON: Do you?

DAVID: I know how I felt, last year, the first time I tried out and the coach told me I didn't make it and I felt like someone threw a football at my stomach. And I felt sick. And I felt like the whole world was lit with a sixty watt bulb.

JASON: That's because you're a wimp, David.

DAVID: Look, I know why you're mad . . .

JUSTINE: Look, Jason, I'm sorry . . .

JASON: Go ahead, David. Play for MTHL. Justine and I don't care, do we, Justine?

DAVID: Justine's playing, Jason.

JASON: Want to bet?

DAVID: They want to sign both of us.

JASON: You want to bet?

JUSTINE: Ask Mr. Johnson, Jason. He's the coach.

JASON: Let me spell it out to you in words of one syllable.

BITSY: Ignore him. He's jealous.

DAVID: Bitsy, mind your own business.

BITSY: I forgot. You're talking hockey. Of which I know nothing. Please. Excuse me for living.

(Exit Bitsy*)*

JASON: The East Enders is an MTHL team, David, isn't it? And

MTHL is a boys' league, isn't it? Boys, guys, males, creatures
of the opposite sex, I mean, opposite from girls. And Justine's
a girl. I mean, oh brother, your sister . . . Point of information . . . she's a girl.

DAVID: She's a girl who plays hockey.

JASON: Don't hold your breath.

DAVID: What are you trying to say?

JASON: My dad's on the board at the MTHL, that's all. And you
know what he'll say if Justine gets signed? Put it this way,
David. It won't be "Congratulations".

JUSTINE: Why shouldn't they sign me?

DAVID: She made the team, Jason. So they have to sign her.

JASON: Do they?

DAVID: What do you mean? Jason?

JUSTINE: Jason, wait . . .

(David *follows* Jason *out. Bitsy* calls Justine *as she is about to
follow. She is dressed as the OWHL* Official.)

OFFICIAL: Wait, Justine . . .

JUSTINE: What?

OFFICIAL: I'd like to talk to you a minute? Do you have a minute?

JUSTINE: What's going on?

OFFICIAL: Look, I'm sorry if I startled you, but I'm from the
Ontario Women's Hockey League, and I was watching your
tryout . . . And I just wanted to say that you were terrific, I
thought you looked good.

JUSTINE: Thank you.

OFFICIAL: . . . And I wanted to say . . . Look, you don't have to
play for the East Enders, you know.

JUSTINE: But I want to play for the East Enders.

OFFICIAL: Because you may not know, but we have a girls' hockey
league. Here in Toronto.

JUSTINE: Yes, I know that.

OFFICIAL: So you could play for us.

JUSTINE: Look, no offense . . .

OFFICIAL: We have a team in Mississauga . . .

JUSTINE: Look, girls' hockey . . . it's just that the level of play's
not the same.

OFFICIAL: I don't know what you're trying to say.

JUSTINE: The East Enders practice two hours a week and your
teams practice one hour a week. Isn't that right?

OFFICIAL: But that gives you more time for yourself.

JUSTINE: But if you don't live in Mississauga, then you have to drive an hour to get to the arena. Then you have to drive to Kingston to find another team to play. Isn't that right?

OFFICIAL: But we only played Kingston twice last year.

JUSTINE: You still spend more time in the car than you do on the ice.

OFFICIAL: There's a lot more to hockey than icetime, Justine.

JUSTINE: Look, no offense . . .

OFFICIAL: You think girls' hockey is inferior, don't you?

JUSTINE: I just want to play the best that I can.

OFFICIAL: You think you'll get more practice time and more support and more competition if you play with the boys.

JUSTINE: I *know* I will.

OFFICIAL: But how is girls' hockey ever going to be any good unless we all work to make it better?

JUSTINE: Look, no offense . . .

OFFICIAL: I wish you'd help us, Justine. Because you might need our help someday.

(She exits.)

JUSTINE: Wait . . . what do you mean?

(David enters with his equipment bag and a letter.)

DAVID: There's a letter for you, Justine. From the MTHL. You want me to open it?

JUSTINE: I can open my own mail, David. Thanks just the same.

DAVID: How come they sent you a letter and they didn't send me a letter?

(Jason enters with Bitsy on a skateboard.)

JASON: David, haven't you heard? You aren't on the team anymore.

DAVID: Very funny.

JASON: I guess they want Justine to break it to you gently.

JUSTINE: *(Is reading the letter)* They don't mean this.

JASON: Don't worry, Justine. He can take it.

JUSTINE: It isn't fair.

DAVID: Justine, what's wrong?

JASON: Don't worry, David. If you're not on the team. You'll have that much more time to play video games.

(Justine has crumpled up the letter and thrown it to the floor. David picks it up.)

DAVID: *(Reads letter)* What is this?

JUSTINE: *(Is on the verge of tears)* It's simple, isn't it? It's in English, isn't it?

DAVID: I don't understand.

JUSTINE: They say I can't play for the MTHL.

DAVID: But they signed you.

JUSTINE: They say MTHL is a boys' hockey league and it's against the rules for me to play. They don't want me.

DAVID: Look, Justine . . . I know how you feel.

JUSTINE: No. You don't.

DAVID: Look, Justine . . . Remember last year . . .

JUSTINE: Look, David, please . . . please don't tell me that you understand. Because I don't care right now. If you understand or not.

DAVID: Last year, I tried out, and I didn't make it, and I felt . . .

JUSTINE: Go and write a poem about last year, David.

DAVID: Sure. Fine. Okay. I'll do that. "Last Year My Sister was a Human". By David Blainey.

(*Exit* David. Bitsy *approaches* Justine.)

BITSY: Look, Justine . . . You feel bad, I know you feel bad . . .

JUSTINE: Go away, Bitsy. Please . . .

BITSY: I want to help.

JUSTINE: I just want to be alone. Is that okay?

BITSY: Justine, you're my friend. And this is important to you.

JUSTINE: And you can't help. No one can help. Go listen to your Walkman.

BITSY: (*Exits*) Sure. Fine. This is hockey, of course. Of which I know nothing.

(Jason *sits on his skateboard. He sighs.*)

JASON: I can help.

JUSTINE: You must be kidding.

JASON: No, really. I didn't make the team either, remember.

JUSTINE: That was different, Jason.

JASON: Okay, I wasn't good enough to make the team. So that was different. But it wasn't any easier.

JUSTINE: (*Sings*)
It makes me mad that
The world runs like a Boys' Club.
With rules that say
The way that we should be
Not just the way I wear my hair
The colours of the clothes I wear
You want to tell me where to go
And what to do when I get there

It makes me angry
Thinking

All I have to do
Is look pretty in pink
I get so angry
Thinking
Nobody thinks I can think

JASON: *(Sings)*
It's too bad that
The world runs like a Boys' Club.
With rules that say
The way that we should be
I know the kind of clothes to wear
And I don't care about my hair
But I don't know which way to go
Or what to do when I get there

It makes me wonder
Sometimes
How I'll get to be
What they want me to be
Because I wonder
Sometimes
What kind of club would take me?

They sing:
It makes us sad that
The world is like a Boys' Club
With rules that say we're
On different teams
Why should we do all the things they tell us to do
If finally we wake up one day
Still wondering
What happened to our dreams

(Bitsy *enters as* Justine's Lawyer. *She hustles* Jason *out.)*

LAWYER: It's all right. We can handle this.

JASON: Hey, wait . . . what's going on?

LAWYER: Don't worry, Justine. You can play hockey. We'll make sure that you play hockey.

JUSTINE: Who are you?

LAWYER: Your lawyer.

JUSTINE: But I don't need a lawyer.

LAWYER: Want to bet?

JUSTINE: Look, this is silly. Why would I need a lawyer?

LAWYER: Because the other side will have them.

JUSTINE: What other side?

LAWYER: I remember the first time I walked into a court room . . . And the judge said "Speak up. I'm not used to listening to women." But you don't have to be afraid, Justine. You just have to stand up and say what you believe in.

JUSTINE: You want me to stand up in court? You want me to speak?

LAWYER: Don't worry. Because under the Charter of Rights no one can discriminate because of sex. So that means no one can stop you playing hockey if you're good enough to make the team.

(Jason enters as Sports Doctor with charts and graphs.)

SPORTS DOC: Unless they look at the evidence.

JUSTINE: Who's that?

(Jason swears himself in.)

SPORTS DOC: I solemnly swear to tell the truth, the whole truth and nothing but the truth.

JUSTINE: What's going on?

SPORTS DOC: Of course, I think that girls are equal to boys, your honour, and women are equal to men, in fact, I think, they're probably superior. But I have here a picture of an adolescent girl hockey player . . . *(He unrolls it.)* And here is a picture of an adolescent boy hockey player.

(He unrolls it. The boy hockey player is much larger.)

JUSTINE: What difference does that make?

SPORTS DOC: May it please the court, as we see there are definitely differences between boys and girls, especially after puberty. There are physiological differences in muscle strength and muscle mass which put the female player at a disadvantage.

JUSTINE: But I made the team.

(Jason ignores Justine. He unrolls another chart.)

SPORTS DOC: In fact, as we see on this graph, the average female hockey player is five foot five inches and weighs 138 pounds and the average male hockey player is six foot one inch and weighs 188 pounds . . . Now those are American figures but that's 138 centim . . .

JUSTINE: But I'm just as tall as David.

LAWYER: Call David Blainey.

SPORTS DOC: Now there's a safety factor involved here . . .

(David enters. Justine pulls him over in front of the Sports Doctor.)

JUSTINE: David . . .

DAVID: What's the matter, Justine?

SPORTS DOC: It's our job to minimize risks for these young people, so putting the post-pubescent male and the post-pubescent female together, the female will be at a disadvantage, that's unhealthy.

JUSTINE: Show him . . . that I'm just as tall as you are . . .

DAVID: Wait a minute . . .

SPORTS DOC: We think sports are supposed to be healthy.

DAVID: You're not taller than I am, Justine.

SPORTS DOC: There is also the psychological factor.

JUSTINE: I didn't say I was taller than . . .

DAVID: You just grew faster, that's all . . .

SPORTS DOC: We have found when girls play on boys' teams, it changes them . . . it changes their character, it makes them more independent, more aggressive, so when they go back to play on girls' teams . . .

JUSTINE: Look, I just want to show him, I'm almost as tall . . .

DAVID: *(To* Justine*)* You have to be right, don't you?

JUSTINE: But he said you were six foot one.

DAVID: Justine, you're embarrassing me.

SPORTS DOC: Girls who play on boys' teams then can't fit in with the other girls.

DAVID: You're making me look like some kind of freak. I'm not a freak. You're the freak.

SPORTS DOC: I rest my case.

(Exit)

JUSTINE: Is that true? What he said? What you said? I'm too independent, I'm too aggressive, I'm a freak?

DAVID: No, of course not.

JUSTINE: But you said it.

DAVID: I got mad, that's all. When you said I was short.

JUSTINE: David, I didn't say you were short. David, he said I was short.

DAVID: I guess everyone has to speak, that's all. Both sides. I guess that's what court's about.

JUSTINE: But I feel like I'm on trial, David. Why am I on trial?

DAVID: You aren't. No, Justine, really. It's more like you're on a breakaway. And you're way out in front of everyone else, so you're the one that everybody watches.

(Jason and Bitsy burst on the scene with cameras and lights, as the CWHO News Team.)

NEWS 1: Lights. Can we please have more lights?

NEWS 2: Her nose is shining, Garth.

NEWS 1: Make-up. Can we have make-up, please. Oh, here it is. *(He passes it to News Team 2.)*

NEWS 2: Close your eyes, dear. Your eyes need a little colour.

JUSTINE: What's going on?

NEWS 1: Now we need a little colour. Background. Whose idea was this, Justine?

JUSTINE: What do you mean?

NEWS 1: This hockey thing. You wanting to play hockey. Was it your mother? Does she believe in women's liberation?

JUSTINE: It was my idea.

NEWS 1: Sure it was.

JUSTINE: I was jealous of my brother.

NEWS 1: Do you believe in women's liberation?

NEWS 2: This will be cute.

NEWS 1: Say anything you want, Justine. Say something really outrageous. We want to make the National.

JUSTINE: I just want to play hockey.

NEWS 2: That's cute.

NEWS 1: I was hoping for cuter.

NEWS 2: No, it's fine, Garth, really. It's sincere, really. It's just she has too much eye make-up, because you know, if her nose was shining, she could do that schtick "I want to play hockey" and people would say it was cute. She has too much make-up, Garth.

(Justine tries to fight her way out from under their attentions.)

JUSTINE: Hey, what's going on?

NEWS 1: I think it's cuter with the make-up.

JUSTINE: What about what I think?

NEWS 1: *(Ignores her)* It's a statement. You know. She paints her toenails, but she still wants to score.

NEWS 2: What colour toenail polish do you wear, Justine?

JUSTINE: Who cares?

NEWS 1: Everyone cares, Justine. You're on the front page.

JUSTINE: Front page? Me? Why?

NEWS 1: Because of your court case, of course.

DAVID: *(Enters, with Justine's hockey bag)* Justine! You won!

NEWS 2: You see. You won.

JUSTINE: I what?

NEWS 1: You won.

NEWS 2: Girl takes on MTHL.

NEWS 1: Girl plays boys' hockey.

NEWS 2: Do you really wear toenail polish?

JUSTINE: David! I won!

DAVID: That's what I said.

JUSTINE: Oh David . . . that means I can play!

DAVID: Hey . . . Yeah . . . Hey . . . Here's your shin pads.

NEWS 2: Garth, are you getting this?

JUSTINE: I can't find my gloves. Have you seen them, David?

NEWS 1: How about you, David? How does all this make you feel?

DAVID: What do you mean?

NEWS 1: Since your sister is getting all this attention. And you're looking for her gloves?

DAVID: I feel fine.

NEWS 1: That's the boy.

DAVID: Why wouldn't I feel fine?

NEWS 1: Because she's on television. And all you've got to do is carry her equipment bag.

(News Team 2 *sets* Justine *up beside her for a stand up interview.*)

NEWS 2: Justine Blainey, the young girl who recently won the historic court case which allows her to play hockey with the Metropolitan Toronto Hockey League, was delighted by the news of her victory today. Well, Justine, are you ready to play?

JUSTINE: David, have you got my equipment?

NEWS 1: *(Pushes* David *"on camera")* David Blainey, Justine's brother, says he finds it hard to get used to the idea of Justine as a role model.

DAVID: Justine for a role model?

NEWS 2: How does it make you feel, David, to know that there are thousands of young people all over the province who are going to look up to your sister? Because she knew what she wanted to do and she did it. Because she took on the adult world and she won. Because she's the first young woman on the East Enders Minor Peewee Hockey team. She reminds me of me. I was a role model. Remember Garth, when I did my first stand-up in the Argos dressing room?

DAVID: I don't think Justine wants to be a role model.

NEWS 2: I don't think she has much choice. Where is she?

JUSTINE: *(Sings)*

Wait a minute

Is this where I want to be

This is more than a joke

It's like going for broke
Is it too fast for me

Wait a minute
Do I really have to be
On that clean sheet of ice
It's so cold, it's so bright
Is it too bright to see

It seems so lonely
When you're the only
Dreamer in the dream
When the ice is as bright
And the ice is as hard
As the eyes on the rest of the team

Wait a minute
This is where I want to be
Right out here in the light
It's so cold
It's so bright
But not too bright to see

If I want it
I can have it
There's a high note
I can reach it
Just watch me!

(Jason *enters*.)

JASON: My father says you shouldn't play. For the East Enders.

DAVID: Want to bet?

JUSTINE: Hasn't he heard about the court case? Didn't he read it in the papers?

JASON: My father doesn't blame you, Justine.

JUSTINE: Blame me for what?

JASON: All this going to court. This legal action. He says it was feminists.

JUSTINE: I just want to play hockey, Jason.

JASON: He says these people are taking advantage of you. They're using you. They want to keep sending you back to court when you haven't got a hope.

JUSTINE: But I won, Jason. And the court said I could play.

JASON: My dad says he has nothing against you personally. But, he says, if you play, other girls will want to play.

JUSTINE: What's wrong with that?

JASON: He says he'll fight you to the death on this.

JUSTINE: To the death?

JASON: He says it's a matter of life or death. It's a matter of principle. He says you could kill organized hockey as we know it.

JUSTINE: Excuse me, Jason, but I have a practice.

JASON: He says you step out on that ice and he'll disqualify your team.

(Bitsy *enters, putting on her* Lawyer's *robes.*)

LAWYER: Don't worry, Justine.

JUSTINE: It isn't fair.

LAWYER: We'll go to court again.

JUSTINE: We went to court. They lost. Now they're changing the rules.

LAWYER: People do that sometimes. When they're losing.

JUSTINE: You know, when they first told me I couldn't play hockey, I felt sick. I thought it was me. They didn't want me on their team. And now that I've thought about it, I still feel sick, because it's true, isn't it? It is me they don't want, no matter how many times they say it isn't personal. It's because I'm a girl, but they still don't want *me*.

LAWYER: Don't worry, Justine. Don't cry.

JUSTINE: I'm not crying. Not exactly.

LAWYER: We'll win the appeal.

JUSTINE: You think so? Really?

LAWYER: They don't have a case. They're just stalling.

JUSTINE: But how long can they stall?

LAWYER: They hope you'll give up. Are you going to give up?

JASON: Hey, Justine. Is she one of the feminists?

LAWYER: I beg your pardon?

JASON: I think you should leave Justine alone.

LAWYER: I beg your pardon?

JASON: My dad says you think you'll make your reputation, taking Justine to court . . .

LAWYER: And what do you think, Jason?

JASON: Justine just wants to play hockey, don't you, Justine?

JUSTINE: Yes, but . . .

JASON: Do you know what will happen if you take the MTHL to court? If you sue the East Enders? The club will collapse, Justine.

LAWYER: Don't believe him, Justine.

JUSTINE: I don't know.

JASON: You won't be able to play. Neither will anyone else. Isn't that more important than what *you* want?

JUSTINE: I don't know.

LAWYER: Don't believe him, Justine.

JUSTINE: I don't know, please, both of you, leave me alone.

LAWYER: *(Exit)* Fight for your rights, Justine.

JASON: *(Exit)* Remember your friends, Justine.

JUSTINE: *(Sings)*
Wait a minute
Does it have to be this tough?
If I've passed every test
And I'm doing my best
Is that still not enough?

(Bitsy *enters*)

BITSY: What's the matter, Justine?

JUSTINE: I can't do it.

BITSY: Do what?

JUSTINE: Be everything everybody wants me to be. All at once.

BITSY: At least you're not Jason. Because his Dad wants him to be a Supreme Court Judge.

(Jason *enters with* David *and a new equipment bag.*)

JASON: Congratulate me, girls.

BITSY: And Jason can't even spell Supreme Court.

JASON: I have signed with an MTHL Team. I'm a Jet.

JUSTINE: Jason, the Jets are jerks.

JASON: Justine, you're jealous.

JUSTINE: They're jerks. They play bozo gazoonie hockey. They're all brain donors.

JASON: You're speaking of my dad's old team.

JUSTINE: I don't care.

DAVID: Justine, calm down . . .

JUSTINE: It isn't fair, David.

DAVID: I know, how you feel but . . .

BITSY: Why do you think it's supposed to be fair?

JUSTINE: Jason gets to play MTHL. Just because he's a guy. It isn't that he knows the plays. It isn't that he has the skills . . .

BITSY: Did you ever think what it would be like if boys could play on girls' teams?

JUSTINE: Bitsy, don't start . . .

BITSY: If they let boys on the gym team or the swim team. They'd take over. There wouldn't be a girls' team.

JUSTINE: Bitsy, please . . . we're supposed to be friends.

BITSY: Or what if all the girls who were any good played for the boys' teams? I guess the girls' teams would get even wimpier, wouldn't they?

JUSTINE: I just want to do my best.

BITSY: You think other girls don't?

JUSTINE: You don't.

BITSY: Thanks Justine.

JUSTINE: You don't care about anything.

BITSY: What you don't understand is, I try not to care. About whether it's fair or not. Because I look at my mother who is just as smart as my father and she was his secretary before he married her. And I look at my sister, she is somewhat smarter than the jerk she married, isn't she? But she quit school to put *him* through school. And I look at my father who has a new secretary and a new wife and a condo in Ajax and my mom has custody and she works at the IGA when he forgets to send support.

JUSTINE: It doesn't have to be that way.

BITSY: Doesn't it?

JUSTINE: Bitsy . . .

BITSY: You have to learn not to care about stuff like that, Justine. And sit back. You can listen to my Walkman.

JUSTINE: You can't just quit, Bitsy. I don't want to quit.

(Exit Bitsy, followed by Justine.)

JASON: Do you think Justine is better than you are? At hockey?

DAVID: That is such a stupid question.

JASON: She's faster than you are.

DAVID: We're different.

JASON: She's stronger than you are. Does that bother you?

DAVID: Look, Jason, she grew faster than I did. That happens. People grow at different rates. People have growth spurts and some people mature faster than other people, that's all.

JASON: You know what my dad heard?

DAVID: I don't care.

JASON: He heard the only reason you got signed was because of Justine.

DAVID: Oh, sure.

JASON: Your coach wanted Justine and your mom said he'd have to take you.

DAVID: Justine isn't playing, Jason. They won't even let her on the ice.

JASON: They say your coach wanted the publicity.

DAVID: Publicity? That's crazy.

JASON: He wants his name in the papers, that's all. Since he hasn't got Justine. And he has to play you.

DAVID: Drop dead, Jason.

JASON: The Jets were talking about Justine. At the practice. I mean in the locker room. The Jets are split about whether she should play or not. But they all want to get her against the boards. Get it? Against the boards?

DAVID: Jason, I'm going to kill you.

JASON: You know what the Jets say when other guys say stuff like that?

DAVID: What?

JASON: Go ahead and try it.

(David *attacks* Jason. *They wrestle.* Justine *enters.*)

JUSTINE: David . . . Jason . . .

JASON: What's that supposed to be? A suplex?

JUSTINE: Let go of him, David. He's bigger than you are.

JASON: This is a hold that our other goalie taught me. Called a camel drop.

(*And* Jason *leaves* David *flat.*)

DAVID: Okay, Jason, you win.

JASON: I won? I really won?

DAVID: Are you happy now?

(*But* Jason *sees* David *is still lying there.*)

JASON: Hey, David, did I hurt you?

DAVID: I'm fine, Jason.

JASON: Look, I'm sorry if I hurt you.

JUSTINE: You shouldn't fight. Either of you.

DAVID: Never mind, Justine.

JUSTINE: Why do guys have to fight all the time? What are they trying to prove?

DAVID: What are you trying to prove?

JUSTINE: I beg your pardon?

DAVID: Why can't you be like everybody else?

JUSTINE: Meaning what?

DAVID: Meaning why do you have to play hockey?

JUSTINE: You play hockey.

DAVID: I mean, why can't you be like your friends and stay home and watch *Dynasty.* Like Bitsy.

JUSTINE: Bitsy doesn't watch *Dynasty.*

DAVID: Bitsy doesn't make waves.

JUSTINE: What are you trying to say?

DAVID: Bitsy doesn't have her name all over the front page and the National news and the locker room walls.

JUSTINE: You don't care about me at all, do you, David?

DAVID: I just got murdered for you, Justine.

JUSTINE: You don't care what I want or what I do. As long as no one notices.

DAVID: Everybody notices everything you do. And everybody thinks you're weird.

JUSTINE: You know what really bothers me. If you want something, really want something, you just assume you can do it. You can play hockey or take off for Mexico, or start a rock band or join the Forest Rangers.

DAVID: You don't want to join the Forest Rangers.

JUSTINE: But if I did, David . . .

DAVID: You'd look pretty silly running through the forest in high heels.

JUSTINE: That's so stupid, David.

(Bitsy enters as Justine's Lawyer.)

LAWYER: Are you ready, Justine?

JUSTINE: You're so childish.

LAWYER: We're going back to court.

JUSTINE: How come you can be so stupid, David, and you can still expect to get to be what you want to be? Can you explain that?

LAWYER: Justine . . .

JUSTINE: And if I want something, all I get to do is dream about it.

LAWYER: We have a plane to catch, Justine. We're going to Ottawa. To the Supreme Court. This is real.

JUSTINE: The Supreme Court?

DAVID: Justine's going to the Supreme Court?

JUSTINE: *(Sings)*
What I remember is
Lions all over the place
And the crest that they have on the
Face of the one dollar bill
In the rest of the space
And a clock like the one that they have at our school
At the side of the men dressed in red
I remember that more than
Just why we were there
What it was that we said
All I remember,
It wasn't a comfortable space

All the chairs were too hard
There were lions all over the place
And the clock was like school
And the judges all had the same face
What I remember is lions
What I remember is lions
What I remember is lions

JASON (as OPPOSING LAWYER): Your honour, may it please the court, we'd like to introduce a few statistics.

(He unfolds a long computer printout.)

JUSTINE: *(Sings)*
And there were lawyers
There were all these lawyers . . .

OPPOSING LAWYER: Your honour, we would like to introduce our list of expert witnesses . . .

(Another printout)

JUSTINE: *(Sings)*
There they were the lawyers
And their old school ties were tied

OPPOSING LAWYER: Your honour, I'd like to introduce our reasons for delaying these proceedings . . .

(An even longer printout)

JUSTINE: *(Sings)*
They talk to you
They smile at you
As if they might agree with you
It's only that they've been employed
By the other side

(David *appears as* Judge *to announce the verdict.*)

JUDGE: Will Justine Blainey approach the bench?

(Justine *approaches.*)

JUDGE: In the matter of Justine Blainey versus the Metropolitan Toronto Hockey League, the Court finds that the Hockey League has discriminated against Justine Blainey in not allowing her to play.

BITSY (as JUSTINE'S LAWYER): Justine, we won!

JUSTINE: We won?

JUDGE: And the court orders that she be allowed to play forthwith.

LAWYER: You can play! They have to let you play!

JUSTINE: They do?

JASON: (as OPPOSING LAWYER, exits) This isn't over.

JUDGE: The court further orders that the Metropolitan Toronto

Hockey League be ordered to pay such court costs as Justine Blainey may have accrued to date.

JUSTINE: Does that mean you get paid?

LAWYER: It means *they* have to pay me.

JUDGE: And the Metropolitan Toronto Hockey League will pay such court costs as may accrue in future.

JUSTINE: Wait a minute . . .

LAWYER: It's wonderful, Justine.

JUSTINE: He said "Such court costs as may accrue in future."

LAWYER: It means they have to pay. If they take us back to court.

JUSTINE: But it's over isn't it?

LAWYER: Not according to the MTHL.

JUSTINE: But I can play, can't I?

(Her Lawyer hesitates.)

The Supreme Court said that I could play. Forthwith.

(Jason enters.)

JASON: My father says the ruling is unfair.

JUSTINE: But it's the *Supreme* Court, Jason.

JASON: He says he's not a quitter and the MTHL shouldn't quit. He says they have to keep fighting. On principle.

JUSTINE: What principle?

JASON: He says the club has rules. He says you can't just change the rules in the middle of the game.

LAWYER: Justine, if they don't let you play, we can take them to court.

JUSTINE: Again?

LAWYER: We can petition the Human Rights Commission.

JASON: My father says what about his rights? What about everyone else's rights?

JUSTINE: Why is it so important? Keeping me off the ice?

LAWYER: Don't worry, Justine. Because you'll win. In the end.

JUSTINE: But how long will it take?

LAWYER: They hope you'll give up. They're just stalling.

JUSTINE: But how long can they stall?

LAWYER: Do you want to quit?

JUSTINE: No.

LAWYER: Even if it takes years?

JUSTINE: No, of course not.

LAWYER: Even if you're too old to play when they let you play?

JUSTINE: I think I'll always want to play some kind of hockey. I'll be an old woman playing hockey. I'll be a hockey playing grandma . . .

LAWYER: Even if you can't play in the MTHL? Even if you can't play for the East Enders?

JUSTINE: But there'll be other girls who want to play.

LAWYER: Yes, there probably will.

JUSTINE: I'll bet there will be. So I can't quit, can I? Because we will win, won't we?

LAWYER: Yes, I hope so.

JUSTINE: We will win. If not this year, then next year. And if it isn't for me, it will be for somebody else.

DAVID: Hey, Justine. Two on one.

(David *passes the puck to* Justine, *who dekes past* Jason *who sprawls trying to save it.*)

LAWYER: She shoots.

DAVID: She scores.

JUSTINE: Thanks, David.

JASON: Hey, look, try that again. I wasn't ready.

JUSTINE and DAVID sing joined by BITSY and JASON:

My dad said
Life is just like hockey
And I said
Hey, Wouldn't that be great?
I mean if
Life were like playing a game
Then if
Somebody told you the rules
You would know what to do
You could be on the team
You could go find some ice
And just skate.

A F T E R W O R D

1. a) Which character in the play do you identify with most, and why? Which character, if any, do you think is right about the issues that are considered? Discuss your point of view with a classmate.

   b) What would you say about Justine's desire to play hockey if you had a chance to record a one-minute message that would be broadcast on local radio? Tape your message and play it for a group or for the class.

2. The same song is sung near the beginning of the play and at the end. Improvise a choral reading of both versions with a group of classmates. What do you think the song is about? What feelings does it express? Is the mood of the song the same both times? Would anything change if Justine sang it by herself? What kind of music would fit the words? (You might name a song you know as an example.) Present your group's answers to the class.

3. If you could talk with Carol Bolt, what might you say to her about the way she presents teenagers in *Icetime*? Write your comments on her characterization in a letter to her.

4. a) With a group, list the "adult" characters in the play, and discuss how the audience is intended to respond to each of them.

   b) As the prop designer for *Icetime*, create props for two adult characters, keeping in mind the effect you want your props to convey to the audience. Present your prop designs to the class as sketches, written descriptions, or actual props. Ask your classmates to suggest how successful you have been in creating props that convey your sense of these two characters.

5. You have been hired by a theatre company to design a program for their production of *Icetime*. The program will be handed to members of the audience as they are being seated.

   With a group, decide what information the program will contain. Consider the following:
- credits for the director, cast, and crew
- photos or illustrations of the actors
- illustrations of highlights from the play
- a summary of the play

A MIDSUMMER NIGHT'S DREAM

BY WILLIAM SHAKESPEARE

DIRECTED BY ANNE STEVENSEN

COSTUME DESIGN
LOUISA MARCOTTE

LIGHTING DESIGN
CANDIDA LUDWIG

SET AND PROP DESIGN
MAURICE GLENDO

COMPOSER/MUSICAL
DIRECTOR
ELIS SZIGETHY

- a statement about the play's theme
- a catchy quotation taken from the play
- quotations from imaginary reviews of the play
- advertisements for local businesses
- a photo or short biography of the playwright

Create a display of all the programs. Which are the most informative? Which are the most eye-catching? As a class, comment on the strengths and weaknesses of each design. Which design should the theatre company choose?

6. Do you think the play has an effective ending? With a partner, invent another ending for the play. Describe your ending to another pair of classmates. Answer any questions they have, and ask them which ending they prefer. You might write a script for the new ending and perform it for your classmates.

7. Research the Justine Blainey story or the story of another girl or woman who has tried to break into male-dominated sports. Try to get articles from different stages in the story's development. Summarize the articles for the class, or display them on a poster.

8. Stage your own talk show, dividing the following roles among the class:
- Bitsy
- David
- Jason
- Justine
- Host
- Studio Audience

In secret, the studio audience brainstorms three questions to ask each guest. The host opens and closes the show, introduces the guests, and asks the questions. The students playing the guests answer the questions in role. The audience might participate by applauding, cheering, or laughing, but the host should control the show. After the show is over, each member of the audience could write a brief review of the show's highlights.

▼ ▼ ▼   *INTRODUCTION TO:*

A Marriage Proposal

Anton Chekhov

"Man will become better when you show him what he is like."
Anton Chekhov

he nineteenth-century writer Anton Chekhov was born in southern Russia in 1860. His grandfather was a serf who managed to buy his freedom. His father was a grocer who had to sneak off to Moscow to avoid his debts. Chekhov was left behind to earn his living and finish his schooling.

To escape the hardships and poverty of his early years, he entered the medical faculty of Moscow University and at the same time began writing for newspapers and magazines. This was the beginning of his dual career as doctor and writer. *A Marriage Proposal* is one of the one-act comedies that Chekhov wrote early in his career to make money to support his parents and large family. Although he called it jokingly "a bad little play," it was an instant success in Moscow and Saint Petersburg (now Leningrad) and is still popular today.

GETTING STARTED

1. Many stories end with lovers who are engaged or newly married and presumably about to live "happily ever after." In your experience, what kind of happiness do couples usually find in marriage? Write a journal entry in which you explore the kinds of happiness to be found in marriage? Share your thoughts with a group.

2. You have been asked to write a magazine article on one of these two topics:
- Five Tips for Finding the Right Partner
- Five Tips for Avoiding the Wrong Partner

In a group, brainstorm a list of ideas for your chosen topic, and then select the five suggestions you think are most valuable. Present your tips to the class.

3. Comedy often makes use of stereotypes or "stock characters": the vain person who is always telling people how wonderful he or she is, for example. The audience laughs at such characters because they behave in ridiculous and predictable ways. What comic stereotypes can you recall from recent movies and television programs? What stereotypes do you know about that were in the movies and television shows of ten years ago? Share your responses with your classmates.

▼ ▼ ▼ STAGE PLAY

A Marriage Proposal

Anton Chekov

CHARACTERS

CHUBUKOV—*a wealthy, middle-aged gentleman who owns an estate in nineteenth-century Russia*

NATALIA—*his daughter, an unmarried woman ready to take a husband*

LOMOV—*a neighbour gentleman, a neurotic bachelor of thirty-five*

(Chubukov's mansion—the living room.
Lomov enters, formally dressed in evening jacket, white gloves, top hat. He is nervous from the start.)

CHUBUKOV: *(Rising)* Well, look who's here! Ivan Vassilevitch! *(Shakes his hand warmly)*
What a surprise, old man! How are you?

LOMOV: Oh, not too bad. And you?

CHUBUKOV: Oh, we manage, we manage. Do sit down, please. You know, you've been neglecting your neighbours, my dear fellow. It's been ages. Say, why the formal dress? Tails, gloves, and so forth. Where's the funeral, my boy? Where are you headed?

LOMOV: Oh, nowhere. I mean, here; just to see you, my dear Stepan Stepanovitch.

CHUBUKOV: Then why the full dress, old boy? It's not New Year's, and so forth.

LOMOV: Well, you see, it's like this. I have come here, my dear Stepan Stepanovitch, to bother you with a request. More than once, or twice, or more than that, it has been my privilege to apply to you for assistance in things, and you've always, well, responded. I mean, well, you have. Yes. Excuse me, I'm

getting all mixed up. May I have a glass of water, my dear
Stepan Stepanovitch? *(Drinks)*

CHUBUKOV: *(Aside)* Wants to borrow some money. Not a chance!
(Aloud) What can I do for you my dear friend?

LOMOV: Well, you see, my dear Stepanitch . . . Excuse me, I mean
Stepan my Dearovitch . . . No, I mean, I get all confused, as
you can see. To make a long story short, you're the only one
who can help me. Of course, I don't deserve it, and there's no
reason why I should expect you to, and all that.

CHUBUKOV: Stop beating around the bush! Out with it!

LOMOV: In just a minute. I mean, now, right now. The truth is, I
have come to ask the hand . . . I mean, your daughter, Natalia
Stepanovna, I, I want to marry her!

CHUBUKOV: *(Overjoyed)* Great heavens! Ivan Vassilevitch! Say it
again!

LOMOV: I have come humbly to ask for the hand . . .

CHUBUKOV: *(Interrupting)* You're a prince! I'm overwhelmed,
delighted, and so forth. Yes, indeed, and all that!
(Hugs and kisses Lomov)
This is just what I've been hoping for. It's my fondest dream
come true. *(Sheds a tear)* And, you know, I've always looked
upon you, my boy, as if you were my own son. May God
grant to both of you His Mercy and His Love, and so forth.
Oh, I have been wishing for this . . . But why am I being so
idiotic? It's just that I'm off my rocker with joy, my boy!
Completely off my rocker! Oh, with all my soul I'm . . . I'll
go get Natalia, and so forth.

LOMOV: *(Deeply moved)* Dear Stepan Stepanovitch, do you think
she'll agree?

CHUBUKOV: Why, of course, old friend. Great heavens! As if she
wouldn't! Why she's crazy for you! Good God! Like a love-
sick cat, and so forth. Be right back. *(Leaves)*

LOMOV: God, it's cold. I'm gooseflesh all over, as if I had to take
a test. But the main thing is, to make up my mind, and keep
it that way. I mean, if I take time out to think, or if I hesitate,
or talk about it, or have ideals, or wait for real love, well, I'll
just never get married! Brrrr, it's cold! Natalia Stepanovna is
an excellent housekeeper. She's not too bad looking. She's
had a good education. What more could I ask? Nothing. I'm
so nervous, my ears are buzzing. *(Drinks)* Besides, I've just got
to get married. I'm thirty-five already. It's sort of a critical
age. I've got to settle down and lead a regular life. I mean,

I'm always getting palpitations, and I'm nervous, and I get upset so easy. Look, my lips are quivering, and my eyebrow's twitching. The worst thing is the night. Sleeping. I get into bed, doze off, and, suddenly, something inside me jumps. First my head snaps, and then my shoulder blade, and I roll out of bed like a lunatic and try to walk it off. Then I try to go back to sleep, but, as soon as I do, something jumps again! Twenty times a night, sometimes . . .

(Natalia Stepanovna enters)

NATALIA: Oh, it's only you. All Papa said was: 'Go inside, there's a merchant come to collect his goods.' How do you do, Ivan Vassilevitch?

LOMOV: How do you do, dear Natalia Stepanovna?

NATALIA: Excuse my apron, and not being dressed. We're shelling peas. You haven't been around lately. Oh, do sit down. *(They do)* Would you like some lunch?

LOMOV: No thanks, I had some.

NATALIA: Well, then smoke if you want. *(He doesn't)* The weather's nice today . . . but yesterday, it was so wet the workmen couldn't get a thing done. Have you got much hay in? I felt so greedy I had a whole field done, but now I'm not sure I was right. With the rain it could rot, couldn't it? I should have waited. But why are you so dressed up? Is there a dance or something? Of course, I must say you look splendid, but . . . Well, tell me, why are you so dressed up?

LOMOV: *(Excited)* Well, you see, my dear Natalia Stepanovna, the truth is, I made up my mind to ask you to . . . well, to, listen to me. Of course, it'll probably surprise you and even maybe make you angry, but . . . *(Aside)* God it's cold in here!

NATALIA: Why, what do you mean? *(A pause)* Well?

LOMOV: I'll try to get it over with. I mean, you know, my dear Natalia Stepanovna that I've known, since childhood, even, known, and had the privilege of knowing, your family. My late aunt, and her husband, who, as you know, left me my estate, they always had the greatest respect for your father, and your late mother. The Lomovs and the Chubukovs have always been very friendly, you might even say affectionate. And, of course, you know, our land borders on each other's. My Oxen Meadows touch your birch grove . . .

NATALIA: I hate to interrupt you, my dear Ivan Vassilevitch, but you said: 'my Oxen Meadows.' Do you really think they're yours?

LOMOV: Why of course they're mine.

NATALIA: What do you mean? The Oxen Meadows are ours, not yours!

LOMOV: Oh, no, my dear Natalia Stepanovna, they're mine.

NATALIA: Well, this is the first I've heard about it! Where did you get that idea?

LOMOV: Where? Why, I mean the Oxen Meadows that are wedged between your birches and the marsh.

NATALIA: Yes, of course, they're ours.

LOMOV: Oh, no, you're wrong, my dear Natalia Stepanovna, they're mine.

NATALIA: Now, come, Ivan Vassilevitch! How long have they been yours?

LOMOV: How long? Why, as long as I can remember!

NATALIA: Well, really, you can't expect me to believe that!

LOMOV: But, you can see for yourself in the deed, my dear Natalia Stepanovna. Of course, there was once a dispute about them, but everyone knows they're mine now. There's nothing to argue about. There was a time when my aunt's grandmother let your father's grandfather's peasants use the land, but they were supposed to bake bricks for her in return. Naturally, after a few years they began to act as if they owned it, but the real truth is . . .

NATALIA: That has nothing to do with the case! Both my grandfather and my great-grandfather said that their land went as far as the marsh, which means that the Meadows are ours! There's nothing whatever to argue about. It's foolish.

LOMOV: But I can show you the deed, Natalia Stepanovna.

NATALIA: You're just making fun of me . . . Great Heavens! Here we have the land for hundreds of years, and suddenly you try to tell us it isn't ours. What's wrong with you, Ivan Vassilevitch? Those meadows aren't even fifteen acres, and they're not worth three hundred rubles, but I just can't stand unfairness! I just can't stand unfairness!

LOMOV: But, you must listen to me. Your father's grandfather's peasants, as I've already tried to tell you, they were supposed to bake bricks for my aunt's grandmother. And my aunt's grandmother, why, she wanted to be nice to them . . .

NATALIA: It's just nonsense, this whole business about aunts and grandfathers and grandmothers. The Meadows are ours! That's all there is to it!

LOMOV: They're mine!

NATALIA: Ours! You can go on talking for two days, and you can put on fifteen evening coats and twenty pairs of gloves, but I tell you they're ours, ours, ours!

LOMOV: Natalia Stepanovna, I don't want the Meadows! I'm just acting on principle. If you want, I'll give them to you.

NATALIA: I'll give them to *you*! Because they're ours! And that's all there is to it! And if I may say so, your behaviour, my dear Ivan Vassilevitch, is very strange. Until now, we've always considered you a good neighbour, even a friend. After all, last year we lent you our threshing machine, even though it meant putting off our own threshing until November. And here you are treating us like a pack of gypsies. Giving me my own land, indeed! Really! Why that's not being a good neighbour. It's sheer impudence, that's what it is . . .

LOMOV: Oh, so you think I'm just a land-grabber? My dear lady, I've never grabbed anybody's land in my whole life, and no-one's going to accuse me of doing it now!
(Quickly walks over to the pitcher and drinks some more water)
The Oxen Meadows are mine!

NATALIA: That's a lie. They're ours!

LOMOV: Mine!

NATALIA: A lie! I'll prove it. I'll send my mowers out there today!

LOMOV: What?

NATALIA: My mowers will mow it today!

LOMOV: I'll kick them out!

NATALIA: You just dare!

LOMOV: *(Clutching his heart)* The Oxen Meadows are mine! Do you understand? Mine!

NATALIA: Please don't shout! You can shout all you want in your own house, but here I must ask you to control yourself.

LOMOV: If my heart wasn't palpitating the way it is, if my insides weren't jumping like mad, I wouldn't talk to you so calmly.
(Yelling) The Oxen Meadows are mine!

NATALIA: Ours!

LOMOV: Mine!

NATALIA: Ours!

LOMOV: Mine!
(Enter Chubukov)

CHUBUKOV: What's going on? Why all the shouting?

NATALIA: Papa, will you please inform this gentleman who owns the Oxen Meadows, he or we?

CHUBUKOV: *(To* Lomov*)* Why, they're ours, old fellow.

LOMOV: But how can they be yours, my dear Stepan Stepanov-itch? Be fair. Perhaps my aunt's grandmother did let your grandfather's peasants work the land, and maybe they did get so used to it that they acted as if it was their own, but . . .

CHUBUKOV: Oh, no, no . . . my dear boy. You forget something. The reason the peasants didn't pay your aunt's grandmother, and so forth, was that the land was disputed, even then. Since then it's been settled. Why, everyone knows it's ours.

LOMOV: I can prove it's mine.

CHUBUKOV: You can't prove a thing, old boy.

LOMOV: Yes I can!

CHUBUKOV: My dear lad, why yell like that? Yelling doesn't prove a thing. Look, I'm not after anything of yours, just as I don't intend to give up anything of mine. Why should I? Besides, if you're going to keep arguing about it, I'd just as soon give the land to the peasants, so there!

LOMOV: There nothing! Where do you get the right to give away someone else's property?

CHUBUKOV: I certainly ought to know if I have the right or not. And you had better realize it, because, my dear young man, I am not used to being spoken to in that tone of voice, and so forth. Besides which, my dear young man, I am twice as old as you are, and I ask you to speak to me without getting yourself into such a tizzy, and so forth!

LOMOV: Do you think I'm a fool? First you call my property yours, and then you expect me to keep calm and polite! Good neighbours don't act like that, my dear Stepan Ste-panovitch. You're no neighbour, you're a land grabber!

CHUBUKOV: What was that? What did you say?

NATALIA: Papa, send the mowers out to the meadows at once!

CHUBUKOV: What did you say, sir?

NATALIA: The Oxen Meadows are ours, and we'll never give them up, never, never, never, never!

LOMOV: We'll see about that. I'll go to court. I'll show you!

CHUBUKOV: Go to court? Well, go to court, and so forth! I know you, just waiting for a chance to go to court, and so forth. You pettifogging shyster, you! All of your family is like that. The whole bunch of them!

LOMOV: You leave my family out of this! The Lomovs have always been honourable, upstanding people, and not a one of them was ever tried for embezzlement, like your grandfather was.

CHUBUKOV: The Lomovs are a pack of lunatics, the whole bunch of them!

NATALIA: The whole bunch!

CHUBUKOV: Your grandfather was a drunkard, and what about your other aunt, the one who ran away with the architect? And so forth.

NATALIA: And so forth!

LOMOV: Your mother was a hunch back! *(Clutches at his heart)* Oh, I've got a stitch in my side . . . My head's whirling . . . Help! Water!

CHUBUKOV: Your father was a rum-soaked gambler.

NATALIA: And your aunt was queen of the scandalmongers!

LOMOV: My left foot's paralyzed. You're a plotter . . . Oh, my heart. It's an open secret that in the last elections you brib . . . I'm seeing stars! Where's my hat?

NATALIA: It's a low-mean, spiteful . . .

CHUBUKOV: And you're a two-faced, malicious schemer!

LOMOV: Here's my hat . . . Oh, my heart . . . Where's the door? How do I get out of here? . . . Oh, I think I'm going to die . . . My foot's numb. *(Goes)*

CHUBUKOV: *(Following him)* And don't you ever set foot in my house again!

NATALIA: Go to court, indeed! We'll see about that!

(Lomov staggers out)

CHUBUKOV: The devil with him!

(Gets a drink, walks back and forth excited)

NATALIA: What a rascal! How can you trust your neighbours after an incident like that?

CHUBUKOV: The villain! The scarecrow!

NATALIA: He's a monster! First he tries to steal our land, and then he has the nerve to yell at you.

CHUBUKOV: Yes, and that turnip, that stupid rooster, has the gall to make a proposal. Some proposal!

NATALIA: What proposal?

CHUBUKOV: Why, he came to propose to you.

NATALIA: To propose? To me? Why didn't you tell me before?

CHUBUKOV: So he gets all dressed up in his formal clothes. That stuffed sausage, that dried up cabbage!

NATALIA: To propose to me? Ohhhh!

(Falls into a chair and starts wailing)

Bring him back! Back! Go get him! Bring him back! Ohhhh!

CHUBUKOV: Bring who back?

NATALIA: Hurry up, hurry up! I'm sick. Get him! *(Complete hysterics)*

CHUBUKOV: What for? *(To her)* What's the matter with you? *(Clutches his head)* Oh, what a fool I am! I'll shoot myself! I'll hang myself! I ruined her chances!

NATALIA: I'm dying. Get him!

CHUBUKOV: All right, all right, right away! Only don't yell! *(He runs out.)*

NATALIA: What are they doing to me? Get him! Bring him back! Bring him back!

(A pause. Chubukov runs in)

CHUBUKOV: He's coming, and so forth, the snake. Oof! You talk to him. I'm not in the mood.

NATALIA: *(Wailing)* Bring him back! Bring him back!

CHUBUKOV: *(Yelling)* I told you, he's coming! Oh Lord, what agony to be the father of a grown-up daughter. I'll cut my throat some day, I swear I will. *(To her)* We cursed him, we insulted him, abused him, kicked him out, and now . . . because you, you . . .

NATALIA: Me? It was all your fault!

CHUBUKOV: My fault? What do you mean my fau..? *(Lomov appears in the doorway)* Talk to him yourself!

(Goes out. Lomov enters, exhausted)

LOMOV: What palpitations! My heart! And my foot's absolutely asleep. Something keeps giving me a stitch in the side . . .

NATALIA: You must forgive us, Ivan Vassilevitch. We all got too excited. I remember now. The Oxen Meadows are yours.

LOMOV: My heart's beating something awful. My Meadows. My eyebrows, they're both twitching!

NATALIA: Yes, the Meadows are all yours, yes, yours. Do sit down. *(They sit)* We were wrong, of course.

LOMOV: I argued on principle. My land isn't worth so much to me, but the principle . . .

NATALIA: Oh, yes, of course, the principle, that's what counts. But let's change the subject.

LOMOV: Besides, I have evidence. You see, my aunt's grandmother let your father's grandfather's peasants use the land . . .

NATALIA: Yes, yes, yes, but forget all that. *(Aside)* I wish I knew how to get him going. *(Aloud)* Are you going to start hunting soon?

LOMOV: After the harvest I'll try for grouse. But oh, my dear

Natalia Stepanovna, have you heard about the bad luck I've had? You know my dog, Guess? He's gone lame.

NATALIA: What a pity. Why?

LOMOV: I don't know. He must have twisted his leg, or got in a fight, or something. *(Sighs)* My best dog, to say nothing of the cost. I paid Mironov 125 rubles for him.

NATALIA: That was too high, Ivan Vassilevitch.

LOMOV: I think it was quite cheap. He's a first class dog.

NATALIA: Why Papa only paid eighty-five rubles for Squeezer, and he's much better than Guess.

LOMOV: Squeezer better than Guess! What an idea! *(Laughs)* Squeezer better than Guess!

NATALIA: Of course he's better. He may still be too young but on points and pedigree, he's a better dog even than any Volcha-netsky owns.

LOMOV: Excuse me, Natalia Stepanovna, but you're forgetting he's overshot, and overshot dogs are bad hunters.

NATALIA: Oh, so he's overshot, is he? Well, this is the first time I've heard about it.

LOMOV: Believe me, his lower jaw is shorter than his upper.

NATALIA: You've measured them?

LOMOV: Yes. He's all right for pointing, but if you want him to retrieve . . .

NATALIA: In the first place, our Squeezer is a thoroughbred, the son of Harness and Chisel, while your mutt doesn't even have a pedigree. He's as old and worn out as a pedlar's horse.

LOMOV: He may be old, but I wouldn't take five Squeezers for him. How can you argue? Guess is a dog, Squeezer's a laugh. Anyone you can name has a dog like Squeezer hanging around somewhere. They're under every bush. If he only cost twenty-five rubles you got cheated.

NATALIA: The devil is in you today, Ivan Vassilevitch! You want to contradict everything. First you pretend the Oxen Meadows are yours, and now you say Guess is better than Squeezer. People should say what they really mean, and you know Squeezer is a hundred times better than Guess. Why say he isn't?

LOMOV: So, you think I'm a fool or a blind man, Natalia Stepa-novna! Once and for all, Squeezer is overshot!

NATALIA: He is not!

LOMOV: He is so!

NATALIA: He is not!

LOMOV: Why shout, my dear lady?

NATALIA: Why talk such nonsense? It's terrible. Your Guess is old enough to be buried, and you compare him with Squeezer!

LOMOV: I'm sorry, I can't go on. My heart . . . it's palpitating!

NATALIA: I've always noticed that the hunters who argue most don't know a thing.

LOMOV: Please! Be quiet a moment. My heart's falling apart . . . *(Shouts)* Shut up!

NATALIA: I'm not going to shut up until you admit that Squeezer's a hundred times better than Guess.

LOMOV: A hundred times worse! His head . . . My eyes . . . shoulder . . .

NATALIA: Guess is half-dead already!

LOMOV: *(Weeping)* Shut up! My heart's exploding!

NATALIA: I won't shut up!

(Chubukov comes in)

CHUBUKOV: What's the trouble now?

NATALIA: Papa, will you please tell us which is the better dog, his Guess or our Squeezer?

LOMOV: Stepan Stepanovitch, I implore you to tell me just one thing. Is your Squeezer overshot or not? Yes or no?

CHUBUKOV: Well what if he is? He's still the best dog in the neigbourhood, and so forth.

LOMOV: Oh, but isn't my dog, Guess, better? Really?

CHUBUKOV: Don't get yourself so fraught up, old man. Of course, your dog has his good points—thoroughbred, firm on his feet, well sprung ribs, and so forth. But, my dear fellow, you've got to admit he has two defects; he's old and he's short in the muzzle.

LOMOV: Short in the muzzle? Oh, my heart! Let's look at the facts! On the Marusinsky hunt my dog ran neck and neck with the Count's, while Squeezer was a mile behind them . . .

CHUBUKOV: That's because the Count's groom hit him with a whip.

LOMOV: And he was right, too! We were fox hunting; what was your dog chasing sheep for?

CHUBUKOV: That's a lie! Look, I'm going to lose my temper . . . *(Controlling himself)* my dear friend, so let's stop arguing, for that reason alone. You're only arguing because we're all jealous of somebody else's dog. Who can help it? As soon as you realize some dog is better than yours, in this case our dog, you start in with this and that, and the next thing you know—pure jealousy! I remember the whole business.

LOMOV: I remember too!

CHUBUKOV: *(Mimicking)* 'I remember too!' What do you remember?

LOMOV: My heart . . . my foot's asleep . . . I can't . . .

NATALIA: *(Mimicking)* 'My heart . . . my foot's asleep.' What kind of a hunter are you? You should be hunting cockroaches in the kitchen, not foxes. 'My heart!'

CHUBUKOV: Yes, what kind of a hunter are you anyway? You should be sitting at home with your palpitations, not tracking down animals. You don't hunt anyhow. You just go out to argue with people and interfere with their dogs, and so forth. For God's sake, let's change the subject before I lose my temper. Anyway, you're just not a hunter.

LOMOV: But you, you're a hunter? Ha! You only go hunting to get in good with the Count, and to plot, and intrigue, and scheme . . . Oh, my heart! You're a schemer, that's what!

CHUBUKOV: What's that? Me a schemer? *(Shouting)* Shut up!

LOMOV: A schemer!

CHUBUKOV: You infant! You puppy!

LOMOV: You old rat! You hawk!

CHUBUKOV: You shut up, or I'll shoot you down like a partridge! You idiot!

LOMOV: Everyone knows that—oh, my heart—that your wife used to beat you . . . Oh, my feet . . . my head . . . I'm seeing stars . . . I'm going to faint!
(He drops into an armchair)
Quick, a doctor! *(Faints)*

CHUBUKOV: *(Going on, oblivious)* Baby! Weakling! Idiot! I'm getting sick. *(Drinks water)* Me! I'm sick!

NATALIA: What kind of a hunter are you? You can't even sit on a horse! *(To her father)* Papa, what's the matter with him? Look, papa! *(Screaming)* Ivan Vassilevitch! He's dead.

CHUBUKOV: I'm choking, I can't breathe . . . Give me air.

NATALIA: He's dead! *(Pulling Lomov's sleeve)* Ivan Vassilevitch! Ivan Vassilevitch! What have you done to me? He's dead!
(She falls into an armchair. Screaming hysterically)
A doctor! A doctor! A doctor!

CHUBUKOV: Ohhhh . . . What's the matter? What happened?

NATALIA: *(Wailing)* He's dead! He's dead!

CHUBUKOV: Who's dead? *(Looks at Lomov)* My God, he is! Quick! Water! A doctor!
(Puts glass to Lomov's lips)

Here, drink this! Can't drink it—he must be dead, and so forth . . . Oh what a miserable life! Why don't I shoot myself! I should have cut my throat long ago! What am I waiting for? Give me a knife! Give me a pistol!
(Lomov stirs)
Look, he's coming to. Here, drink some water. That's it.

LOMOV: I'm seeing stars . . . misty . . . Where am I?

CHUBUKOV: Just you hurry up and get married, and then the devil with you! She accepted.
(Puts Lomov's hand in Natalia's)
She accepts and so forth! I give you my blessing, and so forth! Only leave me in peace!

LOMOV: *(Getting up)* Huh? What? Who?

CHUBUKOV: She accepts! Well! Kiss her, damn you!

NATALIA: He's alive! Yes, yes, I accept.

CHUBUKOV: Kiss each other!

LOMOV: Huh? Kiss? Kiss who? *(They kiss)* That's nice. I mean, excuse me, what happened? Oh, now I get it . . . my heart . . . those stars . . . I'm very happy, Natalia Stepanovna. *(Kisses her hand)* My foot's asleep.

NATALIA: I . . . I'm happy too.

CHUBUKOV: What a load off my shoulders! Whew!

NATALIA: Well, now maybe you'll admit that Squeezer is better than Guess?

LOMOV: Worse!

NATALIA: Better!

CHUBUKOV: What a way to enter matrimonial bliss! Let's have some champagne!

LOMOV: He's worse!

NATALIA: Better! Better, better, better, better!

CHUBUKOV: *(Trying to shout her down)* Champagne! Bring some champagne! Champagne! Champagne!

A F T E R W O R D

1. In pairs, improvise a conversation between Lomov and a marriage counsellor. Lomov should explain his reasons for wanting to marry Natalia; the counsellor should say whether or not Lomov has made a good choice, and should give him some advice about the proposal.

2. Imagine that Chekhov is being interviewed by the host of a talk show:
HOST: Anton, you once said that "man will become better when you show him what he is like." Tell me, is there perhaps a serious side to *A Marriage Proposal*?
Roleplay the rest of the interview with a partner.

3. Part of the humour in this play comes from a "comic misunderstanding" — Natalia doesn't know that Lomov wants to propose to her. Watch several television comedies and note whether the writers use a comic misunderstanding to create the humour. Your notes should include your own response. (Did you find the misunderstanding believable? Did you find it humorous?) Present your findings to a group or to the class. Together, discuss whether similar misunderstandings ever happen in real life.

4. In nineteenth-century Russia, disputes over property were often dramatized because wealth and property were important, and quarrels often arose over money obligations and property rights. How do concerns over money and material possessions cause problems today? Write a journal entry about a time when you had a conflict with someone over money or possessions.

5. Your group is the production team whose job is to create the book cover for a new paperback edition of *A Marriage Proposal*. Your task is to design the front cover, the spine, and the back cover, including a short "blurb" intended to persuade a modern reader to buy the book. Write one or two paragraphs explaining the rationale behind your cover. How does it relate to the play? What audience do you think will buy the book? Why will your cover attract these readers? Post the cover designs in the classroom, and discuss which elements of each cover are most effective.

6. How successful do you think the marriage between Lomov and Natalia will be? What problems might each character encounter

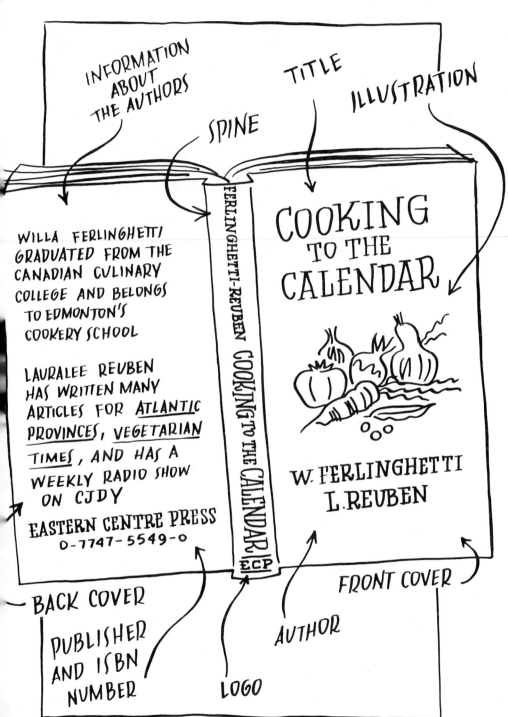

INFORMATION ABOUT THE AUTHORS

TITLE

ILLUSTRATION

SPINE

WILLA FERLINGHETTI GRADUATED FROM THE CANADIAN CULINARY COLLEGE AND BELONGS TO EDMONTON'S COOKERY SCHOOL

LAURALEE REUBEN HAS WRITTEN MANY ARTICLES FOR ATLANTIC PROVINCES, VEGETARIAN TIMES, AND HAS A WEEKLY RADIO SHOW ON CJDY

EASTERN CENTRE PRESS
0-7747-5549-0

FERLINGHETTI-REUBEN COOKING TO THE CALENDAR ECP

COOKING TO THE CALENDAR

W. FERLINGHETTI
L. REUBEN

BACK COVER

PUBLISHER AND ISBN NUMBER

LOGO

AUTHOR

FRONT COVER

after the marriage? Read several horoscopes to see how they are written, and then write horoscopes for both Lomov and Natalia for the day of their wedding. Share your horoscopes with classmates, and see if they can decide which horoscope is Lomov's and which is Natalia's.

7. Choose a scene or part of a scene from the play, and rewrite it as a modern play. (In nineteenth-century drama, a new scene begins whenever a character enters or leaves the stage.) Try to retain the basic character types and the dramatic conflict, but change the characterizations, the dialogue, and the situation to make the scene contemporary.

Present your scene to the class. Ask your audience for their opinions on the strengths of your presentation, and have them comment on how successful you have been in updating the play.

▼ ▼ ▼ *INTRODUCTION TO:*

The Miracle Worker

William Gibson

"Like all plays based upon fact, *The Miracle Worker* contains elements of fiction—but it is the kind of fiction which makes the drama seem more believable than it would be if it clung strictly to fact."
William Gibson

nnie Sullivan became famous as the teacher of Helen Keller, a blind, deaf, and mute child who overcame her disabilities and eventually became one of the most distinguished women of her time. The American playwright William Gibson discovered some of Annie's letters in a library that told the story of her struggle to help the young Helen, and he used these letters as the basis for *The Miracle Worker.*

This is Gibson's description of Helen as Annie first encountered her: "Having lost in infancy sight, hearing, and the resources of language, [Helen] had lived ever since like an animal—worse, with a soul, shackled, wild with rages and despair. Annie arrived in Tuscumbia on March 3, 1887, with the staggering task of putting this deaf, mute, blind bundle of fierce flesh in touch with all human intelligence. She was twenty years old."

On April 5, 1887, Annie managed to perform the needed "miracle." The two women remained lifelong friends.

GETTING STARTED

1. Imagine that you have become deaf and blind. What problems might you encounter if you tried to go through an ordinary day in your life? How do you think family, friends, other students, and teachers would treat you? What feelings might you experience? Jot down some of the key words that come to mind as you think about these questions. Discuss your key words with a classmate.

2. You have been placed in charge of a six-year-old child who has been allowed to throw tantrums whenever she doesn't get what she wants. How would you handle the child? Share your responses with a group. If there are any differences, you might want to try roleplaying the differing approaches and discussing what you think is effective about each one. Which members of your group have actually taken care of a young child?

3. Sometimes a problem someone is having can create conflict within the person's family, especially when each family member has a different idea about how to handle the problem. Have you or people you know faced this situation? What was the problem? How did it affect the other family members? Was the problem ever solved? How? Write about the problem and its effects in your journal, or talk about the situation with a partner.

▼ ▼ ▼   STAGE PLAY

The Miracle Worker

William Gibson

CHARACTERS

HELEN KELLER—*a strong-willed girl of six who has been blind and deaf almost from birth*

KATE KELLER—*Helen's mother, a young woman who is desperate to help her daughter*

CAPTAIN KELLER—*Kate's husband, an Alabama gentleman many years older than Kate*

JAMES KELLER—*the Captain's son by a previous marriage, a young man*

ANNIE SULLIVAN—*a young woman of twenty, specially trained to teach disabled children*

AUNT EV—*Captain Keller's sister*

VINEY—*housekeeper to the Kellers*

MARTHA
PERCY } *Viney's children*

ANAGNOS—*Annie's teacher at the Perkins Institution for the Blind*

A DOCTOR

BLIND GIRLS

OFFSTAGE VOICES

ACT ONE

THE TIME:
The 1880s.

THE PLACE:
In and around the Keller *homestead in Tuscumbia, Alabama; also, briefly, the Perkins Institution for the Blind in Boston.*

DOCTOR : Just let her get well, she knows how to do it better than we do.

(He is packed, ready to leave.)

Main thing is the fever's gone, these things come and go in infants, never know why. Call it acute congestion of the stomach and brain.

KELLER: I'll see you to your buggy, Doctor.

DOCTOR : I've never seen a baby, more vitality, that's the truth.

(He beams a good night at the baby and Kate, *and* Keller *leads him downstairs with a lamp. They go down the porch steps, and across the yard, where the* Doctor *goes off left;* Keller *stands with the lamp aloft,* Kate *meanwhile is bent lovingly over the crib, which emits a bleat; her finger is playful with the baby's face.)*

KATE: Hush. Don't you cry now, you've been trouble enough. Call it acute congestion, indeed, I don't see what's so cute about a congestion, just because it's yours. We'll have your father run an editorial in his paper, the wonders of modern medicine, they don't know what they're curing even when they cure it. Men, men and their battle scars, we women will have to —

(But she breaks off, puzzled, moves her finger before the baby's eyes.)

Will have to — Helen?

(Now she moves her hand, quickly.)

Helen.

(She snaps her fingers at the baby's eyes twice, and her hand falters; after a moment she calls out, loudly.)

Captain. Captain, will you come —

(But she stares at the baby, and her next call is directly at her ears.)

Captain!

(And now, still staring, Kate *screams,* Keller *in the yard hears it, and runs with the lamp back to the house.* Kate *screams again, her look intent on the baby and terrible.* Keller *hurries in and up.)*

KELLER: Kate? What's wrong?

KATE: Look.

(She makes a pass with her hand in the crib, at the baby's eyes.)

KELLER: What, Katie? She's well, she needs only time to —

KATE: She can't see. Look at her eyes.

(She takes the lamp from him, moves it before the child's face.)

She can't *see*!

KELLER: *(Hoarsely)* Helen.

KATE: Or hear. When I screamed she didn't blink. Not an
eyelash —

KELLER: Helen. Helen!

KATE: She can't *hear* you!

KELLER: *Helen*!

(His face has something like fury in it, crying the child's name;
Kate *almost fainting presses her knuckles to her mouth, to stop
her own cry.*

The room dims out quickly.

*Time, in the form of a slow tune of distant belfry chimes
which approaches in a crescendo and then fades, passes; the
light comes up again on a day five years later, on three kneeling
children and an old dog outside around the pump.*

The dog is a setter named Belle, *and she is sleeping. Two of
the children are blacks,* Martha *and* Percy. *The third child is*
Helen, *six and a half years old, quite unkempt, in body a viva-
cious little person with a fine head, attractive, but noticeably
blind, one eye larger and protruding; her gestures are abrupt,
insistent, lacking in human restraint, and her face never smiles.
She is flanked by the other two, in a litter of paper-doll cutouts,
and while they speak* Helen's *hands thrust at their faces in turn,
feeling bafflledly at the movements of their lips.)*

MARTHA: *(Snipping)* First I'm gonna cut off this doctor's legs one,
two, now then —

PERCY: Why you cuttin' off that doctor's legs?

MARTHA: I'm gonna give him a operation. Now I'm gonna cut off
his arms, one, two. Now I'm gonna fix up —

(She pushes Helen's *hand away from her mouth.)*

You stop that.

PERCY: Cut off his stomach, that's a good operation.

MARTHA: No, I'm gonna cut off his head first, he got a bad cold.

PERCY: Ain't gonna be much of that doctor left to fix up, time
you finish all them opera —

(But Helen *is poking her fingers inside his mouth, to feel his
tongue; he bites at them, annoyed and she jerks them away.*
Helen *now fingers her own lips, moving them in imitation, but
soundlessly.)*

MARTHA: What you do, bit her hand?

PERCY: That's how I do, she keep pokin' her fingers in my
mouth, I just bite 'em off.

MARTHA: What she tryin' do now?

PERCY: She tryin' *talk*. She gonna get mad. Looka her tryin' talk. *(Helen is scowling, the lips under her fingertips moving in ghostly silence, growing more and more frantic, until in a bizarre rage she bites at her own fingers. This sends Percy off into laughter, but alarms Martha.)*

MARTHA: Hy, you stop now.

(She pulls Helen's hand down.)

You just sit quiet and —

(But at once Helen topples Martha on her back, knees pinning her shoulders down, and grabs the scissors. Martha screams. Percy darts to the bell string on the porch, yanks it, and the bell rings.

Inside, the lights have been gradually coming up on the main room, where we see the family informally gathered, talking, but in pantomime: Kate sits darning socks near a cradle, occasionally rocking it; Captain Keller in spectacles is working over newspaper pages at a table; a benign visitor in a hat, Aunt Ev, is sharing the sewing basket, putting the finishing touches on a big shapeless doll made out of towels; an indolent young man, James Keller, is at the window watching the children.

With the ring of the bell, Kate is instantly on her feet and out the door onto the porch, to take in the scene; how we see what these five years have done to her, the girlish playfulness is gone, she is a woman steeled in grief.)

KATE: *(For the thousandth time)* Helen.

(She is down the steps at once to them, seizing Helen's wrists and lifting her off Martha; Martha runs off in tears and screams for momma, with Percy after her.)

Let me have those scissors.

(Meanwhile the family inside is alerted, Aunt Ev joining James at the window, Captain Keller resumes work.)

JAMES: *(Blandly)* She only dug Martha's eyes out. Almost dug.

It's always almost, no point worrying till it happens, is there? *(They gaze out, while Kate reaches for the scissors in Helen's hand. But Helen pulls the scissors back, they struggle for them a moment, then Kate gives up, lets Helen keep them. She tries to draw Helen into the house. Helen jerks away. Kate next goes down on her knees, takes Helen's hands gently, and using the scissors like a doll, makes Helen caress and cradle them; she points Helen's finger housewards. Helen's whole body now becomes eager; she surrenders the scissors, Kate turns her toward the door and gives her a little push.* Helen *scrambles up and toward the house, and* Kate *rising follows her.)*

AUNT EV: How does she stand it? Why haven't you seen this Baltimore man? It's not a thing you can let go on and on, like the weather.

JAMES: The weather here doesn't ask permission of me, Aunt Ev. Speak to my father.

AUNT EV: Arthur. Something ought to be done for that child.

KELLER: A refreshing suggestion. What?

(Kate entering turns Helen to Aunt Ev, who gives her the towel doll.)

AUNT EV: Why, this very famous oculist in Baltimore I wrote you about, what was his name?

KATE: Dr. Chisholm.

AUNT EV: Yes. I heard lots of cases of blindness people thought couldn't be cured he's cured, he just does wonders. Why don't you write to him?

KELLER: I've stopped believing in wonders.

KATE: *(Rocks the cradle)* I think the Captain will write to him soon. Won't you, Captain?

KELLER: No.

JAMES: *(Lightly)* Good money after bad, or bad after good. Or bad after bad—

AUNT EV: Well, if it's just a question of money, Arthur, now you're marshal you have this Yankee money. Might as well—

KELLER: Not money. The child's been to specialists all over Alabama and Tennessee. If I thought it would do good I'd have her to every fool doctor in the country.

KATE: I think the Captain will write to him soon.

KELLER: Katie. How many times can you let them break your heart?

KATE: Any number of times.

(Helen meanwhile sits on the floor to explore the doll with her fingers, and her hand pauses over the face; this is no face, a blank area of towel, and it troubles her. Her hand searches for features, and taps questioningly for eyes, but no one notices. She then yanks at her Aunt's dress, and taps again vigorously for eyes.)

AUNT EV: What, child?

(Obviously not hearing, Helen commences to go around, from person to person tapping for eyes, but no one attends or understands.)

KATE: *(No break)* As long as there's the least chance. For her to see, or hear, or —

KELLER: There isn't. Now I must finish here.

KATE: I think, with your permission, Captain, I'd like to write.

KELLER: I said no, Katie.

AUNT EV: Why, writing does no harm, Arthur, only a little bitty letter. To see if he can help her.

KELLER: He can't.

KATE: We won't know that to be a fact, Captain, until after you write.

KELLER: *(Rising, emphatic)* Katie, he can't. *(He collects his papers.)*

JAMES: *(Facetiously)* Father stands up, that makes it a fact.

KELLER: You be quiet! I'm badgered enough here by females without your impudence.

(James shuts up, makes himself scarce. Helen now is groping among things on Keller's desk, and paws his papers to the floor. Keller is exasperated.)
Katie.

(Kate quickly turns Helen away, and retrieves the papers.)
I might as well try to work in a henyard as in this house —

JAMES: *(Placating)* You really ought to put her away, Father.

KATE: *(Staring up)* What?

JAMES: Some asylum. It's the kindest thing.

AUNT EV: Why, she's your sister, James, not a nobody —

JAMES: Half sister, and half — mentally defective, she can't even keep herself clean. It's not pleasant to see her about all the time.

KATE: Do you dare? Complain of what you can see?

KELLER: *(Very annoyed)* This discussion is at an end! I'll thank you not to broach it again, Ev.

(Silence descends at once. Helen gropes the way with the doll, and Keller turns back for a final word, explosive.)
I've done as much as I can bear, I can't give my whole life to it! The house is at sixes and sevens from morning till night over the child, it's time some attention was paid to Mildred here instead!

KATE: *(Gently dry)* You'll wake her up, Captain.

KELLER: I want some peace in the house, I don't care how, but one way we won't have it is by rushing up and down the country every time someone hears of a new quack. I'm as sensible to this affliction as anyone else, it hurts me to look at the girl.

KATE: It was not our affliction I meant you to write about, Captain.

(Helen is back at Aunt Ev, *fingering her dress, and yanks two buttons from it.)*

AUNT EV: Helen! My buttons.

(Helen pushes the buttons into the doll's face. Kate *now sees, comes swiftly to kneel, lifts,* Helen's *hand to her own eyes in question.)*

KATE: Eyes?

(Helen nods energetically.)

She wants the doll to have eyes.

(Another kind of silence now, while Kate *takes pins and buttons from the sewing basket and attaches them to the doll as eyes.* Keller *stands, caught, and watches morosely.* Aunt Ev *blinks, and conceals her emotions by inspecting her dress.)*

AUNT EV: My goodness me, I'm not decent.

KATE: She doesn't know better, Aunt Ev. I'll sew them on again.

JAMES: Never learn with everyone letting her do anything she takes it into her mind to —

KELLER: You be quiet!

JAMES: What did I say now?

KELLER: You talk too much.

JAMES: I was agreeing with you!

KELLER: Whatever it was. Deprived child, the least she can have are the little things she wants.

(James, very wounded, stalks out of the room, onto the porch; he remains here, sulking.)

AUNT EV: *(Indulgently)* It's worth a couple of buttons, Kate, look.

(Helen now has the doll with eyes, and cannot contain herself for joy; she rocks the doll, pats it vigorously, kisses it.)

This child has more sense than all these men Kellers, if there's ever any way to reach that mind of hers.

(But Helen *suddenly has come upon the cradle, and unhesitatingly overturns it; the swaddled baby tumbles out, and* Captain Keller *barely manages to dive and catch it in time.)*

KELLER: *Helen!*

(All are in commotion, the baby screams, but Helen *unperturbed is laying her doll in its place,* Kate *on her knees pulls her hands off the cradle, wringing them;* Helen *is bewildered.)*

KATE: Helen, Helen, you're not to do such things, how can I make you understand —

KELLER: *(Hoarsely)* Katie.

KATE: How can I get it into your head, my darling, my poor —

KELLER: Katie, some way of teaching her an iota of discipline has to be —

KATE: *(Flaring)* How can you discipline an afflicted child? Is it her fault?

(Helen's fingers have fluttered to her mother's lips, vainly trying to comprehend their movements.*)*

KELLER: I didn't say it was her fault.

KATE: Then whose? I don't know what to do! How can I teach her, beat her — until she's black and blue?

KELLER: It's not safe to let her run around loose. Now there must be a way of confining her, somehow, so she can't —

KATE: Where, in a cage? She's a growing child, she has to use her limbs!

KELLER: Answer me one thing, is it fair to Mildred here?

KATE: *(Inexorably)* Are you willing to put her away?

(Now Helen's *face darkens in the same rage as at herself earlier, and her hand strikes at* Kate's *lips.* Kate *catches her hand again, and* Helen *begins to kick, struggle, twist.)*

KELLER: Now what?

KATE: She wants to talk, like — *be* like you and me.

(She holds Helen *struggling until we hear from the child her first sound so far, an inarticulate weird noise in her throat such as an animal in a trap might make; and* Kate *releases her. The second she is free* Helen *blunders away, collides violently with a chair, falls, and sits weeping.* Kate *comes to her, embraces, caresses, soothes her, and buries her own face in her hair, until she can control her voice.)*

Every day she slips further away. And I don't know how to call her back.

AUNT EV: Oh, I've a mind to take her up to Baltimore myself. If that doctor can't help her, maybe he'll know who can.

KELLER: *(Presently, heavily)* I'll write the man, Katie.

(He stands with the baby in his clasp, staring at Helen's *head, hanging down on* Kate's *arm.*

The lights dim out, except the one on Kate *and* Helen. *In the twilight,* James, Aunt Ev, *and* Keller *move off slowly, formally, in separate directions;* Kate *with* Helen *in her arms remains, motionless, in an image which overlaps into the next scene and fades only when it is well under way.*

Without pause, from the dark down left we hear a man's voice with a Greek accent speaking:)

ANAGNOS: —who could do nothing for the girl, of course. It was
Dr. Bell who thought she might somehow be taught. I have
written the family only that a suitable governess, Miss Annie
Sullivan, has been found here in Boston—

*(The lights begin to come up, down left, on a long table and
chair. The table contains equipment for teaching the blind by
touch—a small replica of the human skeleton, stuffed animals,
models of flowers and plants, piles of books. The chair contains a girl of 20,* Annie Sullivan, *with a face which in repose
is grave and rather obstinate, and when active is impudent,
combative, twinkling with all the life that is lacking in
Helen's, and handsome; there is a crude vitality to her. Her
suitcase is at her knee.* Anagnos, *a stocky bearded man, comes
into the light only towards the end of his speech.)*
—and will come. It will no doubt be difficult for you there,
Annie. But it has been difficult for you at our school too, hm?
Gratifying, yes, when you came to us and could not spell
your name, to accomplish so much here in a few years, but
always an Irish battle. For independence.
(He studies Annie, *humorously; she does not open her eyes.)*
This is my last time to counsel you, Annie, and you do lack
some—by some I mean all—what, tact or talent to bend. To
others. And what has saved you on more than one occasion
here at Perkins is that there was nowhere to expel you to.
Your eyes hurt?
ANNIE: My ears, Mr. Anagnos.
*(And now she has opened her eyes; they are inflamed, vague,
slightly crossed, clouded by the granular growth of trachoma,
and she often keeps them closed to shut out the pain of light.)*
ANAGNOS: *(Severely)* Nowhere but back to Tewksbury, where chil-
dren learn to be saucy. Annie, I know how dreadful it was
there, but that battle is dead and done with, why not let it
stay buried?
ANNIE: *(Cheerily)* I think God must owe me a resurrection.
ANAGNOS: *(A bit shocked)* What?
ANNIE: *(Taps her brow)* Well, He keeps digging up that battle!
ANAGNOS: That is not a proper thing to say, Annie. It is what I
mean.
ANNIE: *(Meekly)* Yes. But I know what I'm like, what's this child
like?
ANAGNOS: Like?
ANNIE: Well—bright or dull, to start off.

ANAGNOS: No one knows. And if she is dull, you have no patience with this?

ANNIE: Oh, in grownups you have to, Mr. Anagnos. I mean in children it just seems a little—precocious, can I use that word?

ANAGNOS: Only if you can spell it.

ANNIE: Premature. So I hope at least she's a bright one.

ANAGNOS: Deaf, blind, mute—who knows? She is like a little safe, locked, that no one can open. Perhaps there is a treasure inside.

ANNIE: Maybe it's empty, too?

ANAGNOS: Possible. I should warn you, she is much given to tantrums.

ANNIE: Means something is inside. Well, so am I, if I believe all I hear. Maybe you should warn *them*.

ANAGNOS: *(Frowns)* Annie. I wrote them no word of your history. You will find yourself among strangers now, who know nothing of it.

ANNIE: Well, we'll keep them in a state of blessed ignorance.

ANAGNOS: Perhaps *you* should tell it?

ANNIE: *(Bristling)* Why? I have enough trouble with people who don't know.

ANAGNOS: So they will understand. When you have trouble.

ANNIE: The only time I have trouble is when I'm right.
(But she is amused at herself, as is Anagnos.)
Is it my fault it's so often? I won't give them trouble, Mr. Anagnos, I'll be so ladylike they won't notice I've come.

ANAGNOS: Annie, be—humble. It is not as if you have so many offers to pick and choose. You will need their affection, working with this child.

ANNIE: *(Humorously)* I hope I won't need their pity.

ANAGNOS: Oh, we can all use some pity. *(Crisply)* So. You are no longer our pupil, we throw you into the world, a teacher. If the child can be taught. No one expects you to work miracles, even for twenty-five dollars a month. Now, in this envelope a loan, for the railroad, which you will repay me when you have a bank account. But in this box, a gift. With our love.
(Annie opens the small box he extends, and sees a garnet ring. She looks up, blinking, and down.)
I think other friends are ready to say goodbye.
(He moves as though to open doors.)

ANNIE: Mr. Anagnos.
(Her voice is trembling.)
Dear Mr. Anagnos I—
(But she swallows over getting the ring on her finger, and cannot continue until she finds a woebegone joke.)
Well, what should I say, I'm an ignorant opinionated girl, and everything I am I owe to you?

ANAGNOS: *(Smiles)* That is only half true, Annie.

ANNIE: Which half? I crawled in here like a drowned rat, I thought I died when Jimmie died, that I'd never again—come alive. Well, you say with love so easy, and I haven't *loved* a soul and I never will, I suppose, but this place gave me more than my eyes back. Or taught me how to spell, which I'll never learn anyway, but with all the fights and the trouble I've been here it taught me what help is, and how to live again, and I don't want to say goodbye. Don't open the door, I'm crying.

ANAGNOS: *(Gently)* They will not see.

(He moves again as though opening doors, and in comes a group of Girls, *8-year-olds to 17-year-olds; as they walk we see they are blind.* Anagnos *shepherds them in with a hand.)*

A CHILD: Annie?

ANNIE: *(Her voice cheerful)* Here, Beatrice.

(As soon as they locate her voice they throng joyfully to her, speaking all at once; Annie *is down on her knees to the smallest, and the following are the more intelligible fragments in the general hubbub.)*

CHILDREN: There's a present. We brought you a going-away present, Annie!

ANNIE: Oh, now you shouldn't have—

CHILDREN: We did, we did, where's the present?

SMALLEST CHILD: *(Mournfully)* Don't go, Annie, away.

CHILDREN: Alice has it. Alice! Where's Alice! Here I am! Where? Here!

(An arm is aloft out the group, waving a present; Annie *reaches for it.)*

ANNIE: I have it. I have it, everybody, should I open it?

CHILDREN: Open it! Everyone be quite! Do, Annie! She's opening it. Ssh!

(A settling of silence while Annie *unwraps it. The present is a pair of smoked glasses, and she stands still.)*
Is it open, Annie?

ANNIE: It's open.

CHILDREN: It's for your eyes, Annie. Put them on, Annie! 'Cause Mrs. Hopkins said your eyes hurt since the operation. And she said you're going where the sun is fierce.

ANNIE: I'm putting them on now.

SMALLEST CHILD: Don't go, Annie, where the sun is fierce.

CHILDREN: Do they fit all right?

ANNIE: Oh, they fit just fine.

CHILDREN: Did you put them on? Are they pretty, Annie?

ANNIE: Oh, my eyes feel hundreds of per cent better already, and pretty, why, do you know how I look in them? Splendiloquent. Like a race horse!

CHILDREN: (Delighted) There's another present! Beatrice! We have a present for Helen, too! give it to her, Beatrice. Here, Annie! (This present is an elegant doll, with movable eyelids and a momma sound.) It's for Helen. And we took up a collection to buy it. And Laura dressed it.

ANNIE: It's beautiful!

CHILDREN: So don't forget, you be sure to give it to Helen from us, Annie!

ANNIE: I promise it will be the first thing I give her. If I don't keep it for myself, that is, you know I can't be trusted with dolls!

SMALLEST CHILD: (Mournfully) Don't go, Annie, to her.

ANNIE: (Her arm around her) Sarah, dear. I don't *want* to go.

SMALLEST CHILD: Then why are you going?

ANNIE: (Gently) Because I'm a big girl now, and big girls have to earn a living. It's the only way I can. But if you don't smile for me first, what I'll just have to do is — (She pauses, inviting it.)

SMALLEST CHILD: What?

ANNIE: Put *you* in my suitcase, instead of this doll. And take *you* to Helen in Alabama!

(This strikes the children as very funny, and they begin to laugh and tease the smallest child, who after a moment does smile for Annie.)

ANAGNOS: (Then) Come, children. We must get the trunk into the carriage and Annie into her train, or no one will go to Alabama. Come, come.

(He shepherds them out and Annie is left alone on her knees with the doll in her lap. She reaches for her suitcase, and by a *subtle change in the colour of the light, we go with her thoughts into another time. We hear a* Boy's Voice *whispering; perhaps we see shadowy intimations of these speakers in the background.)*

BOY'S VOICE: Where we goin', Annie?

ANNIE: *(In dread)* Jimmie.

BOY'S VOICE: Where we goin'?

ANNIE: I said — I'm takin' care of you —

BOY'S VOICE: Forever and ever?

MAN'S VOICE: *(Impersonal)* Annie Sullivan, aged nine, virtually blind. James Sullivan, aged seven — What's the matter with your leg, Sonny?

ANNIE: Forever and ever.

MAN'S VOICE: Can't he walk without that crutch?

(Annie *shakes her head, and does not stop shaking it.)*

Girl goes to the women's ward. Boy to the man's.

BOY'S VOICE *(In terror)* Annie! Annie, don't let them take me — Annie!

ANAGNOS: *(Offstage)* Annie! Annie?

(But this voice is real, in the present, and Annie *comes up out of her horror, clearing her head with a final shake; the lights begin to pick out* Kate *in the* Keller *house, as* Annie *in a bright tone calls back.)*

ANNIE: Coming!

(This word catches Kate, *who stands half turned and attentive to it, almost as though hearing it. Meanwhile* Annie *turns and hurries out, lugging the suitcase.*

The room dims out; the sound of railroad wheels begins from off left, and maintains itself in a constant rhythm underneath the following scene; the remaining lights have come up on the Keller *homestead.* James *is lounging on the porch, waiting. In the upper bedroom which is to be* Annie's, Helen *is alone, puzzledly exploring, fingering and smelling things, the curtains, empty drawers in the bureau, water in the pitcher by the washbasin, fresh towels on the bedstead. Downstairs in the family room* Kate *turning to a mirror hastily adjusts her bonnet, watched by a servant in an apron,* Viney.)

VINEY: Let Mr. Jimmy go by hisself, you been pokin' that garden all day, you ought to rest your feet.

KATE: I can't wait to see her, Viney.

VINEY: Maybe she ain't gone be on this train neither.

KATE: Maybe she is.

VINEY: And maybe she ain't.

KATE: And maybe she is. Where's Helen?

VINEY: She upstairs, smellin' around. She knows somethin' funny's goin' on.

KATE: Let her have her supper as soon as Mildred's in bed, and tell Captain Keller when he comes that we'll be delayed tonight.

VINEY: Again.

KATE: I don't think we need say *again*. Simply delayed will do.
(She runs upstairs to Annie's room, Viney speaking after her.)

VINEY: I mean that's what he gone say. "What, again?"

(Viney works at setting the table. Upstairs Kate stands in the doorway, watching Helen's groping explorations.)

KATE: Yes, we're expecting someone. Someone for my Helen.
(Helen happens upon her skirt, clutches her leg; Kate in a tired dismay kneels to tidy her hair and soiled pinafore.)
Oh, dear, this was clean not an hour ago.
(Helen feels her bonnet, shakes her head darkly, and tugs to get it off. Kate retains it with one hand, diverts Helen by opening her other hand under her nose.)
Here. For while I'm gone.
(Helen sniffs, reaches, and pops something into her mouth, while Kate speaks a bit guiltily.)
I don't think one peppermint drop will spoil your supper.
(She gives Helen a quick kiss, evades her hands, and hurries downstairs again. Meanwhile Captain Keller has entered the yard from around the rear of the house, newspaper under arm, cleaning off and munching on some radishes; he sees James lounging at the porch post.)

KELLER: Jimmie?

JAMES: *(Unmoving)* Sir?

KELLER: *(Eyes him)* You don't look dressed for anything useful, boy.

JAMES: I'm not. It's for Miss Sullivan.

KELLER: Needn't keep holding up that porch, we have wooden posts for that. I asked you to see that those strawberry plants were moved this evening.

JAMES: I'm moving your—Mrs. Keller, instead. To the station.

KELLER: *(Heavily)* Mrs. Keller. Must you always speak of her as though you haven't met the lady?

(Kate comes out on the porch, and James inclines his head.)

JAMES: *(Ironic)* Mother.

(He starts off the porch, but sidesteps Keller's glare like a blow.)

I said mother!

KATE: Captain.

KELLER: Evening, my dear.

KATE: We're off to meet the train, Captain. Supper will be a trifle delayed tonight.

KELLER: What, again?

KATE: *(Backing out)* With your permission, Captain?

(And they are gone. Keller watches them offstage, morosely. Upstairs Helen meanwhile has groped for her mother, touched her cheek in a meaningful gesture, waited, touched her cheek, waited, then found the open door, and made her way down. Now she comes into the family room, touches her cheek again; Viney regards her.)

VINEY: What you want, honey, your momma?

(Helen touches her cheek again. Viney goes to the sideboard, gets a tea-cake, gives it into Helen's hand; Helen pops it into her mouth.)

Guess one little tea-cake ain't gone ruin your appetite.

(She turns Helen toward the door. Helen wanders out onto the porch, as Keller comes up the steps. Her hands encounter him, and she touches her cheek again, waits.)

KELLER: She's gone.

(He is awkward with her; when he puts his hand on her head, she pulls away. Keller stands regarding her, heavily.)

She's gone, my son and I don't get along, you don't know I'm your father, no one likes me, and supper's delayed.

(Helen touches her cheek, waits. Keller fishes in his pocket.)

Here. I brought you some stick candy, one nibble of sweets can't do any harm.

(He gives her a large stick candy; Helen falls to it. Viney peers out the window.)

VINEY: *(Reproachfully)* Cap'n Keller, now how'm I gone get her to eat her supper you fill her up wit that trash?

KELLER: *(Roars)* Tend to your work!

(Viney beats a rapid retreat. Keller thinks better of it, and tries to get the candy away from Helen, but Helen hangs on to it; and when Keller pulls, she gives his leg a kick. Keller hops about, Helen takes refuge with the candy down behind the pump, and Keller then irately flings his newspaper on the porch floor, stamps into the house past Viney and disappears.

The lights half dim on the homestead, where Viney *and* Helen *going about their business soon find their way off. Meanwhile, the railroad sounds off left have mounted in a crescendo to a climax typical of a depot at arrival time, the lights come up on stage left, and we see a suggestion of a station. Here* Annie *in her smoked glasses and disarrayed by travel is waiting with her suitcase, while* James *walks to meet her; she has a battered paper-bound book, which is a Perkins report, under her arm.)*

JAMES: *(Coolly)* Miss Sullivan?

ANNIE: *(Cheerily)* Here! At last, I've been on trains so many days I thought they must be backing up every time I dozed off—

JAMES: I'm James Keller.

ANNIE: James? *(The name stops her.)* I had a brother Jimmie. Are you Helen's?

JAMES: I'm only half a brother. You're to be her governess?

ANNIE: *(Lightly)* Well. Try!

JAMES: *(Eying her)* You look like half a governess.

(Kate enters. Annie stands moveless, while James *takes her suitcase. Kate's gaze on her is doubtful, troubled.)*

Mrs. Keller, Miss Sullivan.

(Kate takes her hand.)

KATE: *(Simply)* We've met every train for two days.

(Annie looks at Kate's face, and her good humour comes back.)

ANNIE: I changed trains every time they stopped, the man who sold me that ticket ought to be tied to the tracks—

JAMES: You have a trunk, Miss Sullivan?

ANNIE: Yes.

(She passes James a claim check, and he bears the suitcase out behind them. Annie holds the battered book. Kate is studying her face, and Annie returns the gaze; this is a mutual appraisal, southern gentlewoman and working-class Irish girl, and Annie is not quite comfortable under it.)

You didn't bring Helen, I was hoping you would.

KATE: No, she's home.

(A pause. Annie tries to make ladylike small talk, though her energy now and then erupts; she catches herself up whenever she hears it.)

ANNIE: You—live far from town, Mrs. Keller?

KATE: Only a mile.

ANNIE: Well. I suppose I can wait one more mile. But don't be surprised if I get out to push the horse!

KATE: Helen's waiting for you, too. There's been such a bustle in

the house, she expects something, heaven knows what.
(Now she voices part of her doubt, not as such, but Annie
understands it.)
I expected—a desiccated spinster. You're very young.
ANNIE: *(Resolutely)* Oh, you should have seen me when I left
Boston. I got much older on this trip.
KATE: I mean, to teach anyone as difficult as Helen.
ANNIE: *I* mean to try. They can't put you in jail for trying!
KATE: Is it possible, even? To teach a deaf-blind child *half* of
what an ordinary child learns—has that ever been done?
ANNIE: Half?
KATE: A tenth.
ANNIE: (Reluctantly) No.
*(Kate's face loses its remaining hope, still appraising her
youth.)*
Dr. Howe did wonders, but—an ordinary child? No, never.
But then I thought when I was going over his reports—
(She indicates the one in her hand)
—he never treated them like ordinary children. More like—
eggs everyone was afraid would break.
KATE: *(A pause)* May I ask how old you are?
ANNIE: Well, I'm not in my teens, you know! I'm twenty.
KATE: All of twenty.
(Annie takes the bull by the horns, valiantly.)
ANNIE: Mrs. Keller, don't lose heart just because I'm not on my
last legs. I have three big advantages over Dr. Howe that
money couldn't buy for you. One is his work behind me, I've
read every word he wrote about it and he wasn't exactly what
you'd call a man of few words. Another is to *be* young, why,
I've got energy to do anything. The third is, I've been blind.
(But it costs her something to say this.)
KATE: *(Quietly)* Advantages.
ANNIE: *(Wry)* Well, some have the luck of the Irish some do not.
(Kate smiles, she likes her.)
KATE: What will you try to teach her first?
ANNIE: First, last, and—in between, language.
KATE: Language.
ANNIE: Language is to the mind more than light is to the eye. Dr.
Howe said that.
KATE: Language. *(She shakes her head.)* We can't get through to
teach her to sit still. You *are* young, despite your years, to
have such—confidence. Do you, inside?

(Annie *studies her face; she likes her, too.*)

ANNIE: No, to tell you the truth I'm as shaky inside as a baby's rattle!

(*They smile at each other, and* Kate *pats her hand.*)

KATE: Don't be.

(James *returns to usher them off.*)

We'll do all we can to help, and to make you feel at home. Don't think of us as strangers, Miss Annie.

ANNIE: (*Cheerily*) Oh, strangers aren't so strange to me. I've known them all my life!

(Kate *smiles again,* Annie *smiles back, and they precede* James *offstage.*

The lights dim on them, having simultaneously risen full on the house; Viney *has already entered the family room, taken a water pitcher, and come out and down to the pump. She pumps real water. As she looks offstage, we hear the clop of hoofs, a carriage stopping, and voices.*)

VINEY: Cap'n Keller! Cap'n Keller, they comin'!

(*She goes back into the house, as* Keller *comes out on the porch to gaze.*)

She sure 'nuff came, Cap'n.

(Keller *descends, and crosses toward the carriage; this conversation begins offstage and moves on.*)

KELLER: (*Very courtly*) Welcome to Ivy Green, Miss Sullivan. I take it you are Miss Sullivan —

KATE: My husband, Miss Annie, Captain Keller.

ANNIE: (*Her best behaviour*) Captain, how do you do.

KELLER: A pleasure to see you, at last. I trust you had an agreeable journey?

ANNIE: Oh, I had several! When did this country get so big?

JAMES: Where would you like the trunk, father?

KELLER: Where Miss Sullivan can get at it, I imagine.

ANNIE: Yes, please. Where's Helen?

KELLER: In the hall, Jimmie —

KATE: We've put you in the upstairs corner room, Miss Annie, if there's any breeze at all this summer, you'll feel it —

(*In the house the setter* Belle *flees into the family room, pursued by* Helen *with groping hands; the dog doubles back out the same door, and* Helen *still groping for her makes her way out to the porch; she is messy, her hair tumbled, her pinafore now ripped, her shoelaces untied.* Keller *acquires the suitcase, and* Annie *gets her hands on it too though still endeavouring to*

live up to the general air of propertied manners.)
KELLER: *And* the suitcase —
ANNIE: *(Pleasantly)* I'll take the suitcase, thanks.
KELLER: Not at all, I have it, Miss Sullivan.
ANNIE: I'd like it.
KELLER: *(Gallantly)* I couldn't think of it, Miss Sullivan. You'll
find in the south we —
ANNIE: Let me.
KELLER: — view women as the flowers of civiliza —
ANNIE: *(Impatiently)* I've got something in it for Helen.
(She tugs it free; Keller stares.)
Thank you. When do I see her?
KATE: There. There is Helen.
*(Annie turns, and sees Helen on the porch. A moment of
silence. Then Annie begins across the yard to her, lugging
her suitcase.)*
KELLER: *(Sotto voce)* Katie —
*(Kate silences him with a hand on his arm. When Annie finally
reaches the porch steps she stops, contemplating Helen for a
last moment before entering her world. Then she drops the suitcase on the porch with intentional heaviness, Helen starts with
the jar, and comes to grope over it. Annie puts forth her hand,
and touches Helen's. Helen at once grasps it, and commences
to explore it, like reading a face. She moves her hand on to
Annie's forearm, and dress; and Annie brings her face within
reach of Helen's fingers, which travel over it, quite without
timidity, until they encounter and push aside the smoked
glasses. Annie's gaze is grave, unpitying, very attentive. She puts
her hands on Helen's arms, but Helen at once pulls away, and
they confront each other with a distance between. Then Helen
returns to the suitcase, tries to open it, cannot. Annie points
Helen's hand overhead. Helen pulls away, tries to open the
suitcase again; Annie points her hand overhead again. Helen
points overhead, a question, and Annie drawing Helen's hand
to her own face, nods. Helen now begins tugging the suitcase
toward the door; when Annie tries to take it from her, she fights
her off and backs through the doorway with it. Annie stands a
moment, then follows her in, and together they get the suitcase
up the steps into Annie's room.)*
KATE: Well?
KELLER: She's very rough, Katie.
KATE: I like her, Captain.

KELLER: Certainly rear a peculiar kind of young woman in the north. How old is she?

KATE: *(Vaguely)* Ohh—Well, she's not in her teens, you know.

KELLER: She's only a child. What's her family like shipping her off alone this far?

KATE: I couldn't learn. She's very closemouthed about some things.

KELLER: Why does she wear those glasses? I like to see a person's eyes when I talk to—

KATE: For the sun. She was blind.

KELLER: Blind.

KATE: She's had nine operations on her eyes. One just before she left.

KELLER: Blind, good heavens, do they expect one blind child to teach another? Has she experience at least, how long did she teach there?

KATE: She was a pupil.

KELLER: *(Heavily)* Katie, Katie. This is her first position?

KATE: *(Bright voice)* She was valedictorian—

KELLER: Here's a houseful of grownups can't cope with the child, how can an inexperienced half-blind Yankee schoolgirl manage her?

(James moves in with the trunk on his shoulder.)

JAMES: *(Easily)* Great improvement. Now we have two of them to look after.

KELLER: You look after those strawberry plants!

(James stops with the trunk, Keller turns from him without another word, and marches off.)

JAMES: Nothing I say is right.

KATE: Why say anything? *(She calls.)* Don't be long, Captain, we'll have supper right away—

(She goes into the house, and through the rear door of the family room. James trudges in with the trunk, takes it up the steps to Annie's room, and sets it down outside the door. The lights elsewhere dim somewhat.

Meanwhile, inside, Annie has given Helen a key; while Annie removes her bonnet, Helen unlocks and opens the suitcase. The first thing she pulls out is a voluminous shawl. She fingers it until she perceives what it is; then she wraps it around her, and acquiring Annie's bonnet and smoked glasses as well, dons the lot: the shawl swamps her, and the bonnet settles down upon the glasses, but she stands before a mirror cocking her head to

one side, then to the other, in a mockery of adult action. Annie
*is amused, and talks to her as one might to a kitten, with no
trace of company manners.)*

ANNIE: All the trouble I went to and that's how I look?
*(Helen then comes back to the suitcase, gropes for more, lifts
out a pair of female drawers.)*
Oh, no. Not the drawers!
(But Helen *discarding them comes to the elegant doll. Her fingers explore its features, and when she raises it and finds its
eyes open and close, she is at first startled, then delighted. She
picks it up, taps its head vigorously, taps her own chest, and
nods questioningly.* Annie *takes her finger, points it to the
doll, points it to* Helen, *and touching it to her own face, also
nods.* Helen *sits back on her heels, clasps the doll to herself,
and rocks it.* Annie *studies her, still in bonnet and smoked
glasses like a caricature of herself, and addresses her
humorously.)*
All right, Miss O'Sullivan. Let's begin with doll.
(She takes Helen's *hand; in her palm* Annie's *forefinger points,
thumb holding her other fingers clenched.)*
D.
(Her thumb next holds all her fingers clenched, touching
Helen's *palm.)*
O.
(Her thumb and forefinger extend.)
L.
(Same contact repeated.)
L.
(She puts Helen's *hand to the doll.)*
Doll.

JAMES: You spell pretty well.
*(Annie in one hurried move gets the drawers swiftly back into
the suitcase, the lid banged shut, and her head turned, to see
James leaning in the doorway.)*
Finding out if she's ticklish? She is.
(Annie regards him stonily, but Helen *after a scowling moment tugs at her hand again, imperious.* Annie *repeats the letters, and* Helen *interrupts her fingers in the middle, feeling
each of them, puzzled.* Annie *touches* Helen's *hand to the
doll, and begins spelling into it again.)*
What is it, a game?

ANNIE: *(Curtly)* An alphabet.

JAMES: Alphabet?

ANNIE: For the deaf.

(Helen now repeats the finger movements in air, exactly, her head cocked to her own hand, and Annie's eyes suddenly gleam.)

Ho. How *bright* she is!

JAMES: You think she knows what she's doing?

(He takes Helen's hand, to throw a meaningless gesture into it; she repeats this one too.)

She imitates everything, she's a monkey.

ANNIE: *(Very pleased)* Yes, she's a bright little monkey, all right.

(She takes the doll from Helen, and reaches for her hand; Helen instantly grabs the doll back. Annie takes it again, and Helen's hand next, but Helen is incensed now; when Annie draws her hand to her·face to shake her head no, then tries to spell to her, Helen slaps at Annie's face. Annie grasps Helen by both arms, and swings her into a chair, holding her pinned there, kicking, while glasses, doll, bonnet fly in various directions. James laughs.)

JAMES: She wants her doll back.

ANNIE: When she spells it.

JAMES: Spell, she doesn't know the thing has a name, even.

ANNIE: Of course not, who expects her to, now? All I want is her fingers to learn the letters.

JAMES: Won't mean anything to her.

(Annie gives him a look. She then tries to form Helen's fingers into the letters, but Helen swings a haymaker instead, which Annie barely ducks, at once pinning her down again.)

Doesn't like that alphabet, Miss Sullivan. You invent it yourself?

(Helen is now in a rage, fighting tooth and nail to get out of the chair, and Annie answers while struggling and dodging her kicks.)

ANNIE: Spanish monks under a — vow of silence. Which I wish *you'd* take!

(And suddenly releasing Helen's hands, she comes and shuts the door in James' face. Helen drops to the floor, groping around for the doll. Annie looks around desperately, sees her purse on the bed, rummages in it, and comes up with a battered piece of cake wrapped in newspaper; with her foot she moves the doll deftly out of the way of Helen's groping, and going on her knee she lets Helen smell the cake. When Helen

grabs for it, Annie *removes the cake and spells quickly into the reaching hand.)*
Cake. From Washington up north, it's the best I can do.
*(*Helen's *hand waits, baffled.* Annie *repeats it.)*
C, a, k, e. Do what my fingers do, never mind what it means.
(She touches the cake briefly to Helen's *nose, pats her hand, presents her own hand.* Helen *spells the letters rapidly back.* Annie *pats her hand enthusiastically, and gives her the cake;* Helen *crams it into her mouth with both hands.* Annie *watches her, with humour.)*
Get it down fast, maybe I'll steal that back too. Now.
(She takes the doll, touches it to Helen's *nose, and spells again into her hand.)*
D, o, l, l. Think it over.
*(*Helen *thinks it over, while* Annie *presents her own hand. Then* Helen *spells three letters.* Annie *waits a second, then completes the word for* Helen *in her palm.)*
L.
(She hands over the doll, and Helen *gets a good grip on its leg.)*
Imitate now, understand later. End of the first les—
(She never finishes, because Helen *swings the doll with a furious energy, it hits* Annie *squarely in the face, and she falls back with a cry of pain, her knuckles up to her mouth.* Helen *waits, tensed for further combat. When* Annie *lowers her knuckles she looks at blood on them; she works her lips, gets to her feet, finds the mirror, and bares her teeth at herself. Now she is furious herself.)*
You little wretch, no one's taught you *any* manners? I'll—
(But rounding from the mirror she sees the door slam, Helen *and the doll are on the outside, and* Helen *is turning the key in the lock.* Annie *darts over, to pull the knob, the door is locked fast. She yanks it again.)*
Helen! Helen, let me out of—
(She bats her brow at the folly of speaking, but James, *now downstairs, hears her and turns to see* Helen *with the key and doll groping her way down the steps,* James *takes in the whole situation, makes a move to intercept* Helen, *but then changes his mind, lets her pass, and amusedly follows her out onto the porch. Upstairs* Annie *meanwhile rattles the knob, kneels, peers through the keyhole, gets up. She goes to the window, looks down, frowns.* James *from the yard sings gaily up to her:)*

JAMES: Buffalo girl, are you coming out tonight,
  Coming out tonight,
  Coming out—
(He drifts back into the house, Annie takes a handkerchief, nurses her mouth, stands in the middle of the room, staring at door and window in turn, and so catches sight of herself in the mirror, her cheek scratched, her hair dishevelled, her handkerchief bloody, her face disgusted with herself. She addresses the mirror, with some irony.)
ANNIE: Don't worry. They'll find you, you're not lost. Only out of place.
(But she coughs, spits something into her palm, and stares at it, outraged.)
And toothless. (She winces.) Oo! It hurts.
(She pours some water into the basin, dips the handkerchief, and presses it to her mouth. Standing there, bent over the basin in pain—with the rest of the set dim and unreal, and the lights upon her taking on the subtle color of the past—she hears again, as do we, the faraway voices, and slowly she lifts her head to them; the Boy's Voice *is the same, the others are cracked old crones in a nightmare, and perhaps we see their shadows.)*
BOY'S VOICE: It hurts, Annie, it hurts.
FIRST CRONE'S VOICE: Keep that brat shut up, can't you, girlie, how's a body to get any sleep in this damn ward?
BOY'S VOICE: It hurts, it hurts.
SECOND CRONE'S VOICE: Shut up, you!
BOY'S VOICE: Annie, when are we goin' home? You promised!
ANNIE: Jimmie—
BOY'S VOICE: Forever and ever, you said forever—
  (Annie drops the handkerchief, averts to the window, and is arrested there by the next cry.)
  Annie? Annie, you there? Annie! It hurts!
THIRD CRONE'S VOICE: Grab him, he's fallin'!
BOY'S VOICE: *Annie!*
DOCTOR'S VOICE: *(A pause, slowly)* Little girl. Little girl, I must tell you your brother will be going on a—
(But Annie *claps her hands to her ears, to shut this out, there is instant silence.*

As the lights bring the other areas in again, James *goes to the steps to listen for any sound from upstairs.* Keller *re-entering from left crosses toward the house; he passes* Helen *en route to her retreat under the pump.* Kate *re-enters the rear door of the family room, with flowers for the table.)*

KATE: Supper is ready, Jimmie, will you call your father?

JAMES: Certainly.

(But he calls up the stairs, for Annie's *benefit:)*

Father! Supper!

KELLER: *(At the door)* No need to shout, I've been cooling my heels for an hour. Sit down.

JAMES: Certainly.

KELLER: Viney!

(Viney backs in with a roast, while they get settled around the table.)

VINEY: Yes, Cap'n, right here.

KATE: Mildred went directly to sleep, Viney?

VINEY: Oh yes, that babe's a angel.

KATE: And Helen had a good supper?

VINEY: *(Vaguely)* I dunno, Miss Kate, somehow she didn't have much of a appetite tonight —

KATE: *(A bit guilty)* Oh. Dear.

KELLER: *(Hastily)* Well, now. Couldn't say the same for my part, I'm famished. Katie, your plate.

KATE: *(Looking)* But where is Miss Annie?

(A silence.)

JAMES: *(Pleasantly)* In her room.

KELLER: In her room? Doesn't she know hot food must be eaten hot? Go bring her down at once, Jimmie.

JAMES: *(Rises)* Certainly, I'll get a ladder.

KELLER: *(Stares)* What?

JAMES: I'll need a ladder. Shouldn't take me long.

KATE: *(Stares)* What shouldn't take you —

KELLER: Jimmie, do as I say! Go upstairs at once and tell Miss Sullivan supper is getting cold —

JAMES: She's locked in her room.

KELLER: Locked in her —

KATE: What on earth are you —

JAMES: Helen locked her in and made off with the key.

KATE: *(Rising)* And you sit here and say nothing?

JAMES: Well, everyone's been telling me not to say anything.

(He goes serenely out and across the yard, whistling. Keller thrusting up from his chair makes for the stairs.)

KATE: Viney, look out in back for Helen. See if she has that key.

VINEY: Yes, Miss Kate.

(Viney *goes out the rear door.*)

KELLER: *(Calling down)* She's out by the pump!

(Kate *goes out on the porch after* Helen, *while* Keller *knocks on* Annie's *door, then rattles the knob, imperiously.*) Miss Sullivan! Are you in there?

ANNIE: Oh, I'm in here, all right.

KELLER: Is there no key on your side?

ANNIE: *(With some asperity)* Well, if there was a key in here, *I* wouldn't be in here. Helen took it, the only thing on my side is me.

KELLER: Miss Sullivan. I —

(He tries, but cannot hold it back.)

Not in the house ten minutes, I don't see *how* you managed it!

(He stomps downstairs again, while Annie *mutters to herself.)*

ANNIE: And even I'm not on my side.

KELLER: *(Roaring)* Viney!

VINEY: *(Reappearing)* Yes, Cap'n?

KELLER: Put that meat back in the oven!

(Viney bears the roast off again, while Keller *strides out onto the porch.* Kate *is with Helen at the pump, opening her hands.)*

KATE: She has no key.

KELLER: Nonsense, she must have the key. Have you searched in her pockets?

KATE: Yes. She doesn't have it.

KELLER: Katie, she must have the key.

KATE: Would you prefer to search her yourself, Captain?

KELLER: No, I would not prefer to search her! She almost took my kneecap off this evening, when I tried merely to —

(James reappears carrying a long ladder, with Percy *running after him to be in on things.)*

KELLER: Take that ladder back!

JAMES: Certainly.

(He turns around with it. Martha *comes skipping around the upstage corner of the house to be in on things, accompanied by the setter* Belle.)

KATE: She could have hidden the key.

KELLER: Where?

KATE: Anywhere. Under a stone. In the flower beds. In the grass —

KELLER: Well, I can't plow up the entire grounds to find a missing key! Jimmie!

JAMES: Sir?

KELLER: Bring me a ladder!

JAMES: Certainly.

(Viney comes around the downstage side of the house to be in on things; she has Mildred over her shoulder, bleating. Keller places the ladder against Annie's window and mounts. Annie meanwhile is running about making herself presentable, washing the blood off her mouth, straightening her clothes, tidying her hair. Another Servant enters to gaze in wonder, increasing the gathering ring of spectators.)

KATE: *(Sharply)* What is Mildred doing up?

VINEY: Cap'n woke her, ma'am, all that hollerin'.

KELLER: Miss Sullivan!

(Annie comes to the window, with as much air of gracious normality as she can manage; Keller is at the window.)

ANNIE: *(Brightly)* Yes, Captain Keller?

KELLER: Come out!

ANNIE: I don't see how I can. There isn't room.

KELLER: I intend to carry you. Climb onto my shoulder and hold tight.

ANNIE: Oh, no. It's—very chivalrous of you, but I'd rather prefer to—

KELLER: Miss Sullivan, follow instructions! I will not have you also tumbling out of our windows.

(Annie obeys, with some misgivings.)

I hope this is not a sample of what we may expect from you. In the way of simplifying the work of looking after Helen.

ANNIE: Captain Keller, I'm perfectly able to go down a ladder under my own—

KELLER: I doubt it, Miss Sullivan. Simply hold onto my neck.

(He begins down with her, while the spectators stand in a wide and somewhat awe-stricken circle, watching. Keller half-misses a rung, and Annie grabs at his whiskers.)

My *neck*, Miss Sullivan!

ANNIE: I'm sorry to inconvenience you this way—

KELLER: No inconvenience, other than having that door taken down and the lock replaced, if we fail to find that key.

ANNIE: Oh, I'll look everywhere for it.

KELLER: Thank you. Do not look in any rooms that can be locked. There.

(He stands her on the ground. James applauds.)

ANNIE: Thank you very much.

(*She smooths her skirt, looking as composed and ladylike as possible.* Keller *stares around at the spectators.*)

KELLER: Go, go, back to your work. What are you looking at here? There's nothing here to look at.

(*They break up, move off.*)

Now would it be possible for us to have supper, like other people?

(*He marches into the house.*)

KATE: Viney, serve supper. I'll put Mildred to sleep.

(*They all go in.* James *is the last to leave, murmuring to* Annie *with a gesture.*)

JAMES: Might as well leave the l, a, d, d, e, r, hm?

(Annie *ignores him, looking at* Helen; James *goes in too. Imperceptibly, the lights commence to narrow down.* Annie *and* Helen *are now alone in the yard,* Helen *seated at the pump, where she has been oblivious to it all, a battered little savage, playing with the doll in a picture of innocent contentment.* Annie *comes near, leans against the house, and taking off her smoked glasses, studies her, not without awe. Presently* Helen *rises, gropes around to see if anyone is present;* Annie *evades her hand, and when* Helen *is satisfied she is alone, the key suddenly protrudes out of her mouth. She takes it in her fingers, stands thinking, gropes to the pump, lifts a loose board, drops the key into the well, and hugs herself gleefully.* Annie *stares. But after a moment she shakes her head to herself, she cannot keep the smile from her lips.*)

ANNIE: You *devil*.

(*Her tone is one of great respect, humour, and acceptance of challenge.*)

You think I'm so easily gotten rid of? You have a thing or two to learn, first. I have nothing else to do.

(*She goes up the steps to the porch, but turns for a final word, almost of warning.*)

And nowhere to go.

(*And presently she moves into the house to the others, as the lights dim down and out, except for the small circle upon* Helen *solitary at the pump, which ends the act.*)

ACT TWO

(It is evening.

The only room visible in the Keller *house is* Annie's, *where by lamplight* Annie *in a shawl is at a desk writing a letter; at her bureau* Helen *in her customary unkempt state is tucking her doll in the bottom drawer as a cradle, the contents of which she has dumped out, creating as usual a fine disorder.*

Annie *mutters each word as she writes her letter, slowly, her eyes close to and almost touching the page, to follow with difficulty her penwork.)*

ANNIE: " . . . and, nobody, here, has, attempted, to, control, her. The, greatest, problem, I, have, is, how, to, discipline, her, without, breaking, her, spirit." *(Resolute voice)* "But, I, shall, insist, on, reasonable, obedience, from, the, start—"

(At which point Helen, *groping about on the desk, knocks over the inkwell.* Annie *jumps up, rescues her letter, rights the inkwell, grabs a towel to stem the spillage, and then wipes at* Helen's *hands;* Helen *as always pulls free, but not until* Annie *first gets three letters into her palm.)*

Ink.

*(*Helen *is enough interested in and puzzled by this spelling that she proffers her hand again; so* Annie *spells and impassively dunks it back in the spillage.)*

Ink. It has a name.

(She wipes the hand clean, and leads Helen *to her bureau, where she looks for something to engage her. She finds a sewing card, with needle and thread, and going to her knees, shows* Helen's *hand how to connect one row of holes.)*

Down. Under. Up. And be careful of the needle—

*(*Helen *gets it, and* Annie *rises.)*

Fine. You keep out of the ink and perhaps I can keep out of—the soup.

(She returns to the desk, tidies it, and resumes writing her letter, bent close to the page.)

"These, blots, are, her, handiwork. I—"

(She is interrupted by a gasp: Helen *has stuck her finger, and sits sucking at it, darkly. Then with vengeful resolve she seizes her doll, and is about to dash its brains out on the floor when* Annie *diving catches it in one hand, which she at once shakes with hopping pain but otherwise ignores, patiently.)*

All right, let's try temperance.

(Taking the doll, she kneels, goes through the motion of

knocking its head on the floor, spells into Helen's *hand:)*
Bad, girl.
(She lets Helen *feel the grieved expression on her face.* Helen *imitates it. Next she makes* Helen *caress the doll and kiss the hurt spot and hold it gently in her arms, then spells into her hand:)*
Good, girl.
(She lets Helen *feel the smile on her face.* Helen *sits with a scowl, which suddenly clears; she pats the doll, kisses it, wreathes her face in a large artificial smile, and bears the doll to the washstand, where she carefully sits it.* Annie *watches, pleased.)*
Very good girl—
(Whereupon Helen *elevates the pitcher and dashes it on the floor instead.* Annie *leaps to her feet, and stands inarticulate;* Helen *calmly gropes back to sit to the sewing card and needle.*

Annie *manages to achieve self-control. She picks up a fragment or two of the pitcher, sees* Helen *is puzzling over the card, and resolutely kneels to demonstrate it again. She spells into* Helen's *hand.*

Kate *meanwhile coming around the corner with folded sheets on her arm, halts at the doorway and watches them for a moment in silence; she is moved, but level.)*
KATE: *(Presently)* What are you saying to her?
(Annie glancing up is a bit embarrassed, and rises from the spelling, to find her company manners.)
ANNIE: Oh, I was just making conversation. Saying it was a sewing card.
KATE: But does that—
(She imitates with her fingers)
—mean that to her?
ANNIE: No. No, she won't know what spelling is till she knows what a word is.
KATE: Yet you keep spelling to her. Why?
ANNIE: *(Cheerily)* I like to hear myself talk!
KATE: The Captain says it's like spelling to the fence post.
ANNIE: *(A pause)* Does he, now.
KATE: Is it?
ANNIE: No, it's how I watch you talk to Mildred.
KATE: Mildred.
ANNIE: Any baby. Gibberish, grown-up gibberish, baby-talk gibberish, do they understand one word of it to start? Somehow

they begin to. If they hear it, I'm letting Helen hear it.

KATE: Other children are not—impaired.

ANNIE: Ho, there's nothing impaired in that head, it works like a mousetrap!

KATE: *(Smiles)* But after a child hears how many words, Miss Annie, a million?

ANNIE: I guess no mother's ever minded enough to count.

(She drops her eyes to spell into Helen's hand, again indicating the card; Helen spells back, and Annie is amused.)

KATE: *(Too quickly)* What did she spell?

ANNIE: I spelt card. She spelt cake!

(She takes in Kate's quickness, and shakes her head, gently.) No, it's only a finger-game to her, Mrs. Keller. What she has to learn first is that things have names.

KATE: And when will she learn?

ANNIE: Maybe after a million and one words.

(They hold each other's gaze; Kate then speaks quietly.)

KATE: I should like to learn those letters, Miss Annie.

ANNIE: *(Pleased)* I'll teach you tomorrow morning. That makes only half a million each!

KATE: *(Then)* It's her bedtime.

(Annie reaches for the sewing card, Helen objects, Annie insists, and Helen gets rid of Annie's hand by jabbing it with the needle. Annie gasps, and moves to grip Helen's wrist; but Kate intervenes with a proffered sweet, and Helen drops the card, crams the sweet into her mouth, and scrambles up to search her mother's hand for more. Annie nurses her wound, staring after the sweet.)

I'm sorry, Miss Annie.

ANNIE: *(Indignantly)* Why does she get a reward? For stabbing me?

KATE: Well—*(Then, tiredly)* We catch our flies with honey, I'm afraid. We haven't the heart for much else, and so many times she simply cannot be compelled.

ANNIE: *(Ominous)* Yes. I'm the same way myself.

(Kate smiles, and leads Helen off around the corner. Annie alone in her room picks up things and in the act of removing Helen's doll gives way to unmannerly temptation: she throttles it. She drops it on her bed, and stands pondering. Then she turns back, sits decisively, and writes again, as the lights dim on her.)

(Grimly) "The, more, I, think, the, more, certain, I, am, that,

obedience, is, the gateway, through, which, knowledge, enters, the, mind, of, the, child—"

(On the word "obedience" a shaft of sunlight hits the water pump outside, while Annie's *voice ends in the dark, followed by a distant cockcrow; daylight comes up over another corner of the sky, with* Viney's *voice heard at once.)*

VINEY: Breakfast ready!

*(*Viney *comes down into the sunlight beam, and pumps a pitcherful of water. While the pitcher is brimming we hear conversation from the dark; the light grows to the family room of the house where all are either entering or already seated at breakfast, with* Keller *and* James *arguing the war.* Helen *is wandering around the table to explore the contents of the other plates. When* Annie *is in her chair, she watches* Helen. Viney *re-enters, sets the pitcher on the table;* Kate *lifts the almost empty biscuit plate with an inquiring look,* Viney *nods and bears it off back, neither of them interrupting the men.* Annie *meanwhile sits with fork quiet, watching* Helen, *who at her mother's plate pokes her hand among some scrambled eggs.* Kate *catches* Annie's *eyes on her, smiles with a wry gesture.* Helen *moves on to* James's *plate, the male talk continuing,* James *deferential and* Keller *overriding.)*

JAMES: —no, but shouldn't we give the devil his due, father? The fact is we lost the South two years earlier when he outthought us behind Vicksburg.

KELLER: Outthought is a peculiar word for a butcher.

JAMES: Harness maker, wasn't he?

KELLER: I said butcher, his only virtue as a soldier was numbers and he led them to slaughter with no more regard than for so many sheep.

JAMES: But even if in that sense he was a butcher, the fact is he—

KELLER: And a drunken one, half the war.

JAMES: Agreed, father. If his own people said he was I can't argue he—

KELLER: Well, what is it you find to admire in such a man, Jimmie, the butchery or the drunkenness?

JAMES: Neither, father, only the fact that he beat us.

KELLER: He didn't.

JAMES: Is it your contention we won the war, sir?

KELLER: He didn't beat us at Vicksburg. We lost Vicksburg because Pemberton gave Bragg five thousand of his cavalry and

Loring, whom I knew personally for a nincompoop before you were born, marched away from Champion's Hill with enough men to have held them, we lost Vicksburg by stupidity verging on treason.

JAMES: I would have said we lost Vicksburg because Grant was one thing no Yankee general was before him —

KELLER: Drunk? I doubt it.

JAMES: Obstinate.

KELLER: Obstinate. Could any of them compare even in that with old Stonewall? If he'd been there we would still have Vicksburg.

JAMES: Well, the butcher simply wouldn't give up, he tried four ways of getting around Vicksburg and on the fifth try he got around. Anyone else would have pulled north and —

KELLER: He wouldn't have got around if we'd had a Southerner in command, instead of a half-breed Yankee traitor like Pemberton —

(While this background talk is in progress, Helen *is working around the table, ultimately toward* Annie's *plate. She messes with her hands in* James's *plate, then in* Keller's, *both men taking it so for granted they hardly notice. Then* Helen *comes groping with soiled hands past her own plate, to* Annie's; *her hand goes to it, and* Annie, *who has been waiting, deliberately lifts and removes her hand.* Helen *gropes again,* Annie *firmly pins her by the wrist, and removes her hand from the table.* Helen *thrusts her hands again,* Annie *catches them, and* Helen *begins to flail and make noises; the interruption brings* Keller's *gaze upon them.)*

What's the matter there?

KATE: Miss Annie. You see, she's accustomed to helping herself from our plates to anything she —

ANNIE: *(Evenly)* Yes, but *I'm* not accustomed to it.

KELLER: No, of course not. Viney!

KATE: Give her something, Jimmie, to quiet her.

JAMES: *(Blandly)* But her table manners are the best she has. Well.

(He pokes across with a chunk of bacon at Helen's *hand, which* Annie *releases; but* Helen *knocks the bacon away and stubbornly thrusts at* Annie's *plate,* Annie *grips her wrists again, the struggle mounts.)*

KELLER: Let her this time, Miss Sullivan, it's the only way we get any adult conversation. If my son's half merits that description.

(*He rises*) I'll get you another plate.

ANNIE: (*Gripping* Helen) I have a plate, thank you.

KATE: (*Calling*) Viney! I'm afraid what Captain Keller says is only too true, she'll persist in this until she gets her own way.

KELLER: (*At the door*) Viney, bring Miss Sullivan another plate—

ANNIE: (*Stonily*) I have a plate, nothing's wrong with the *plate*, I intend to keep it.

(*Silence for a moment, except for* Helen's *noises as she struggles to get loose; the* Kellers *are a bit nonplussed, and* Annie *is too darkly intent on* Helen's *manners to have any thoughts now of her own.*)

JAMES: Ha. You see why they took Vicksburg?

KELLER: (*Uncertainly*) Miss Sullivan. One plate or another is hardly a matter to struggle with a deprived child about.

ANNIE: Oh, I'd sooner have a more—

(Helen *begins to kick,* Annie *moves her ankles to the opposite side of the chair.*)

heroic issue myself, I —

KELLER: No, I really must insist you—

(Helen *bangs her toe on the chair and sinks to the floor, crying with rage and feigned injury;* Annie *keeps hold of her wrists, gazing down, while* Kate *rises.*)

Now she's hurt herself.

ANNIE: (*Grimly*) No, she hasn't.

KELLER: Will you please let her hands go?

KATE: Miss Annie, you don't know the child well enough yet, she'll keep—

ANNIE: I know an ordinary tantrum well enough, when I see one, and a badly spoiled child—

JAMES: Hear, hear.

KELLER: (*Very annoyed*) Miss Sullivan! You would have more understanding of your pupil if you had some pity in you. Now kindly do as I—

ANNIE: Pity?

(*She releases* Helen *to turn equally annoyed on* Keller *across the table; instantly* Helen *scrambles up and dives at* Annie's *plate. This time* Annie *intercepts her by pouncing on her wrists like a hawk, and her temper boils.*)

For this *tyrant*? The whole house turns on her whims, is there anything she wants she doesn't get? I'll tell you what I pity, that the sun won't rise and set for her all her life, and every day you're telling her it will, what good will your pity do her when you're under the strawberries, Captain Keller?

KELLER: *(Outraged)* Kate, for the love of heaven will you —

KATE: Miss Annie, please, I don't think it serves to lose our —

ANNIE: It does you good, that's all. It's less trouble to feel sorry for her than to teach her anything better, isn't it?

KELLER: I fail to see where you have taught her anything yet, Miss Sullivan!

ANNIE: I'll begin this minute, if you'll leave the room, Captain Keller!

KELLER: *(Astonished)* Leave the —

ANNIE: Everyone, please.

(She struggles with Helen, while Keller endeavors to control his voice.)

KELLER: Miss Sullivan, you are here only as a paid teacher. Nothing more, and not to lecture —

ANNIE: I can't *un*teach her six years of pity if you can't stand up to one tantrum! Old Stonewall, indeed. Mrs. Keller, you promised me help.

KATE: Indeed I did, we truly want to —

ANNIE: Then leave me alone with her. Now!

KELLER: *(In a wrath)* Katie, will you come outside with me? At once, please.

(He marches to the front door. Kate and James follow him. Simultaneously Annie releases Helen's wrists, and the child again sinks to the floor, kicking and crying her weird noises; Annie steps over her to meet Viney coming in the rear doorway with biscuits and a clean plate, surprised at the general commotion.)

VINEY: Heaven sakes —

ANNIE: Out, please.

(She backs Viney out with one hand, closes the door on her astonished mouth, locks it, and removes the key. Keller meanwhile snatches his hat from a rack, and Kate follows him down the porch steps. James lingers in the doorway to address Annie across the room with a bow.)

JAMES: If it takes all summer, general.

(Annie comes over to his door in turn, removing her glasses grimly; as Keller outside begins speaking, Annie closes the door on James, locks it, removes the key, and turns with her back against the door to stare ominously at Helen, kicking on the floor.

James takes his hat from the rack, and going down the porch steps joins Kate and Keller talking in the yard, Keller in a sputter of ire.)*

KELLER: This girl, this—cub of a girl—*presumes*! I tell you, I'm of half a mind to ship her back to Boston before the week is out. You can inform her so from me!

KATE: *(Eyebrows up)* I, Captain?

KELLER: She's a *hireling*! Now I want it clear, unless there's an apology and complete change of manner she goes back on the next train! Will you make that quite clear?

KATE: Where will you be, Captain, while I am making it quite—

KELLER: At the office!

(He begins off left, finds his napkin still in his irate hand, is uncertain with it, dabs his lips with dignity, gets rid of it in a toss to James, *and marches off.* James *turns to eye* Kate.*)*

JAMES: Will you?

*(*Kate's *mouth is set, and* James *studies it lightly.)*
I thought what she said was exceptionally intelligent. I've been saying it for years.

KATE: *(Not without scorn)* To his face?

(She comes to relieve him of the white napkin, but reverts again with it.)
Or will you take it, Jimmie? As a flag?

*(*James *stalks out, much offended, and* Kate *turning stares across the yard at the house; the lights narrowing down to the following pantomime in the family room leave her motionless in the dark.*

Annie *meanwhile has begun by slapping both keys down on a shelf out of* Helen's *reach; she returns to the table, upstage.* Helen's *kicking has subsided, and when from the floor her hand finds* Annie's *chair empty she pauses.* Annie *clears the table of* Kate's, James's, *and* Keller's *plates; she gets back to her own across the table just in time to slide it deftly away from* Helen's *pouncing hand. She lifts the hand and moves it to* Helen's *plate, and after an instant's exploration,* Helen *sits again on the floor and drums her heels.* Annie *comes around the table and resumes her chair. When* Helen *feels her skirt again, she ceases kicking, waits for whatever is to come, renews some kicking, waits again.* Annie *retrieving her plate takes up a forkful of food, stops it halfway to her mouth, gazes at it devoid of appetite, and half-lowers it; but after a look at* Helen *she sighs, dips the forkful toward* Helen *in a for-your-sake toast, and puts it in her own mouth to chew, not without an effort.*

Helen *now gets hold of the chair leg, and half-succeeds in pulling the chair out from under her.* Annie *bangs it down with*

her rear, heavily, and sits with all her weight. Helen's *next attempt to topple it is unavailing, so her fingers dive in a pinch at*
Annie's *flank.* Annie *in the middle of her mouthful almost loses
it with startle, and she slaps down her fork to round on* Helen.
The child comes up with curiosity to feel what Annie *is doing,
so* Annie *resumes eating, letting* Helen's *hand follow the movement of her fork to her mouth; whereupon* Helen *at once
reaches into* Annie's *plate.* Annie *firmly removes her hand to
her own plate.* Helen *in reply pinches* Annie's *thigh, a good
mean pinchful that makes* Annie *jump.* Annie *sets the fork
down, and sits with her mouth tight.* Helen *digs another pinch
into her thigh, and this time* Annie *slaps her hand smartly
away;* Helen *retaliates with a roundhouse fist that catches*
Annie *on the ear, and* Annie's *hand leaps at once in a forceful
slap across* Helen's *cheek;* Helen *is the startled one now.*
Annie's *hand in compunction falters to her own face, but when*
Helen *hits at her again,* Annie *deliberately slaps her again.*
Helen *lifts her fist irresolute for another roundhouse,* Annie *lifts
her hand resolute for another slap, and they freeze in this
posture, while* Helen *mulls it over. She thinks better of it, drops
her fist, and giving* Annie *a wide berth, gropes around to her
mother's chair, to find it empty; she blunders her way along the
table upstage, and encountering the empty chairs and missing
plates, she looks bewildered; she gropes back to her mother's
chair, again touches her cheek and indicates the chair, and waits
for the world to answer.*

Annie *now reaches over to spell into her hand, but* Helen
*yanks it away; she gropes to the front door, tries the knob, and
finds the door locked, with no key. She gropes to the rear door,
and finds it locked, with no key. She commences to bang on it.*
Annie *rises, crosses, takes her wrists, draws her resisting back to
the table, seats her, and releases her hands upon her plate; as*
Annie *herself begins to sit,* Helen *writhes out of her chair, runs
to the front door, and tugs and kicks at it.* Annie *rises again,
crosses, draws her by one wrist back to the table, seats her, and
sits;* Helen *escapes back to the door, knocking over her mother's
chair en route.* Annie *rises again in pursuit, and this time lifts*
Helen *bodily from behind and bears her kicking to her chair.
She deposits her, and once more turns to sit.* Helen *scrambles
out, but as she passes,* Annie *catches her up again from behind
and deposits her in the chair;* Helen *scrambles out on the other
side, for the rear door, but* Annie *at her heels catches her up*

*and deposits her again in the chair. She stands behind it. Helen
scrambles out to her right, and the instant her feet hit the floor
Annie lifts and deposits her back; she scrambles out to her left,
and is at once lifted and deposited back. She tries right again
and is deposited back, and tries left again and is deposited back,
and now feints Annie to the right but is off to her left, and is
promptly deposited back. She sits a moment, and then starts
straight over the tabletop, dishware notwithstanding; Annie
hauls her in and deposits her back, with her plate spilling in her
lap, and she melts to the floor and crawls under the table, labo-
rious among its legs and chairs; but Annie is swift around the
table and waiting on the other side when she surfaces, immediately bearing her aloft; Helen clutches at James's chair for an-
chorage, but it comes with her, and halfway back she abandons
it to the floor. Annie deposits her in her chair, and waits. Helen
sits tensed motionless. Then she tentatively puts out her left
foot and hand, Annie interposes her own hand, and at the contact Helen jerks hers in. She tries her right foot, Annie blocks it
with her own, and Helen jerks hers in. Finally, leaning back,
she slumps down in her chair, in a sullen biding.*

*Annie backs off a step, and watches; Helen offers no move.
Annie takes a deep breath. Both of them and the room are in
considerable disorder, two chairs down and the table a mess,
but Annie makes no effort to tidy it; she only sits on her own
chair, and lets her energy refill. Then she takes up knife and
fork, and resolutely addresses her food. Helen's hand comes out
to explore, and seeing it Annie sits without moving; the child's
hand goes over her hand and fork, pauses—Annie still does not
move—and withdraws. Presently it moves for her own plate,
slaps about for it, and stops, thwarted. At this, Annie again
rises, recovers Helen's plate from the floor and a handful of
scattered food from the deranged tablecloth, drops it on the
plate, and pushes the plate into contact with Helen's fist. Neither of them now moves for a pregnant moment—until Helen
suddenly takes a grab of food and wolfs it down. Annie permits
herself the humor of a minor bow and warming of her hands
together; she wanders off a step or two, watching. Helen cleans
up the plate.*

*After a glower of indecision, she holds the empty plate out for
more. Annie accepts it, and crossing to the removed plates,
spoons food from them onto it; she stands debating the spoon,
tapping it a few times on Helen's plate; and when she returns*

with the plate she brings the spoon, too. She puts the spoon first into Helen's *hand, then sets the plate down.* Helen *discarding the spoon reaches with her hand, and* Annie *stops it by the wrist; she replaces the spoon in it.* Helen *impatiently discards it again, and again.* Annie *stops her hand, to replace the spoon in it. This time* Helen *throws the spoon on the floor.* Annie *after considering it lifts* Helen *bodily out of the chair, and in a wrestling match on the floor closes her fingers upon the spoon, and returns her with it to the chair.* Helen *again throws the spoon on the floor.* Annie *lifts her out of the chair again; but in the struggle over the spoon.* Helen *with* Annie *on her back sends her sliding over her head;* Helen *flees back to her chair and scrambles into it.* When Annie *comes after her she clutches it for dear life;* Annie *pries one hand loose, then the other, then the first again, then the other again, and then lifts* Helen *by the waist, chair and all, and shakes the chair loose.* Helen *wrestles to get free, but* Annie *pins her to the floor, closes her fingers upon the spoon, and lifts her kicking under one arm; with her other hand she gets the chair in place again, and plunks* Helen *back on it. When she releases her hand,* Helen *throws the spoon at her.*

Annie *now removes the plate of food.* Helen *grabbing finds it missing, and commences to bang with her fists on the table.* Annie *collects a fistful of spoons and descends with them and the plate on* Helen; *she lets her smell the plate, at which* Helen *ceases banging, and* Annie *puts the plate down and a spoon in* Helen's *hand.* Helen *throws it on the floor.* Annie *puts another spoon in her hand.* Helen *throws it on the floor.* Annie *puts another spoon in her hand.* Helen *throws it on the floor.* When Annie *comes to her last spoon she sits next to* Helen, *and gripping the spoon in* Helen's *hand, compels her to take food in it up to her mouth.* Helen *sits with lips shut.* Annie *waits a stolid moment, then lowers* Helen's *hand. She tries again.* Helen's *lips remain shut.* Annie *waits, lowers* Helen's *hand. She tries again; this time* Helen *suddenly opens her mouth and accepts the food.* Annie *lowers the spoon with a sigh of relief, and* Helen *spews the mouthful out at her face.* Annie *sits a moment with eyes closed, then takes the pitcher and dashes its water into* Helen's *face, who gasps astonished.* Annie *with* Helen's *hand takes up another spoonful, and shoves it into her open mouth.* Helen *swallows involuntarily, and while she is catching her breath* Annie *forces her palm open, throws four swift letters into it, then another four, and bows toward her with devastating pleasantness.)*

ANNIE: Good girl.

(Annie lifts Helen's hand to feel her face nodding; Helen grabs a fistful of her hair, and yanks. The pain brings Annie to her knees, and Helen pummels her; they roll under the table, and the lights commence to dim out on them.

Simultaneously the light at left has been rising, slowly, so slowly that it seems at first we only imagine what is intimated in the yard: a few ghostlike figures, in silence, motionless, waiting. Now the distant belfry chimes commence to toll the hour, also very slowly, almost—it is twelve— interminably; the sense is that of a long time passing. We can identify the figures before the twelfth stroke, all facing the house in a kind of watch; Kate is standing exactly as before, but now with the baby Mildred sleeping in her arms, and placed here and there, unmoving, are Aunt Ev in her hat with a hanky to her nose, and the two children, Percy and Martha with necks outstretched eagerly, and Viney with a knotted kerchief on her head and a feather duster in her hand.

The chimes cease, and there is silence. For a long moment none of the group moves.)

VINEY: *(Presently)* What am I gone do, Miss Kate? It's noontime, dinner's comin', I didn't get them breakfast dishes out of there yet.

(Kate says nothing, stares at the house. Martha shifts Helen's doll in her clutch, and it plaintively says momma.)

KATE: *(Presently)* You run along, Martha.

(Aunt Ev blows her nose.)

AUNT EV: *(Wretchedly)* I can't wait out here a minute longer, Kate, why, this could go on all afternoon, too.

KATE: I'll tell the Captain you called.

VINEY: *(To the* Children*)* You hear what Miss Kate say? Never you mind what's going on here.

(Still no one moves.)

You run along tend your own bizness.

(Finally Viney *turns on the* Children *with the feather duster.)* Shoo!

(The two Children *divide before her. She chases them off.* Aunt Ev *comes to* Kate, *on her dignity.)*

AUNT EV: Say what you like, Kate, but that child is a *Keller.*

(She opens her parasol, preparatory to leaving.)

I needn't remind you that all the Kellers are cousins to General Robert E. Lee. I don't know *who* that girl is.
(She waits; but Kate *staring at the house is without response.)*
The only Sullivan I've heard of — from Boston too, and I'd think twice before locking her up with that kind — is that man John L.
(And Aunt Ev *departs, with head high. Presently* Viney *comes to* Kate, *her arms out for the baby.)*
VINEY: You give me her, Miss Kate, I'll sneak her in back, to her crib.
(But Kate *is moveless, until* Viney *starts to take the baby;* Kate *looks down at her before relinquishing her.)*
KATE: *(Slowly)* This child never gives me a minute's worry.
VINEY: Oh yes, this one's the angel of the family, no question 'bout that.

(She begins off rear with the baby, heading around the house; and Kate *now turns her back on it, her hand to her eyes. At this moment there is the slamming of a door, and when* Kate *wheels* Helen *is blundering down the porch steps into the light, like a ruined bat out of hell.* Viney *halts, and* Kate *runs in;* Helen *collides with her mother's knees, and reels off and back to clutch them as her savior.* Annie *with smoked glasses in hand stands on the porch, also much undone, looking as though she had indeed just taken Vicksburg.* Kate *taking in* Helen's *ravaged state becomes steely in her gaze up at* Annie.)
KATE: What happened?
*(Annie *meets* Kate's *gaze, and gives a factual report, too exhausted for anything but a flat voice.)*
ANNIE: She ate from her own plate. *(She thinks a moment.)* She ate with a spoon. Herself.
*(Kate *frowns, uncertain with thought, and glances down at* Helen.)
And she folded her napkin.
*(Kate's *gaze now wavers, from* Helen *to* Annie, *and back.)*
KATE: *(Softly)* Folded — her napkin?
ANNIE: The room's a wreck, but her napkin is folded. *(She pauses, then:)* I'll be in my room, Mrs. Keller.
(She moves to re-enter the house; but she stops at Viney's *voice.)*
VINEY: *(Cheery)* Don't be long, Miss Annie. Dinner be ready right away!
*(Viney *carries Mildred around the back of the house.* Annie

stands unmoving, takes a deep breath, stares over her shoulder at Kate *and* Helen, *then inclines her head graciously, and goes with a slight stagger into the house. The lights in her room above steal up in readiness for her.*

Kate *remains alone with* Helen *in the yard, standing protectively over her, in a kind of wonder.)*

KATE: *(Slowly)* Folded her napkin.

(She contemplates the wild head in her thighs, and moves her fingertips over it, with such a tenderness, and something like a fear of its strangeness, that her own eyes close; she whispers, bending to it:)

My Helen—folded her napkin—

(And still erect, with only her head in surrender, Kate *for the first time that we see loses her protracted war with grief; but she will not let a sound escape her, only the grimace of tears comes, and sobs that shake her in a grip of silence. But* Helen *feels them, and her hand comes up in its own wondering, to interrogate her mother's face, until* Kate *buries her lips in the child's palm.*

Upstairs, Annie *enters her room, closes the door, and stands back against it; the lights, growing on her with their special color, commence to fade on* Kate *and* Helen. *Then* Annie *goes wearily to her suitcase, and lifts it to take it toward the bed. But it knocks an object to the floor, and she turns to regard it. A new* Voice *comes in a cultured murmur, hesitant as with the effort of remembering a text:)*

MAN'S VOICE: This—soul—

(Annie puts the suitcase down, and kneels to the object: it is the battered Perkins report, and she stands with it in her hand, letting memory try to speak:)

This—blind, deaf, mute woman—

(Annie sits on her bed, opens the book, and finding the passage, brings it up an inch from her eyes to read, her face and lips following the overhead words, the voice quite factual now:)

Can nothing be done to disinter this human soul? The whole neighborhood would rush to save this woman if she were buried alive by the caving in of a pit, and labor with zeal until she were dug out. Now if there were one who had as much patience as zeal, he might awaken her to a consciousness of her immortal—

(When the Boy's *Voice comes,* Annie *closes her eyes, in pain.)*

BOY'S VOICE: Annie? Annie, you there?

ANNIE: Hush.

BOY'S VOICE: Annie, what's that noise?

(Annie *tries not to answer; her own voice is drawn out of her, unwilling.*)

ANNIE: Just a cot, Jimmie.

BOY'S VOICE: Where they pushin' it?

ANNIE: To the deadhouse.

BOY'S VOICE: Annie. Does it hurt, to be dead?

(Annie *escapes by opening her eyes, her hand works restlessly over her cheek; she retreats into the book again, but the cracked old* Crones *interrupt, whispering.* Annie *slowly lowers the book.*)

FIRST CRONE'S VOICE: There is schools.

SECOND CRONE'S VOICE: There is schools outside —

THIRD CRONE'S VOICE: — schools where they teach blind ones, worse'n you —

FIRST CRONE'S VOICE: To read —

SECOND CRONE'S VOICE: To read and write —

THIRD CRONE'S VOICE: There is schools outside where they —

FIRST CRONE'S VOICE: There is schools —

(*Silence.* Annie *sits with her eyes shining, her hand almost in a caress over the book. Then:*)

BOY'S VOICE: You ain't goin' to school, are you, Annie?

ANNIE: *(Whispering)* When I grow up.

BOY'S VOICE: You ain't either, Annie. You're goin' to stay here take care of me.

ANNIE: I'm goin' to school when I grow up.

BOY'S VOICE: You said we'll be together, forever and ever and ever —

ANNIE: *(Fierce)* I'm goin' to school when I grow up!

DOCTOR'S VOICE: *(Slowly)* Little girl. Little girl, I must tell you. Your brother will be going on a journey, soon.

(Annie *sits rigid, in silence. Then the* Boy's Voice *pierces it, a shriek of terror.*)

BOY'S VOICE: *Annie!*

(*It goes into* Annie *like a sword, she doubles onto it; the book falls to the floor. It takes her a racked moment to find herself and what she was engaged in here; when she sees the suitcase she remembers, and lifts it once again toward the bed. But the* Voices *are with her, as she halts with suitcase in hand.*)

FIRST CRONE'S VOICE: Goodbye, Annie.

DOCTOR'S VOICE: Write me when you learn how.

SECOND CRONE'S VOICE: Don't tell anyone you came from here. Don't tell anyone—

THIRD CRONE'S VOICE: Yeah, don't tell anyone you came from—

FIRST CRONE'S VOICE: Yeah, don't tell anyone—

SECOND CRONE'S VOICE: Don't tell any—

(The echoing Voices *fade. After a moment* Annie *lays the suitcase on the bed; and the last* Voice *comes faintly, from far away.)*

BOY'S VOICE: Annie. It hurts, to be dead. Forever.

(Annie falls to her knees by the bed, stifling her mouth in it. When at last she rolls blindly away from it, her palm comes down on the open report; she opens her eyes, regards it dully, and then, still on her knees, takes in the print.)

MAN'S VOICE: *(Factual)*—might awaken her to a consciousness of her immortal nature. The chance is small indeed; but with a smaller chance they would have dug desperately for her in the pit; and is the life of the soul of less import than that of the body?

(Annie gets to her feet. She drops the book on the bed, and pauses over her suitcase; after a moment she unclasps and opens it. Standing before it, she comes to her decision; she at once turns to the bureau, and taking her things out of its drawers, commences to throw them into the open suitcase.

In the darkness down left a hand strikes a match, and lights a hanging oil lamp. It is Keller's *hand, and his voice accompanies it, very angry; the lights rising here before they fade on* Annie *show* Keller *and* Kate *inside a suggestion of a garden house, with a bay-window seat towards center and a door at back.)*

KELLER: Katie, I will not *have* it! Now you did not see when that girl after supper tonight went to look for Helen in her room—

KATE: No.

KELLER: The child practically climbed out of her window to escape from her! What kind of teacher *is* she? I thought I had seen her at her worst this morning, shouting at me, but I come home to find the entire house disorganized by her— Helen won't stay one second in the same room, won't come to the table with her, won't let herself be bathed or undressed or put to bed by her, or even by Viney now, and the end result is that *you* have to do more for the child than before we hired this girl's services! From the moment she stepped off the train she's been nothing but a burden, incompetent, impertinent, ineffectual, immodest —

KATE: She folded her napkin, Captain.

KELLER: What?

KATE: Not ineffectual. Helen did fold her napkin.

KELLER: What in heaven's name is so extraordinary about folding a napkin?

KATE: (With some humor) Well. It's more than you did, Captain.

KELLER: Katie. I did not bring you all the way out here to the garden house to be frivolous. Now, how does Miss Sullivan propose to teach a deaf-blind pupil who won't let her even touch her?

KATE: (A pause) I don't know.

KELLER: The fact is, today she scuttled any chance she ever had of getting along with the child. If you can see any point or purpose to her staying on here longer, it's more than —

KATE: What do you wish me to do?

KELLER: I want you to give her notice.

KATE: I can't.

KELLER: Then if you won't, I must. I simply will not —

(He is interrupted by a knock at the back door. Keller after a glance at Kate moves to open the door; Annie in her smoked glasses is standing outside. Keller contemplates her, heavily.) Miss Sullivan.

ANNIE: Captain Keller.

(She is nervous, keyed up to seizing the bull by the horns again, and she assumes a cheeriness which is not unshaky.) Viney said I'd find you both over here in the garden house. I thought we should — have a talk?

KELLER: (Reluctantly) Yes, I — Well, come in.

(Annie enters, and is interested in this room; she rounds on her heel, anxiously, studying it. Keller turns the matter over to Kate, sotto voce.) Katie.

KATE: (Turning it back, courteously) Captain.

(Keller clears his throat, makes ready.)

KELLER: I, ah — wanted first to make my position clear to Mrs. Keller, in private. I have decided I — am not satisfied — in fact, am deeply dissatisfied — with the manner in which —

ANNIE: (Intent) Excuse me, is this little house ever in use?

KELLER: (With patience) In the hunting season. If you will give me your attention, Miss Sullivan.

(Annie *turns her smoked glasses upon him; they hold his unwilling stare.*)
I have tried to make allowances for you because you come from a part of the country where people are—women, I should say—come from who—well, for whom—
(*It begins to elude him.*)
—allowances must—be made. I have decided, nevertheless, to—that is, decided I— (*Vexedly*) Miss Sullivan, I find it difficult to talk through those glasses.

ANNIE: (*Eagerly, removing them*) Oh, of course.

KELLER: (*Dourly*) Why do you wear them, the sun has been down for an hour.

ANNIE: (*Pleasantly, at the lamp*) Any kind of light hurts my eyes.
(*A silence; Keller ponders her, heavily.*)

KELLER: Put them on. Miss Sullivan, I have decided to—give you another chance.

ANNIE: (*Cheerfully*) To do what?

KELLER: To—remain in our employ.
(Annie's *eyes widen.*)
But on two conditions. I am not accustomed to rudeness in servants or women, and that is the first. If you are to stay, there must be a radical change of manner.

ANNIE: (*A pause*) Whose?

KELLER: (*Exploding*) Yours, young lady, isn't it obvious? And the second is that you persuade me there's the slightest hope of your teaching a child who flees from you now like the plague, to anyone else she can find in this house.

ANNIE: (*A pause*) There isn't.
(Kate *stops sewing, and fixes her eyes upon* Annie.)

KATE: What, Miss Annie?

ANNIE: It's hopeless here. I can't teach a child who runs away.

KELLER: (*Nonplussed*) Then—do I understand you—propose—

ANNIE: Well, if we all agree it's hopeless, the next question is what—

KATE: Miss Annie.
(*She is leaning toward* Annie, *in deadly earnest; it commands both* Annie *and* Keller.)
I am not agreed. I think perhaps you—underestimate Helen.

ANNIE: I think everybody else here does.

KATE: She did fold her napkin. She learns, she learns, do you know she began talking when she was six months old? She could say "water." Not really—"wahwah." "Wahwah," but

she meant water, she knew what it meant, and only six
months old, I never saw a child so — bright, or outgoing —
(Her voice is unsteady, but she gets it level.)
It's still in her, somewhere, isn't it? You should have seen her
before her illness, such a good-tempered child —
ANNIE: *(Agreeably)* She's changed.
*(A pause, Kate not letting her eyes go; her appeal at last is un-
conditional, and very quiet.)*
KATE: Miss Annie, put up with it. And with us.
KELLER: Us!
KATE: Please? Like the lost lamb in the parable, I love her all the
more.
ANNIE: Mrs. Keller, I don't think Helen's worst handicap is deaf-
ness or blindness. I think it's your love. And pity.
KELLER: Now what does that mean?
ANNIE: All of you here are so sorry for her you've kept her — like
a pet, why, even a dog you housebreak. No wonder she won't
let me come near her. It's useless for me to try to teach her
language or anything else here. I might as well —
KATE: *(Cuts in)* Miss Annie, before you came we spoke of putting
her in an asylum.
(Annie turns back to regard her. A pause.)
ANNIE: What kind of asylum?
KELLER: For mental defectives.
KATE: I visited there. I can't tell you what I saw, people like —
animals, with — rats, in the halls, and —
(She shakes her head on her vision.)
What else are we to do, if you give up?
ANNIE: Give up?
KATE: You said it was hopeless.
ANNIE: Here. Give up, why, I only today saw what has to be
done, to begin!
*(She glances from Kate to Keller, who stare, waiting; and she
makes it as plain and simple as her nervousness permits.)*
I — want complete charge of her.
KELLER: You already have that. It has resulted in —
ANNIE: No, I mean day and night. She has to be dependent on me.
KATE: For what?
ANNIE: Everything. The food she eats, the clothes she wears,
fresh —
(She is amused at herself, though very serious.)
— air, yes, the air she breathes, whatever her body needs is

a—primer, to teach her out of it. It's the only way, the one who lets her have it should be her teacher.
(She considers them in turn; they digest it, Keller *frowning,* Kate *perplexed.)*
Not anyone who *loves* her, you have so many feelings they fall over each other like feet, you won't use your chances and you won't let me.
KATE: But if she runs from you—*to* us—
ANNIE: Yes, that's the point. I'll have to live with her somewhere else.
KELLER: What!
ANNIE: Till she learns to depend on and listen to me.
KATE: *(Not without alarm)* For how long?
ANNIE: As long as it takes. *(A pause. She takes a breath.)* I packed half my things already.
KELLER: Miss—Sullivan!
(But when Annie *attends upon him he is speechless, and she is merely earnest.)*
ANNIE: Captain Keller, it meets both your conditions. It's the one way I can get back in touch with Helen, and I don't see how I can be rude to you again if you're not around to interfere with me.
KELLER: *(Red-faced)* And what is your intention if I say no? Pack the other half, for home, and abandon your charge to—to—
ANNIE: The asylum?
(She waits, appraises Keller's *glare and* Kate's *uncertainty, and decides to use her weapons.)*
I grew up in such an asylum. The state almshouse.
*(Kate's *head comes up on this, and* Keller *stares hard;* Annie's *tone is cheerful enough, albeit level as gunfire.)*
Rats—why, my brother Jimmie and I used to play with the rats because we didn't have toys. Maybe you'd like to know what Helen will find there, not on visiting days? One ward was full of the—old women, crippled, blind, most of them dying, but even if what they had was catching there was no-where else to move them, and that's where they put us. There were younger ones across the hall, prostitutes mostly, with T.B., and epileptic fits, and a couple of the kind who—keep after other girls, especially young ones, and some insane. Some just had the D.T.'s. The youngest were in another ward to have babies they didn't want, they started at thirteen, four-teen. They'd leave afterwards, but the babies stayed and we

played with them, too, though a lot of them had—sores all over from diseases you're not supposed to talk about, but not many of them lived. The first year we had eighty, seventy died. The room Jimmie and I played in was the deadhouse, where they kept the bodies till they could dig—

KATE: *(Closes her eyes)* Oh, my dear—

ANNIE: —the graves.

(She is immune to Kate's *compassion.)*

No, it made me strong. But I don't think you need send Helen there. She's strong enough.

(She waits again; but when neither offers her a word, she simply concludes.)

No, I have no conditions, Captain Keller.

KATE: *(Not looking up)* Miss Annie.

ANNIE: Yes.

KATE: *(A pause)* Where would you—take Helen?

ANNIE: Ohh— *(Brightly)* Italy?

KELLER: *(Wheeling)* What?

ANNIE: Can't have everything, how would this garden house do? Furnish it, bring Helen here after a long ride so she won't recognize it, and you can see her every day. If she doesn't know. Well?

KATE: *(A sigh of relief)* Is that all?

ANNIE: That's all.

KATE: Captain.

(Keller turns his head; and Kate's *request is quiet but firm.)*

With your permission?

KELLER: *(Teeth in cigar)* Why must she depend on you for the food she eats?

ANNIE: *(A pause)* I want control of it.

KELLER: Why?

ANNIE: It's a way to reach her.

KELLER: *(Stares)* You intend to *starve* her into letting you touch her?

ANNIE: She won't starve, she'll learn. All's fair in love and war, Captain Keller, you never cut supplies?

KELLER: This is hardly a war!

ANNIE: Well, it's not love. A siege is a siege.

KELLER: *(Heavily)* Miss Sullivan. Do you *like* the child?

ANNIE: *(Straight in his eyes)* Do you?

(A long pause)

KATE: You could have a servant here—

ANNIE: *(Amused)* I'll have enough work without looking after a servant! But that boy Percy could sleep here, run errands —

KATE: *(Also amused)* We can let Percy sleep here, I think, Captain?

ANNIE: *(Eagerly)* And some old furniture, all our own —

KATE: *(Also eager)* Captain? Do you think that walnut bedstead in the barn would be too —

KELLER: I have not yet consented to Percy! Or to the house, or to the proposal! Or to Miss Sullivan's — staying on when I —
(But he erupts in an irate surrender.)
Very well, I consent to everything!
(He shakes the cigar at Annie.*)*
For two weeks. I'll give you two weeks in this place, and it will be a miracle if you get the child to tolerate you.

KATE: Two weeks? Miss Annie, can you accomplish anything in two weeks?

KELLER: Anything or not, two weeks, then the child comes back to us. Make up your mind, Miss Sullivan, yes or no?

ANNIE: Two weeks. For only one miracle? *(She nods at him, nervously.)* I'll get her to tolerate me.
(Keller marches out, and slams the door. Kate *on her feet regards* Annie, *who is facing the door.)*

KATE: *(Then)* You can't think as little of love as you said.
(Annie glances questioning.*)*
Or you wouldn't stay.

ANNIE: *(A pause)* I didn't come here for love. I came for money!
(Kate shakes her head to this, with a smile; after a moment she extends her open hand. Annie *looks at it, but when she puts hers out it is not to shake hands, it is to set her fist in* Kate's *palm.)*

KATE: *(Puzzled)* Hm?

ANNIE: A. It's the first of many. Twenty-six!
(Kate squeezes her fist, squeezes it hard, and hastens out after Keller. Annie *stands as the door closes behind her, her manner so apprehensive that finally she slaps her brow, holds it, sighs, and, with her eyes closed, crosses herself for luck.*
The lights dim into a cool silhouette scene around her, the lamp paling out, and now, in formal entrances, persons appear around Annie *with furniture for the room:* Percy *crosses the stage with a rocking chair and waits;* Martha *from another direction bears in a stool,* Viney *bears in a small table, and the other* Servant *rolls in a bed partway from left; and* Annie, *opening her eyes to put her glasses back on, sees them. She*

turns around in the room once, and goes into action, pointing out locations for each article; the Servants place them and leave, and Annie *then darts around, interchanging them. In the midst of this—while* Percy *and* Martha *reappear with a tray of food and a chair, respectively—* James *comes down from the house with* Annie's *suitcase, and stands viewing the room and her quizzically;* Annie *halts abruptly under his eyes, embarrassed, then seizes the suitcase from his hand, explaining herself brightly.)*

I always wanted to live in a doll's house!

(She sets the suitcase out of the way, and continues; Viney *at left appears to position a rod with drapes for a doorway, and the other* Servant *at center pushes in a wheelbarrow loaded with a couple of boxes of* Helen's *toys and clothes.* Annie *helps lift them into the room, and the* Servant *pushes the wheelbarrow off. In none of this is any heed taken of the imaginary walls of the garden house, the furniture is moved in from every side and itself defines the walls.*

Annie *now drags the box of toys into center, props up the doll conspicuously on top; with the people melted away, except for* James, *all is again still. The lights turn again without pause, rising warmer.)*

JAMES: You don't let go of things easily, do you? How will you—win her hand now, in this place?

ANNIE: *(Curtly)* Do I know? I lost my temper, and here we are!

JAMES: *(Lightly)* No touching, no teaching. Of course, you *are* bigger—

ANNIE: I'm not counting on force, I'm counting on her. That little imp is dying to know.

JAMES: Know what?

ANNIE: Anything. Any and every crumb in God's creation. I'll have to use that appetite too.

(She gives the room a final survey, straightens the bed, arranges the curtains.)

JAMES: *(A pause)* Maybe she'll teach you.

ANNIE: Of course.

JAMES: That she isn't. That there's such a thing as—dullness of heart. Acceptance. And letting go. Sooner or later we all give up, don't we?

ANNIE: Maybe you all do. It's my idea of the original sin.

JAMES: What is?

ANNIE: *(Witheringly)* Giving up.

JAMES: *(Nettled)* You won't open her. Why can't you let her be? Have some — pity on her, for being what she is —

ANNIE: If I'd ever once thought like that, I'd be dead!

JAMES: *(Pleasantly)* You will be. Why trouble?

(Annie turns to glare at him; he is mocking.)

Or will you teach me?

(And with a bow, he drifts off.

Now in the distance there comes the clopping of hoofs, drawing near, and nearer, up to the door; and they halt. Annie wheels to face the door. When it opens this time, the Kellers — Kate in travelling bonnet, Keller also hatted — are standing there with Helen between them; she is in a cloak. Kate gently cues her into the room. Helen comes in groping, baffled, but interested in the new surroundings; Annie evades her exploring hand, her gaze not leaving the child.)

ANNIE: Does she know where she is?

KATE: *(Shakes her head)* We rode her out in the country for two hours.

KELLER: For all she knows, she could be in another town —

(Helen stumbles over the box on the floor and in it discovers her doll and other battered toys, is pleased, sits to them, then becomes puzzled and suddenly very wary. She scrambles up and back to her mother's thighs, but Annie steps in, and it is hers that Helen embraces. Helen recoils, gropes, and touches her cheek instantly.)

KATE: That's her sign for me.

ANNIE: I know.

(Helen waits, then recommences her groping, more urgently. Kate stands indecisive, and takes an abrupt step toward her, but Annie's hand is a barrier.)

In two weeks.

KATE: Miss Annie, I — Please be good to her. These two weeks, try to be very good to her —

ANNIE: I will.

(Kate, turning then, hurries out. The Kellers cross back of the main house.

Annie closes the door. Helen starts at the door jar, and rushes it. Annie holds her off. Helen kicks her, breaks free, and careens around the room like an imprisoned bird, colliding with furniture, groping wildly, repeatedly touching her cheek in a growing panic. When she has covered the room, she commences her weird screaming. Annie moves to comfort her, but

her touch sends Helen *into a paroxysm of rage: she tears
away, falls over her box of toys, flings its contents in handfuls
in* Annie's *direction, flings the box too, reels to her feet, rips
curtains from the window, bangs and kicks at the door, sweeps
objects off the mantelpiece and shelf, a little tornado incar-
nate, all destruction, until she comes upon her doll and, in the
act of hurling it, freezes. Then she clutches it to herself, and in
exhaustion sinks sobbing to the floor.* Annie *stands contemplating her, in some awe.)*
Two weeks.
*(She shakes her head, not without a touch of disgusted
bewilderment.)*
What did I get into now?
*(The lights have been dimming throughout, and the garden
house is lit only by moonlight now, with* Annie *lost in the
patches of dark.*
Kate, *now hatless and coatless, enters the family room by the
rear door, carrying a lamp.* Keller, *also hatless, wanders simultaneously around the back of the main house to where* James
has been waiting, in the rising moonlight, on the porch.)
KELLER: I can't understand it. I had every intention of dismissing
   that girl, not setting her up like an empress.
JAMES: Yes, what's her secret, sir?
KELLER: Secret?
JAMES: *(Pleasantly)* That enables her to get anything she wants
   out of you? When I can't.
(James turns to go into the house, but Keller *grasps his wrist,
twisting him half to his knees.* Kate *comes from the porch.)*
KELLER: *(Angrily)* She does *not* get anything she —
JAMES: *(In pain)* Don't — don't —
KATE: Captain.
KELLER: He's afraid.
   (He throws James *away from him, with contempt.)*
   What *does* he want out of me?
JAMES: *(An outcry)* My God, don't you know?
   (He gazes from Keller *to* Kate.)
   Everything you forgot, when you forgot my mother.
KELLER: What!
   (James wheels into the house. Keller *takes a stride to the
porch, to roar after him.)*
   One thing that girl's secret is not, she doesn't fire one shot
   and disappear!

(Kate stands rigid, and Keller comes back to her.)
Katie. Don't mind what he—
KATE: Captain, *I* am proud of you.
KELLER: For what?
KATE: For letting this girl have what she needs.
KELLER: Why can't my son be? He can't bear me, you'd think I treat him as hard as this girl does Helen—
(He breaks off, as it dawns in him.)
KATE: *(Gently)* Perhaps you do.
KELLER: But he has to learn some respect!
KATE: *(A pause, wryly) Do* you like the child?
(She turns again to the porch, but pauses, reluctant.)
How empty the house is, tonight.
(After a moment she continues on in. Keller stands moveless, as the moonlight dies on him.
The distant belfry chimes toll, two o'clock, and with them, a moment later, comes the Boy's Voice *on the wind, in a whisper:)*
BOY'S VOICE: Annie. Annie.
(In her patch of dark Annie, now in her nightgown, hurls a cup into a corner as though it were her grief, getting rid of its taste through her teeth.)
ANNIE: No! No pity. I won't have it.
(She comes to Helen, prone on the floor.)
On either of us.
(She goes to her knees, but when she touches Helen's *hand the child starts up awake, recoils, and scrambles away from her under the bed. Annie stares after her. She strikes her palm on the floor, with passion.)*
I *will* touch you!
(She gets to her feet, and paces in a kind of anger around the bed, her hands in her hair, and confronting Helen at each turn.)
How, how? How do I—
(Annie stops. Then she calls out urgently, loudly.)
Percy! Percy!
(She moves swiftly to the drapes, at left.)
Percy, wake up!
(Percy's voice comes in a thick sleepy mumble, unintelligible.)
Get out of bed and come in here, I need you.
(Annie darts away, finds and strikes a match, and touches it to the hanging lamp; the lights come up dimly in the room, and

Percy *stands bare to the waist in torn overalls between the drapes, with eyes closed, swaying.* Annie *goes to him, pats his cheeks vigorously.)*
Percy. You awake?
PERCY: No'm.
ANNIE: How would you like to play a nice game?
PERCY: Whah?
ANNIE: With Helen. She's under the bed. Touch her hand.
(She kneels Percy *down at the bed, thrusting his hand under it to contact* Helen's; Helen *emits an animal sound and crawls to the opposite side, but commences sniffing.* Annie *rounds the bed with* Percy *and thrusts his hand again at* Helen; *this time* Helen *clutches it, sniffs in recognition, and comes scrambling out after* Percy *to hug him with delight.* Percy *alarmed struggles, and* Helen's *fingers go to his mouth.)*
PERCY: Lemme go. Lemme go—
(Helen fingers her own lips, as before, moving them in dumb imitation.)
She tryin' talk. She gonna hit me—
ANNIE: *(Grimly)* She can talk. If she only knew, I'll show you how. She makes letters.
(She opens Percy's *other hand, and spells into it:)*
This one is C. C.
(She hits his palm with it a couple of times, her eyes upon Helen *across from him;* Helen *gropes to feel what* Percy's *hand is doing, and when she encounters* Annie's *she falls back from them.)*
She's mad at me now, though, she won't play. But she knows lots of letters. Here's another, A. C, a. C, a.
(But she is watching Helen, *who comes groping, consumed with curiosity;* Annie *makes the letters in* Percy's *hand, and* Helen *pokes to question what they are up to. Then* Helen *snatches* Percy's *other hand, and quickly spells four letters into it.* Annie *follows them aloud.)*
C, a, k, e! She spells cake, she gets cake.
(She is swiftly over to the tray of food, to fetch cake and a jug of milk.)
She doesn't know yet it means this. Isn't it funny she knows how to spell it and doesn't *know* she knows?
(She breaks the cake in two pieces, and extends one to each; Helen *rolls away from her offer.)*
Well, if she won't play it with me, I'll play it with you.

Would you like to learn one she doesn't know?
PERCY: No'm.
(But Annie *seizes his wrist, and spells to him.)*
ANNIE: M, i, l, k. M is this. I, that's an easy one, just the little finger. L is this—
(And Helen *comes back with her hand, to feel the new word.* Annie *brushes her away, and continues spelling aloud to* Percy. Helen's *hand comes back again, and tries to get in;* Annie *brushes it away again.* Helen's *hand insists, and* Annie *puts it away rudely.)*
No, why should I talk to you? I'm teaching Percy a new word. L. K is this—
(Helen now *yanks their hands apart; she butts* Percy *away, and thrusts her palm out insistently.* Annie's *eyes are bright, with glee.)*
Ho, you're *jealous, are you!*
*(Helen's *hand waits, intractably waits.)*
All *right.*
*(Annie *spells into it, milk; and* Helen *after a moment spells it back to* Annie. Annie *takes her hand, with her whole face shining. She gives a great sigh.)*
Good! So I'm finally back to where I can touch you, hm? Touch and go! No love lost, but here we go.
(She puts the jug of milk into Helen's *hand and squeezes* Percy's *shoulder.)*
You can go to bed now, you've earned your sleep. Thank you.
*(Percy *stumbling up weaves his way out through the drapes.* Helen *finishes drinking, and holds the jug out, for* Annie; *when* Annie *takes it,* Helen *crawls onto the bed, and makes for sleep.* Annie *stands, looks down at her.)*
Now all I have to teach you is—one word. Everything.
(She sets the jug down. On the floor now Annie *spies the doll, stoops to pick it up, and with it dangling in her hand, turns off the lamp. A shaft of moonlight is left on* Helen *in the bed, and a second shaft on the rocking chair; and* Annie, *after putting off her smoked glasses, sits in the rocker with the doll. She is rather happy, and dangles the doll on her knee, and it makes its momma sound.* Annie *whispers to it in mock solicitude.)*
Hush, little baby. Don't—say a word—
(She lays it against her shoulder, and begins rocking with it, patting its diminutive behind; she talks the lullaby to it,

humorously at first.)
Momma's gonna buy you—a mockingbird:
If that—mockingbird don't sing—
(The rhythm of the rocking takes her into the tune, softly, and more tenderly.)
Momma's gonna buy you a diamond ring:
If that diamond ring turns to brass—
(A third shaft of moonlight outside now rises to pick out James *at the main house, with one foot on the porch step; he turns his body, as if hearing the song.)*
Momma's gonna buy you a looking-glass:
If that looking-glass gets broke—
(In the family room a fourth shaft picks out Keller *seated at the table, in thought; and he, too, lifts his head, as if hearing.)*
Momma's gonna buy you a billy goat:
If that billy goat won't pull—
(The fifth shaft is upstairs in Annie's *room, and picks out* Kate, *pacing there; and she halts, turning her head, too, as if hearing.)*
Momma's gonna buy you a cart and bull:
If that cart and bull turns over,
Momma's gonna buy you a
dog named Rover:
If that dog named Rover won't bark—
(With the shafts of moonlight on Helen, *and* James, *and* Keller, *and* Kate, *all moveless, and* Annie *rocking the doll, the curtain ends the act.)*

ACT THREE

(The stage is totally dark, until we see Annie *and* Helen *silhouetted on the bed in the garden house.* Annie's *voice is audible, very patient, and worn; it has been saying this for a long time.)*
ANNIE: Water, Helen. This is water. W, a, t, e, r. It has a *name.*
(A silence. Then:) Egg, e, g, g. It has a *name,* the name stands for the thing. Oh, it's so simple, simple as birth, to explain.
(The lights have commenced to rise, not on the garden house but on the homestead. Then:)
Helen, Helen, the chick *has* to come out of its shell, sometime. You come out, too.
(In the bedroom upstairs, we see Viney *unhurriedly washing the window, dusting, turning the mattress, readying the room for use again; then in the family room a diminished group at one end of the table —* Kate, Keller, James *— finishing up a quiet breakfast; then outside, down right, the other* Servant *on his knees, assisted by* Martha, *working with a trowel around a new trellis and wheelbarrow. The scene is one of everyday calm, and all are oblivious to* Annie's *voice.)*
There's only one way out, for you, and it's language. To learn that your fingers can talk. And say anything, anything you can name. This is mug. Mug, m, u, g. Helen, it has a *name.* It — has — a — *name —*
(Kate *rises from the table.)*
KELLER: *(Gently)* You haven't eaten, Katie.
KATE: *(Smiles, shakes her head)* I haven't the appetite. I'm too — restless, I can't sit to it.
KELLER: You should eat, my dear. It will be a long day, waiting.
JAMES: *(Lightly)* But it's been a short two weeks. I never thought life could be so — noiseless, went much too quickly for me.
(Kate *and* Keller *gaze at him, in silence.* James *becomes uncomfortable.)*
ANNIE: C, a, r, d. Card. C, a —
JAMES: Well, the house has been practically normal, hasn't it?
KELLER: *(Harshly)* Jimmie.
JAMES: Is it wrong to enjoy a quiet breakfast, after five years? And you two even seem to enjoy each other —
KELLER: It could be even more noiseless, Jimmie, without your tongue running every minute. Haven't you enough feeling to imagine what Katie has been undergoing, ever since —
(Kate *stops him, with her hand on his arm.)*
KATE: Captain. *(To* James) It's true. The two weeks have been

normal, quiet, all you say. But not short. Interminable.
(She rises, and wanders out; she pauses on the porch steps, gazing toward the garden house.)
ANNIE: *(Fading)* W, a, t, e, r. But it means *this*. W, a, t, e, r. *This.*
W, a, t—
JAMES: I only meant that Miss Sullivan is a boon. Of contention, though, it seems.
KELLER: *(Heavily)* If and when you're a parent, Jimmie, you will understand what separation means. A mother loses a—
protector.
JAMES: *(Baffled)* Hm?
KELLER: You'll learn, we don't just keep our children safe. They keep us safe.
(He rises, with his empty coffee cup and saucer.)
There are of course all kinds of separation, Katie has lived with one kind for five years. And another is disappointment. In a child.
(He goes with the cup out the rear door. James sits for a long moment of stillness. In the garden house the lights commence to come up; Annie, haggard at the table, is writing a letter, her face again almost in contact with the stationery; Helen, apart on the stool, and for the first time as clean and neat as a button, is quietly crocheting an endless chain of wool, which snakes all around the room.)
ANNIE: "I, feel, every, day, more, and, more, in—"
(She pauses, and turns the pages of a dictionary open before her; her finger descends the words to a full stop. She elevates her eyebrows, then copies the word.)
"—adequate."
(In the main house James pushes up, and goes to the front doorway, after Kate.)
JAMES: Kate?
(Kate turns her glance. James is rather weary.)
I'm sorry. Open my mouth, like that fairy tale, frogs jump out.
KATE: No. It has been better. For everyone.
(She starts away, up center.)
ANNIE: *(Writing)* "If, only, there, were, someone, to, help, me, I, need, a, teacher, as, much, as, Helen—"
JAMES: Kate.
(Kate halts, waits.)
What does he want from me?

KATE: That's not the question. Stand up to the world, Jimmie, that comes first.

JAMES: *(A pause, wryly)* But the world is him.

KATE: Yes. And no one can do it for you.

JAMES: Kate. *(His voice is humble.)* At least we — Could you — be my friend?

KATE: I am.

(Kate turns to wander, up back of the garden house. Annie's murmur comes at once; the lights begin to die on the main house.)

ANNIE: " — my, mind, is, undisciplined, full, of, skips, and, jumps, and — "

(She halts, rereads, frowns.) Hm.

(Annie puts her nose again in the dictionary, flips back to an earlier page, and fingers down the words; Kate presently comes down toward the bay window with a trayful of food.)

Disinter — disinterested — disjoin — dis — *(She backtracks, indignant.)* Disinterested, disjoin — Where's discipline?

(She goes a page or two back, searching with her finger, muttering.)

What a dictionary, have to know how to spell it before you can look up how to spell it, disciple, *discipline*! Diskipline.

(She corrects the word in her letter.)

Undisciplined.

(But her eyes are bothering her, she closes them in exhaustion and gently fingers the eyelids. Kate watches her through the window.)

KATE: What are you doing to your eyes?

(Annie glances around; she puts her smoked glasses on, and gets up to come over, assuming a cheerful energy.)

ANNIE: It's worse on my vanity! I'm learning to spell. It's like a surprise party, the most unexpected characters turn up.

KATE: You're not to overwork your eyes, Miss Annie.

ANNIE: Well.

(She takes the tray, sets it on her chair, and carries chair and tray to Helen.)

Whatever I spell to Helen I'd better spell right.

KATE: *(Almost wistful)* How — serene she is.

ANNIE: She learned this stitch yesterday. Now I can't get her to stop!

(She disentangles one foot from the wool chain, and sets the chair before Helen. Helen at its contact with her knee feels

the plate, promptly sets her crocheting down, and tucks the napkin in at her neck, but Annie *withholds the spoon; when* Helen *finds it missing, she folds her hands in her lap, and quietly waits.* Annie *twinkles at* Kate *with mock devoutness.)*
Such a little lady, she'd sooner starve than eat with her fingers.
(She gives Helen *the spoon, and* Helen *begins to eat, neatly.)*
KATE: You've taught her so much, these two weeks. I would never have—
ANNIE: Not enough.
(She is suddenly gloomy, shakes her head.)
Obedience isn't enough. Well, she learned two nouns this morning, key and water, brings her up to eighteen nouns and three verbs.
KATE: (Hesitant) But—not—
ANNIE: No. Not that they mean things. It's still a finger-game, no meaning.
(She turns to Kate, *abruptly.)*
Mrs. Keller—
(But she defers it; she comes back, to sit in the bay and lift her hand.)
Shall we play our finger-game?
KATE: How will she learn it?
ANNIE: It will come.
(She spells a word; Kate *does not respond.)*
KATE: How?
ANNIE: *(A pause)* How does a bird learn to fly? *(She spells again.)* We're born to use words, like wings, it has to come.
KATE: How?
ANNIE: *(Another pause, wearily)* All right. I don't know how.
(She pushes up her glasses, to rub her eyes.)
I've done everything I could think of. Whatever she's learned here—keeping herself clean, knitting, stringing beads, meals, setting-up exercises each morning, we climb trees, hunt eggs, yesterday a chick was born in her hands— all of it I spell, everything we do, we never stop spelling. I go to bed with— writer's cramp from talking so much!
KATE: I worry about you, Miss Annie. You must rest.
ANNIE: Now? She spells back in her *sleep,* her fingers make letters when she doesn't know! In her bones those five fingers know, that hand aches to—speak out, and something in her mind is asleep, how do I—nudge that awake? That's the one question.

KATE: With no answer.

ANNIE: *(Long pause)* Except keep at it. Like this.

(She again begins spelling—I, need—and Kate's *brows gather, following the words.)*

KATE: More—time?

(She glances at Annie, *who looks her in the eyes, silent.)* Here?

ANNIE: Spell it.

(Kate spells a word—no—shaking her head; Annie *spells two words—why, not— back, with an impatient question in her eyes; and* Kate *moves her head in pain to answer it.)*

KATE: Because I can't—

ANNIE: Spell it! If she ever learns, you'll have a lot to tell each other, start now.

(Kate painstakingly spells in air. In the midst of this the rear door opens, and Keller *enters with the setter* Belle *in tow.)*

KELLER: Miss Sullivan? On my way to the office, I brought Helen a playmate—

ANNIE: Outside please, Captain Keller.

KELLER: My dear child, the two weeks are up today, surely you don't object to—

ANNIE: *(Rising)* They're not up till six o'clock.

KELLER: *(Indulgent)* Oh, now. What difference can a fraction of one day—

ANNIE: An agreement is an agreement. Now you've been very good, I'm sure you can keep it up for a few more hours.

(She escorts Keller *by the arm over the threshold; he obeys, leaving* Belle.)

KELLER: Miss Sullivan, you are a tyrant.

ANNIE: Likewise, I'm sure. You can stand there, and close the door if she comes.

KATE: I don't think you know how eager we are to have her back in our arms—

ANNIE: I do know, it's my main worry.

KELLER: It's like expecting a new child in the house. Well, she *is*, so—composed, so—*(Gently)* Attractive. You've done wonders for her, Miss Sullivan.

ANNIE: *(Not a question)* Have I.

KELLER: If there's anything you want from us in repayment tell us, it will be a privilege to—

ANNIE: I just told Mrs. Keller. I want more time.

KATE: Miss Annie—

ANNIE: Another week.

(Helen *lifts her head, and begins to sniff.*)

KELLER: We miss the child. *I* miss her, I'm glad to say, that's a different debt I owe you—

ANNIE: Pay it to Helen. Give *her* another week.

KATE: *(Gently)* Doesn't she miss us?

KELLER: Of course she does. What a wrench this unexplainable— exile must be to her, can you say it's not?

ANNIE: No. But I—

(Helen *is off the stool, to grope about the room; when she encounters* Belle, *she throws her arms around the dog's neck in delight.*)

KATE: Doesn't she need affection too, Miss Annie?

ANNIE: *(Wavering)* She—never shows me she needs it, she won't have any—caressing or—

KATE: But you're not her mother.

KELLER: And what would another week accomplish? We are more than satisfied, you've done more than we ever thought possible, taught her constructive—

ANNIE: I can't promise anything. All I can—

KELLER: *(No break)*—things to do, to behave like—even look like—a human child, so manageable, contented, cleaner, more—

ANNIE: *(Withering)* Cleaner.

KELLER: Well. We say cleanliness is next to godliness, Miss—

ANNIE: Cleanliness is next to nothing, she has to learn that everything has its name! That words can be her *eyes*, to everything in the world outside her, and inside too, what is she without words? With them she can think, have ideas, be reached, there's not a thought or fact in the world that can't be hers. You publish a newspaper, Captain Keller, do I have to tell you what words are? And she has them already—

KELLER: Miss Sullivan.

ANNIE: —eighteen nouns and three verbs, they're in her fingers now, I need only time to push *one* of them into her mind! One, and everything under the sun will follow. Don't you see what she's learned here is only clearing the way for that? I can't risk her unlearning it, give me more time alone with her, another week to—

KELLER: Look.

(He points, and Annie *turns.* Helen *is playing with* Belle's *claws; she makes letters with her fingers, shows them to* Belle,

waits with her palm, then manipulates the dog's claws.)
What is she spelling?
(A silence.)
KATE: Water?
(Annie nods.)
KELLER: Teaching a dog to spell. *(A pause.)* The dog doesn't
know what she means, any more than she knows what you
mean, Miss Sullivan. I think you ask too much, of her and
yourself. God may not have meant Helen to have the — eyes
you speak of.
ANNIE: *(Toneless)* I mean her to.
KELLER: *(Curiously)* What is it to you?
(Annie's head comes slowly up.)
You make us see how we indulge her for our sake. Is the
opposite true, for you?
ANNIE: *(Then)* Half a week?
KELLER: An agreement *is* an agreement.
ANNIE: Mrs. Keller?
KATE: *(Simply)* I want her back.
(A wait; Annie then lets her hands drop in surrender, and nods.)
KELLER: I'll send Viney over to help you pack.
ANNIE: Not until six o'clock. I have her till six o'clock.
KELLER: *(Consenting)* Six o'clock. Come, Katie.
*(Kate leaving the window joins him around back, while Keller
closes the door; they are shut out.*

*Only the garden house is daylit now, and the light on it is
narrowing down. Annie stands watching Helen work Belle's
claws. Then she settles beside them on her knees, and stops
Helen's hand.)*
ANNIE: *(Gently)* No.
*(She shakes her head, with Helen's hand to her face, then
spells.)*
Dog. D, o, g. dog.
*(She touches Helen's hand to Belle. Helen dutifully pats the
dog's head, and resumes spelling to its paw.)*
Not water.
*(Annie rolls to her feet, brings a tumbler of water back from
the tray, and kneels with it, to seize Helen's hand and spell.)*
Here. Water. *Water.*
*(She thrusts Helen's hand into the tumbler. Helen lifts her
hand out dripping, wipes it daintily on Belle's hide, and taking
the tumbler from Annie, endeavors to thrust Belle's paw*

into it. Annie *sits watching, wearily.)*
I don't know how to tell you. Not a soul in the world knows
how to tell you. Helen, Helen.
(She bends in compassion to touch her lips to Helen's *temple,
and instantly* Helen *pauses, her hands off the dog, her head
slightly averted. The lights are still narrowing, and* Belle *slinks
off. After a moment* Annie *sits back.)*
Yes, what's it to me? They're satisfied. Give them back their
child and dog, both housebroken, everyone's satisfied. But
me, and you.
(Helen's hand comes out into the light, groping.)
Reach. *Reach!*
(Annie extending her own hand grips Helen's; *the two hands
are clasped, tense in the light, the rest of the room changing in
shadow.)*
I wanted to teach you — oh, everything the earth is full of,
Helen, everything on it that's ours for a wink and it's gone,
and what we are on it, the — light we bring to it and leave behind in — words, why, you can see five thousand years back in
a light of words, everything we feel, think, know — and share,
in words, so not a soul is in darkness, or done with, even in
the grave. And I know, I *know*, one word and I can — put the
world in your hand — and whatever it is to me, I won't take
less! How, how, how do I tell you that *this — (She spells.) —*
means a *word*, and the word means this *thing*, wool?
(She thrusts the wool at Helen's *hand;* Helen *sits, puzzled.*
Annie *puts the crocheting aside.)*
Or this — s, t, o, o, l — means this *thing*, stool?
(She claps Helen's *palm to the stool.* Helen *waits, uncompre-
hending.* Annie *snatches up her napkin, spells:)*
Napkin!
(She forces it on Helen's *hand, waits, discards it, lifts a fold of
the child's dress, spells:)*
Dress!
(She lets it drop, spells:)
F, a, c, e, face!
(She draws Helen's *hand to her cheek and pressing it there,
staring into the child's responseless eyes, hears the distant bel-
fry begin to toll, slowly: one, two, three, four, five, six.*
   *On the third stroke the lights stealing in around the garden
house show us figures waiting:* Viney, *the other* Servant, Mar-
tha, Percy *at the drapes, and* James *on the dim porch.* Annie

and Helen *remain, frozen. The chimes die away. Silently* Percy
moves the drape-rod back out of sight; Viney *steps into the
room—not using the door—and unmakes the bed; the other*
Servant *brings the wheelbarrow over, leaves it handy, rolls the
bed off;* Viney *puts the bed linens on top of a waiting boxful
of* Helen's *toys, and loads the box on the wheelbarrow;*
Martha *and* Percy *take out the chairs, with the trayful, then
the table; and* James, *coming down and into the room, lifts*
Annie's *suitcase from its corner.* Viney *and the other* Servant
*load the remaining odds and ends on the wheelbarrow, and
the* Servant *wheels it off.* Viney *and the* Children *departing
leave only* James *in the room with* Annie *and* Helen. James
*studies the two of them, without mockery, and then, quietly
going to the door and opening it, bears the suitcase out, and
housewards. He leaves the door open.*

Kate *steps into the doorway, and stands.* Annie *lifting her
gaze from* Helen *sees her; she takes* Helen's *hand from her
cheek, and returns it to the child's own, stroking it there
twice, in her mother-sign, before spelling slowly into it:)*
M, o, t, h, e, r. Mother.
(Helen *with her hand free strokes her cheek, suddenly forlorn.*
Annie *takes her hand again.*

But Kate *is trembling with such impatience that her voice
breaks from her, harsh.)*

KATE: Let her *come!*
(Annie *lifts* Helen *to her feet, with a turn, and gives her a little
push. Now* Helen *begins groping, sensing something, trembling
herself; and* Kate *falling one step in onto her knees clasps her,
kissing her.* Helen *clutches her, tight as she can.* Kate *is inarticulate, choked, repeating* Helen's *name again and again. She
wheels with her in her arms, to stumble away out the doorway;*
Annie *stands unmoving, while* Kate *in a blind walk carries*
Helen *like a baby behind the main house, out of view.*

Annie *is now alone on the stage. She turns, gazing around at
the stripped room, bidding it silently farewell, impassively, like
a defeated general on the deserted battlefield. All that remains is
a stand with a basin of water; and here* Annie *takes up an eyecup, bathes each of her eyes, empties the eyecup, drops it in her
purse, and tiredly locates her smoked glasses on the floor. The
lights alter subtly; in the act of putting on her glasses* Annie
*hears something that stops her, with head lifted. We hear it too,
the* Voices *out of the past, including her own now, in a whisper:)*

BOY'S VOICE: You said we'd be together, forever—You promised, forever and—*Annie!*

ANAGNOS' VOICE: But that battle is dead and done with, why not let it stay buried?

ANNIE'S VOICE: *(Whispering)* I think God must owe me a resurrection.

ANAGNOS' VOICE: What?

(A pause, and Annie *answers it herself, heavily.)*

ANNIE: And I owe God one.

BOY'S VOICE: Forever and ever—

(Annie *shakes her head.)*

—forever, and ever, and—

(Annie *covers her ears.)*

—forever, and ever, and ever—

(It pursues Annie; *she flees to snatch up her purse, wheels to the doorway, and* Keller *is standing in it. The lights have lost their special color.)*

KELLER: Miss—Annie.

(He has an envelope in his fingers.)

I've been waiting to give you this.

ANNIE: *(After a breath)* What?

KELLER: Your first month's salary.

(He puts it in her hand.)

With many more to come, I trust. It doesn't express what we feel, it doesn't pay our debt. For what you've done.

ANNIE: What have I done?

KELLER: Taken a wild thing, and given us back a child.

ANNIE: *(Presently)* I taught her one thing, no. Don't do this, don't do that—

KELLER: It's more than all of us could, in all the years we—

ANNIE: I wanted to teach her what language is. I wanted to teach her yes.

KELLER: You will have time.

ANNIE: I don't know how. I know without it to do nothing but obey is—no gift, obedience without understanding is a—blindness, too. Is that all I've wished on her?

KELLER: *(Gently)* No, no—

ANNIE: Maybe. I don't know what else to do. Simply go on, keep doing what I've done, and have—faith that inside she's—That inside it's waiting. Like water, underground. All I can do is keep on.

KELLER: It's enough. For us.

ANNIE: You can help, Captain Keller.

KELLER: How?

ANNIE: Even learning no has been at a cost. Of much trouble and pain. Don't undo it.

KELLER: Why should we wish to—

ANNIE: *(Abruptly)* The world isn't an easy place for anyone, I don't want her just to obey but to let her have her way in everything is a lie, to her, I can't—
(Her eyes fill, it takes her by surprise, and she laughs through it.)
And I don't even love her, she's not my child! Well. You've got to stand between that lie and her.

KELLER: We'll try.

ANNIE: Because *I* will. As long as you let me stay, that's one promise I'll keep.

KELLER: Agreed. We've learned something too, I hope. *(A pause)* Won't you come now, to supper?

ANNIE: Yes.
(She wags the envelope, ruefully.)
Why doesn't God pay His debts each month?

KELLER I beg your pardon?

ANNIE: Nothing. I used to wonder how I could—
(The lights are fading on them, simultaneously rising on the family room of the main house, where Viney *is polishing glassware at the table set for dinner.)*
—earn a living.

KELLER: Oh, you do.

ANNIE: I really do. Now the question is, can I survive it!
(Keller smiles, offers his arm.)

KELLER: May I?
*(Annie takes it, and the lights lose them as he escorts her out.
Now in the family room the rear door opens, and* Helen *steps in. She stands a moment, then sniffs in one deep grateful breath, and her hands go out vigorously to familiar things, over the door panels, and to the chairs around the table, and over the silverware on the table, until she meets* Viney; *she pats her flank approvingly.)*

VINEY: Oh, we glad to have you back too, prob'ly.
(Helen hurries groping to the front door, opens and closes it, removes its key, opens and closes it again to be sure it is unlocked, gropes back to the rear door and repeats the procedure, removing its key and hugging herself gleefully.

Aunt Ev *is next in by the rear door, with a relish tray; she bends to kiss* Helen's *cheek.* Helen *finds* Kate *behind her, and thrusts the keys at her.)*
KATE: What? Oh. (To *Ev*) Keys.
(She pockets them, lets Helen *feel them.)*
Yes, *I'll* keep the keys. I think we've had enough of locked doors, too.
*(*James, *having earlier put* Annie's *suitcase inside her door upstairs and taken himself out of view around the corner, now reappears and comes down the stairs as* Annie *and* Keller *mount the porch steps. Following them into the family room, he pats* Annie's *hair in passing, rather to her surprise.)*
JAMES: Evening, general.
(He takes his own chair opposite.
Viney *bears the empty water pitcher out to the porch. The remaining suggestion of garden house is gone now, and the water pump is unobstructed;* Viney *pumps water into the pitcher.*
Kate *surveying the table breaks the silence.)*
KATE: Will you say grace, Jimmie?
(They bow their heads, except for Helen, *who palms her empty plate and then reaches to be sure her mother is there.* James *considers a moment, glances across at* Annie, *lowers his head again, and obliges.)*
JAMES: *(Lightly)* And Jacob was left alone, and wrestled with an angel until the breaking of the day; and the hollow of Jacob's thigh was out of joint, as he wrestled with him; and the angel said, Let me go, for the day breaketh. And Jacob said, I will not let thee go, except thou bless me. Amen.
*(*Annie *has lifted her eyes suspiciously at* James, *who winks expressionlessly and inclines his head to* Helen.)*
Oh, you angel.
(The others lift their faces; Viney *returns with the pitcher, setting it down near* Kate, *then goes out the rear door; and* Annie *puts a napkin around* Helen.)*
AUNT EV: That's a very strange grace, James.
KELLER: Will you start the muffins, Ev?
JAMES: It's from the Good Book, isn't it?
AUNT EV: *(Passing a plate)* Well, of course it is. Didn't you know?
JAMES: Yes, I knew.
KELLER: *(Serving)* Ham, Miss Annie?
ANNIE: Please.
AUNT EV: Then why ask?

JAMES: I meant it *is* from the Good Book, and therefore a fitting grace.

AUNT EV: Well. I don't know about *that.*

KATE: *(With the pitcher)* Miss Annie?

ANNIE: Thank you.

AUNT EV: There's an awful *lot* of things in the Good Book that I wouldn't care to hear just before eating.

(When Annie reaches for the pitcher, Helen removes her napkin and drops it to the floor. Annie is filling Helen's glass when she notices it; she considers Helen's bland expression a moment, then bends, retrieves it, and tucks it around Helen's neck again.)

JAMES: Well, fitting in the sense that Jacob's thigh was out of joint, and so is this piggie's.

AUNT EV: I declare, James—

KATE: Pickles, Aunt Ev?

AUNT EV: Oh, I should say so, you know my opinion of your pickles—

KATE: This is the end of them, I'm afraid. I didn't put up nearly enough last summer, this year I intend to—

(She interrupts herself, seeing Helen deliberately lift off her napkin and drop it again to the floor. She bends to retrieve it, but Annie stops her arm.)

KELLER: *(Not noticing)* Reverend looked in at the office today to complain his hens have stopped laying. Poor fellow, *he* was out of joint, all he could—

(He stops too, to frown down the table at Kate, Helen, and Annie in turn, all suspended in mid-motion.)

JAMES: *(Not noticing)* I've always suspected those hens.

AUNT EV: Of what?

JAMES: I think they're Papist. Has he tried—

(He stops, too, following Keller's eyes. Annie now stops to pick the napkin up.)

AUNT EV: James, now you're pulling my—lower extremity, the first thing you know we'll be—

(She stops, too, hearing herself in the silence. Annie, with everyone now watching, for the third time puts the napkin on Helen. Helen yanks it off, and throws it down. Annie rises, lifts Helen's plate, and bears it away. Helen, feeling it gone, slides down and commences to kick up under the table; the dishes jump. Annie contemplates this for a moment, then coming back takes Helen's wrists firmly and swings her off the chair. Helen

*struggling gets one hand free, and catches at her mother's skirt;
when* Kate *takes her by the shoulders,* Helen *hangs quiet.)*

KATE: Miss Annie.

ANNIE: No.

KATE: *(A pause)* It's a very special day.

ANNIE: *(Grimly)* It will be, when I give in to that.

(She tries to disengage Helen's *hand;* Kate *lays hers on* Annie's.*)*

KATE: Please. I've hardly had a chance to welcome her home —

ANNIE: Captain Keller.

KELLER: *(Embarrassed)* Oh. Kate, we — had a little talk, Miss
Annie feels that if we indulge Helen in these —

AUNT EV: But what's the child done?

ANNIE: She's learned not to throw things on the floor and kick. It
took us the best part of two weeks and —

AUNT EV: But only a napkin, it's not as if it were breakable!

ANNIE: And everything she's learned *is*? Mrs. Keller, I don't think
we should — play tug-of-war for her, either give her to me or
you keep her from kicking.

KATE: What do you wish to do?

ANNIE: Let me take her from the table.

AUNT EV: Oh, let her stay, my goodness, she's only a child, she
doesn't have to wear a napkin if she doesn't want to to her first
evening —

ANNIE: *(Level)* And ask outsiders not to interfere.

AUNT EV: *(Astonished)* Out — outsi — I'm the child's *aunt*!

KATE: *(Distressed)* Will once hurt so much, Miss Annie? I've —
made all Helen's favorite foods, tonight.

(A pause)

KELLER: *(Gently)* It's a homecoming party, Miss Annie.

(Annie after a moment releases Helen. *But she cannot accept it,
at her own chair she shakes her head and turns back, intent on*
Kate.)

ANNIE: She's testing you. You realize?

JAMES: *(To Annie)* She's testing you.

KELLER: Jimmie, be quiet.

(James sits, tense.)

Now she's home, naturally she —

ANNIE: And wants to see what will happen. At your hands. I said
it was my main worry, is this what you promised me not half
an hour ago?

KELLER: *(Reasonably)* But she's *not* kicking, now —

ANNIE: And not learning not to. Mrs. Keller, teaching her is bound to be painful, to everyone. I know it hurts to watch, but she'll live up to just what you demand of her, and no more.

JAMES: *(Palely)* She's testing *you*.

KELLER: *(Testily)* Jimmie.

JAMES: I have an opinion, I think I should—

KELLER: No one's interested in hearing your opinion.

ANNIE: *I'm* interested, of course she's testing me. Let me keep her to what she's learned and she'll go on learning from me. Take her out of my hands and it all comes apart.

(Kate closes her eyes, digesting it; Annie sits again, with a brief comment for her.)

Be bountiful, it's at her expense.

(She turns to James, flatly.)

Please pass me more of—her favorite foods.

(Then Kate lifts Helen's hand, and turning her toward Annie, surrenders her; Helen makes for her own chair.)

KATE: *(Low)* Take her, Miss Annie.

ANNIE: *(Then)* Thank you.

(But the moment Annie rising reaches for her hand, Helen begins to fight and kick, clutching to the tablecloth, and uttering laments. Annie again tries to loosen her hand, and Keller rises.)

KELLER: *(Tolerant)* I'm afraid you're the difficulty, Miss Annie. Now I'll keep her to what she's learned, you're quite right there—

(He takes Helen's hands from Annie, pats them; Helen quiets down.)

—but I don't see that we need send her from the table, after all, she's the guest of honor. Bring her plate back.

ANNIE: If she was a seeing child, none of you would tolerate one—

KELLER: Well, she's not, I think some compromise is called for. Bring her plate, please.

(Annie's jaw sets, but she restores the plate, while Keller fastens the napkin around Helen's neck; she permits it.)

There. It's not unnatural, most of us take some aversion to our teachers, and occasionally another hand can smooth things out.

(He puts a fork in Helen's hand; Helen takes it. Genially:)

Now. Shall we start all over?

(He goes back around the table, and sits. Annie stands watching. Helen is motionless, thinking things through, until with a

wicked glee she deliberately flings the fork on the floor. After another moment she plunges her hand into her food, and crams a fistful into her mouth.)

JAMES: *(Wearily)* I think we've started all over—

(Keller shoots a glare at him, as Helen *plunges her other hand into* Annie's *plate.* Annie *at once moves in, to grasp her wrist, and* Helen *flinging out a hand encounters the pitcher; she swings with it at* Annie; Annie *falling back blocks it with an elbow, but the water flies over her dress.* Annie *gets her breath, then snatches the pitcher away in one hand, hoists* Helen *up bodily under the other arm, and starts to carry her out, kicking.* Keller *stands.)*

ANNIE: *(Savagely polite)* Don't get up!

KELLER: Where are you going?

ANNIE: Don't smooth anything else out for me, don't interfere in any way! I treat her like a seeing child because I *ask* her to see, I *expect* her to see, don't undo what I do!

KELLER: Where are you taking her?

ANNIE: To make her fill this pitcher again!

(She thrusts out with Helen *under her arm, but* Helen *escapes up the stairs and* Annie *runs after her.* Keller *stands rigid.* Aunt Ev *is astounded.)*

AUNT EV: You let her speak to you like that, Arthur? A creature who *works* for you?

KELLER: *(Angrily)* No. I don't.

(He is starting after Annie *when* James, *on his feet with shaky resolve, interposes his chair between them in* Keller's *path.)*

JAMES: Let her go.

KELLER: What!

JAMES: *(A swallow)* I said—let her go. She's right.

(Keller glares at the chair and him. James takes a deep breath, then headlong:)

She's right, Kate's right, I'm right, and you're wrong. If you drive her away from here it will be over my dead—chair, has it never occurred to you that on one occasion you might be consummately wrong?

(Keller's stare is unbelieving, even a little fascinated. Kate rises in trepidation, to mediate.)

KATE: Captain.

(Keller stops her with his raised hand; his eyes stay on James' *pale face, for a long hold. When he finally finds his voice, it is gruff.)*

KELLER: Sit down, everyone.
(He sits. Kate *sits.* James *holds onto his chair.* Keller *speaks mildly.)*
Please sit down, Jimmie.
(James sits, and a moveless silence prevails; Keller's *eyes do not leave him.*
Annie *has pulled* Helen *downstairs again by one hand, the pitcher in her other hand, down the porch steps, and across the yard to the pump. She puts* Helen's *hand on the pump handle, grimly.)*
ANNIE: All right. Pump.
(Helen touches her cheek, waits uncertainly.)
No, she's not here. Pump!
(She forces Helen's *hand to work the handle, then lets go. And* Helen *obeys. She pumps till the water comes, then* Annie *puts the pitcher in her other hand and guides it under the spout, and the water tumbling half into and half around the pitcher douses* Helen's *hand.* Annie *takes over the handle to keep water coming, and does automatically what she has done so many times before, spells into* Helen's *free palm:)*
Water. W, a, t, e, r. *Water.* It has a —*name*—
(And now the miracle happens. Helen *drops the pitcher on the slab under the spout, it shatters. She stands transfixed.* Annie *freezes on the pump handle: there is a change in the sundown light, and with it a change in* Helen's *face, some light coming into it we have never seen there, some struggle in the depths behind it; and her lips tremble, trying to remember something the muscles around them once knew, till at last it finds its way out, painfully, a baby sound buried under the debris of years of dumbness.)*
HELEN: Wah. Wah. *(And again, with great effort)* Wah. Wah.
(Helen plunges her hand into the dwindling water, spells into her own palm. Then she gropes frantically, Annie *reaches for her hand, and* Helen *spells into* Annie's *hand.)*
ANNIE: *(Whispering)* Yes.
(Helen spells into it again.)
Yes!
(Helen grabs at the handle, pumps for more water, plunges her hand into its spurt and grabs Annie's *to spell it again.)*
Yes! Oh, my dear —
(She falls to her knees to clasp Helen's *hand, but* Helen *pulls it free, stands almost bewildered, then drops to the ground,*

pats it swiftly, holds up her palm, imperious. Annie *spells into it:)*
Ground.
(Helen spells it back.)
Yes!
(Helen whirls to the pump, pats it, holds up her palm, and Annie *spells into it.)*
Pump.
(Helen spells it back.)
Yes! Yes!
(Now Helen *is in such an excitement she is possessed, wild, trembling, cannot be still, turns, runs, falls on the porch steps, claps it, reaches out her palm, and* Annie *is at it instantly to spell:)*
Step.
(Helen has no time to spell back now, she whirls groping, to touch anything, encounters the trellis, shakes it, thrusts out her palm, and Annie *while spelling to her cries wildly at the house.)*
Trellis. Mrs. Keller! *Mrs. Keller!*
(Inside, Kate *starts to her feet.* Helen *scrambles back onto the porch, groping, and finds the bell string, tugs it; the bell rings, the distant chimes begin tolling the hour, all the bells in town seem to break into speech while* Helen *reaches out and* Annie *spells feverishly into her hand.* Kate *hurries out, with* Keller *after her;* Aunt Ev *is on her feet, to peer out the window; only* James *remains at the table, and with a napkin wipes his damp brow. From up right and left the servants—*Viney, *the two* Children, *the other* Servant—*run in, and stand watching from a distance as* Helen, *ringing the bell, with her other hand encounters her mother's skirt; when she throws a hand out,* Annie *spells into it:)*
Mother.
(Keller now seizes Helen's *hand, she touches him, gestures a hand, and* Annie *again spells:)*
Papa—She *knows!*
(Kate and Keller *go to their knees, stammering, clutching* Helen *to them, and* Annie *steps unsteadily back to watch the threesome,* Helen *spelling wildly into* Kate's *hand, then into* Keller's, Kate *spelling back into* Helen's; *they cannot keep their hands off her, and rock her in their clasp.*
Then Helen *gropes, feels nothing, turns all around, pulls free,*

and comes with both hands groping, to find Annie. *She encounters* Annie's *thighs,* Annie *kneels to her,* Helen's *hand
pats* Annie's *cheek impatiently, points a finger, and waits; and*
Annie *spells into it:)*
Teacher.
(Helen *spells it back, slowly;* Annie *nods.)*
Teacher.
(She holds Helen's *hand to her cheek. Presently* Helen *withdraws it, not jerkily, only with reserve, and retreats a step. She
stands thinking it over, then turns again and stumbles back to
her parents. They try to embrace her, but she has something else
in mind, it is to get the keys, and she hits* Kate's *pocket until*
Kate *digs them out for her.*

Annie *with her own load of emotion has retreated, her back
turned, toward the pump, to sit;* Kate *moves to* Helen, *touches
her hand questioningly, and* Helen *spells a word to her.* Kate
*comprehends it, their first act of verbal communication, and she
can hardly utter the word aloud, in wonder, gratitude, and dep-
rivation; it is a moment in which she simultaneously finds and
loses a child.)*
KATE: Teacher?
*(*Annie *turns; and* Kate, *facing* Helen *in her direction by the
shoulders, holds her back, holds her back, and then relinquishes
her.* Helen *feels her way across the yard, rather shyly, and when
her moving hands touch* Annie's *skirt she stops. Then she holds
out the keys and places them in* Annie's *hand. For a moment
neither of them moves. Then* Helen *slides into* Annie's *arms,
and lifting away her smoked glasses, kisses her on the cheek.*
Annie *gathers her in.*

Kate *torn both ways turns from this, gestures the* Servants *off,
and makes her way into the house, on* Keller's *arm. The* Servants *go, in separate directions.*

The lights are half down now, except over the pump. Annie
and Helen *are here, alone in the yard.* Annie *has found* Helen's
*hand, almost without knowing it, and she spells slowly into it,
her voice unsteady, whispering:)*
ANNIE: I, love, Helen.
*(She clutches the child to her, tight this time, not spelling,
whispering into her hair.)*
Forever, and—
*(She stops. The lights over the pump are taking on the color of
the past, and it brings* Annie's *head up, her eyes opening, in*

fear; and as slowly as though drawn she rises, to listen, with her hand on Helen's *shoulders. She waits, waits, listening with ears and eyes both, slowly here, slowly there: and hears only silence. There are no voices. The color passes on, and when her eyes come back to* Helen *she can breathe the end of her phrase without fear:)*

—ever.

(In the family room Kate *has stood over the table, staring at* Helen's *plate, with* Keller *at her shoulder; now* James *takes a step to move her chair in, and* Kate *sits, with head erect, and* Keller *inclines his head to* James; *so it is* Aunt Ev, *hesitant, and rather humble, who moves to the door.*

Outside Helen *tugs at* Annie's *hand, and* Annie *comes with it.* Helen *pulls her toward the house; and hand in hand, they cross the yard, and ascend the porch steps, in the rising lights, to where* Aunt Ev *is holding the door open for them.)*

The curtain ends the play.

AFTERWORD

1. Create a sound collage for *The Miracle Worker*. Have a group discussion about the sounds that are important to the meaning of the play. Your collage might contain words and lines of dialogue, and sounds that are part of the action. Once you have agreed on a list of sounds, decide what order to put them in and tape-record your collage. Play your collage for another group. Be prepared to answer any questions they might have about the significance of the sounds you chose.

2. In Act Two, Annie writes that her greatest problem is how to discipline Helen without breaking her spirit. What does Annie mean by this? Do you think she succeeds? Write a paragraph explaining why you might or might not recommend Annie's method of handling a child who is badly behaved. Suggest alternative or additional strategies you might use.

3. Collect examples of current movie advertisements and share them with a group. Discuss what information most movie advertisements contain and what techniques they use to attract attention. Create a newspaper advertisement for a new movie version of *The Miracle Worker*. Use your imagination in deciding who the director and major actors might be. You might quote some class reviews as part of your advertisement.

4. In his stage directions, Gibson is often quite specific about the lighting. Your group's task is to choose a scene from the play, to read the stage directions carefully to see how the lighting

changes, and to explain the reasons for these changes to your classmates. Be prepared to answer their questions.

5. In the play, Annie has hallucinations; that is, she "hears voices." Imagine that you are a researcher piecing together the story behind Annie's hallucinations. Write a brief report explaining why she hears voices and why the voices suddenly stop at the end of the play. Compare your "case study" with those of some other classmates.

6. *The Miracle Worker* is based on events that really happened. With a group, do some research to find out more about Helen Keller, her family, and Annie Sullivan. Present your group's findings to the class, or create a display for your classmates to refer to as they discuss the play.

7. With a group, create a tableau of the last moments of the play. (In a tableau, all the characters "freeze" at a particular moment in a scene.) Once the tableau is established, have each character step forward in turn, and describe what he or she is feeling and what changes, if any, he or she has undergone since the beginning of the play.

   Ask the audience to discuss the major strengths of your presentation, and to suggest any changes that might make your tableau more effective.

8. When *The Miracle Worker* was first performed, with only one exception the reviewers were unanimous in their praise. These are excerpts from the worst and best reviews:

   "If the journeymen who made an acceptable play out of [William Gibson's] *Two for the Seesaw* had gone to work on *The Miracle Worker* they could probably have made something more acceptable than the disarray that is now on stage. It has the loose narrative technique of a TV script."
   Brooks Atkinson, *The New York Times*

   "All reviewers are adjective-happy, and most of us overpraise . . . How, then, are you going to believe me when I tell you that *The Miracle Worker* is really and truly powerful, hairraising, spine-tingling, touching, and just plain wonderful?"
   Walter Kerr, *The Herald Tribune*

   Read entertainment reviews in the newspaper for a few days to see how they are written. Then write your own review of *The Miracle Worker*. Post all the reviews in the classroom.

▼ ▼ ▼ *INTRODUCTION TO:*

The Veldt

Ray Bradbury

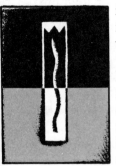

f you were to ask for the name of a famous science-fiction writer, chances are that Ray Bradbury's name would be mentioned. In fact, he has been called the "uncrowned king of science fiction." By the time Bradbury was twelve, he was completely hooked on fantasy and science fiction. His favourite reading included the Oz books, *Amazing Stories* (which was the first science fiction magazine published in the United States), Tarzan comics, and Jules Verne stories. His early fascination with science fiction had a great effect on his writing.

Even though he is best known for his short stories and novels, Bradbury's real love is drama. He and his wife even decided to set up their own theatre: the Pandemonium Theater Company. As he says, "when you came into our theatre you never knew what special kind of hell might break loose." *The Veldt* is one of the plays Bradbury wrote for his theatre. To his delight, the play opened to uniformly excellent reviews.

As you read *The Veldt,* you will encounter both the unexpected and the very familiar. Although the play is futuristic, it is really about families and what it is that either holds them together or tears them apart. Bradbury wrote the play in 1972, setting it in the year 1991. Surprisingly, the play predicts some of the problems actually facing people today.

GETTING STARTED

1. With your classmates, discuss some of the topics that parents and teenagers usually disagree about. In your journal, describe a family conflict that was successfully resolved.

2. If people were visiting your home for the first time, what are some of the mechanical or electrical devices they might notice? With a group, select three of these devices, and discuss how

you feel about them. You might consider the following questions:
- Do these devices make your life easier or more pleasant?
- Do they cause arguments or interfere with family relationships?

Decide whether these devices help or hinder a good home life.

3. In your group, discuss whether you think life ten years from now will be better or worse than it is today. Write a paragraph on your ideas, and share it with a partner.

▼ ▼ ▼   *STAGE PLAY*

The Veldt

Ray Bradbury

CHARACTERS

GEORGE HADLEY—*only thirty-six, but already a successful executive*

LYDIA HADLEY—*a busy woman in her early thirties, married to George*

WENDY HADLEY—*their thirteen-year-old daughter*

PETER HADLEY—*their twelve-year-old son*

DAVID MACLEAN—*a psychiatrist and a friend of the Hadleys*

ELECTRICIAN

OFFSTAGE VOICES

(The curtain rises to find a completely empty room with no furniture of any kind in it. This room encompasses the entire front half of the stage. Its walls are scrim which appear when lighted from the front, vanish when lighted from the rear. In the center of the room is a door which leads to the living quarters of a house circa 1991. The living quarters dominate the entire rear half of the stage. There we see armchairs, lamps, a dining table and chairs, some abstract paintings. When the characters in the play are moving about the living area, the lights in the "empty" room, the playroom, will be out, and we will be able to see through into the back quarters of the house. Similarly, when the characters enter the empty playroom, the lights will vanish in the living room and come on, in varying degrees, as commanded, in the play area.

At rise of curtain, the playroom is dimly lit. An Electrician, bent to the floor, is working by flashlight, fingering and testing electrical equipment set under a trapdoor. From above and all around come ultrahigh-frequency hummings and squealings, as volume and tone are adjusted.

George Hadley, *about thirty-six, enters and moves through*

the living area to look through the playroom door. He is fasci-
nated, delighted in fact, by the sounds and the flicker of shad-
ows in the playroom. He looks out through the fourth wall, as
he will do often in the play, and treats the audience area, on all
sides, as if it were the larger part of the playroom. Much light-
ing, and vast quantities of sound, will come from the sides and
back of the theater itself.
   At last, excited, George *turns and calls.)*
GEORGE: Lydia! Lydia, come here!
   (She appears, a woman about thirty-two, very clean and fresh,
   dressed simply but rather expensively.)
   (Waving) Come on! It's almost ready!
(She joins him at the door as the humming, squealing dies. The
Electrician *slams the trapdoor, rises, and comes toward them*
with his kit.)
ELECTRICIAN: It's all yours, Mr. Hadley.
GEORGE: Thanks, Tom.
(The Electrician *turns to point a screwdriver into the room.)*
ELECTRICIAN: There's your new — how does the advertisement
   read? — Happylife Electrodynamic Playroom! And *what* a
   room!
LYDIA: *(Ruefully)* It ought to be. It cost thirty thousand dollars.
GEORGE: *(Taking her arm)* You'll forget the cost when you see
   what the room can do.
ELECTRICIAN: You sure you know how to work it?
GEORGE: You taught me well!
ELECTRICIAN: I'll run on, then. Wear it in health! *(Exits)*
GEORGE: Good-bye, Tom.
   (George turns to find Lydia *staring into the room.)*
   Well!
LYDIA: Well . . .
GEORGE: Let me call the children!
   (He steps back to call down a hall.)
   Peter! Wendy! *(Winks at his wife)* They wouldn't want to
   miss this.
(The boy and the girl, twelve and thirteen, respectively, appear
after a moment. Both are rather pale and look as if they slept
poorly. Peter is engrossed in putting a point to his sister as they
enter.)
PETER: Sure, I know, I know, you don't like fish. OK. But fish is
   one thing and fishing is something else! *(Turning)* Dad and I'll
   catch whoppers, won't we, dad?

GEORGE: *(Blinking)* What, what?

PETER: *(Apprehensively)* Fishing. Loon Lake. You remember . . . *today . . . you promised . . .*

GEORGE: Of course. Yes.

(A buzzer and bell cut in. A TV screen, built into one wall at an angle so we cannot see it, flashes on and off. George jabs a button. We see the flickering shadows on his face as the screen glows.)

Yes?

SECRETARY'S RADIO VOICE: Mr. Hadley . . .

GEORGE: *(Aware of his son's eyes)* Yes? Yes . . .

SECRETARY'S VOICE: A special board meeting is called for 11. A helicopter is on its way to pick you up.

GEORGE: I . . . thanks.

(George snaps the screen off, but cannot turn to face his son.)

I'm sorry, Peter. They own me, don't they?

(Peter nods mutely.)

LYDIA: *(Helpfully)* Well, now, it isn't all bad. Here's the new playroom finished and ready.

GEORGE: *(Hearing)* Sure, sure . . . you children don't know how lucky you are.

(The children stare silently into the room, as George opens the door very wide so we get a good view.)

WENDY: Is that all there is to it?

PETER: But—it's *empty.*

GEORGE: It only *looks* empty. It's a machine, but more than a machine!

(He has fallen into the salesman's cadence as he tries to lead the children through the door. They will not move. Perturbed, he reaches in past them and touches a switch. Immediately the room begins to hum. Slowly, George Hadley steps gingerly into the room.)

Here, now. Watch me. If you please.

(George has addressed this last to the ceiling, in a pompous tone.

The humming becomes louder.

The children wait, unimpressed.

George glances at them and then says, quickly:)

Let there be light.

(The dull ceiling dissolves into very bright light as if the sun had come from a cloud! Electronic music begins to build edifices of sound.)

*The children, startled, shield their eyes, looking in at their
father.)*
Paris. The blue hour of twilight. The gold hour of sunset. An
Eiffel Tower, please, of bronze! An Arc de Triomphe of shin-
ing brass! Let fountains toss forth fiery lava. Let the Seine be
a torrent of gold!
(The light becomes golden within the room, bathing him.)
Egypt now! Shape pyramids of white-hot stone. Carve Sphinx
from ancient sand! There! There! Do you see, children?
Come in! Don't stand out there!
*(The children, standing on either side of the door, do not
move. George pretends not to notice.)*
Enough! Begone!
*(The lights go out, leaving only a dim light spotted on
George's face. The electronic music dies.)*
There! What do you think, eh?

WENDY: It's great.

GEORGE: Great? It's a miracle, that's what it is. There's a giant's
eye, a giant's ear, a giant's brain in each of those walls, that
remembers every city, town, hill, mountain, ocean, every
birdsong, every language, all the music of the world. In three
dimensions, by God. Name anything. The room will hear and
obey.

PETER: *(Looking steadily at him)* You sound like a salesman.

GEORGE: *(Off balance)* Do I? Well, no harm. We all have some
melodrama in us needs bleeding out on occasion. Tones the
system. Go in, kids, go on.
(Wendy creeps in a toe. Peter does not move.)
Peter, you heard me!
*(Helicopter thunder floods the house. All look up. Huge shad-
ows flutter in a side window. George, relieved, breaks, moves
from the room.)*
There's my helicopter. Lydia, will you see me to the door?

LYDIA: *(Hesitating)* George . . . ?

GEORGE: *(Still moving)* Have fun, kids! *(Stops, suddenly, thinking)*
Peter? Wendy? Not even "Thanks"?

WENDY: *(Calmly)* Thanks a lot, dad.
(She nudges Peter, who does not even look at his father.)

PETER: *(Quietly)* Thanks . . .
*(The children, left behind, turn slowly to face the door of the
playroom. Wendy puts one hand into the room. The room
hums, strangely, now, at her approach. It is a different sound*

from the one we heard when George *entered the place. The hum now has an* atonal *quality.*

Wendy *moves out into the empty space, turns, and waits for* Peter *to follow, reluctantly. The humming grows.)*

WENDY: I don't know what to ask it for. You. Go ahead. Please. Ask it to show us something.

(Peter relents, shuts his eyes, thinks, then whispers.)

What? I didn't hear you.

PETER: The room did. Look.

(He nods. Shadows stir on the walls, colors dilate. The children look about, obviously fascinated at what is only suggested to the audience.)

WENDY: That's a lake. *Loon* Lake!

PETER: Yes.

WENDY: Oh, it's so blue! It's like the sky turned upside down. And there's a boat, white as snow, on the water! It's moving toward us.

(We hear the sound of water lapping, the sound of oars at a distance.)

Someone's rowing the boat.

PETER: A boy.

WENDY: Someone's behind the boy.

PETER: A man.

WENDY: Why, it's you, and dad!

PETER: Is it? Yes. Now we've stopped, the lines are out, fishing.

(Suddenly excited) There. I've caught a big one! A big one!

(We hear a distant splash of water.)

WENDY: It's beautiful. It's all silver coins!

PETER: It's a beaut, all right. Boy! Boy!

WENDY: Oh, it slipped off the line! It's gone!

PETER: That isn't—

WENDY: *(Disappointed)* The boat . . . it's going away. The fog's coming up. I can hardly see the boat . . . or you or dad.

PETER: Neither can I . . .

WENDY: *(Forlorn)* The boat's gone. Bring it back, Peter.

PETER: Come back!

(An echo, way off, repeats his words. The playroom grows dimmer.)

It's no use. The room's broken.

WENDY: You're not trying. Come back! Come back!

PETER: Come back!

(Lydia enters on this last, slightly concerned.)

LYDIA: Peter, Wendy? Is everything all right?

PETER: Sure, swell . . .

LYDIA: *(Checks her watch)* Have you tried Mexico yet? The instructions book said the most wonderful things about the Aztec ruins there. Well! I'll be downtown at 10:45, at Mrs. Morgan's at 11:30, at Mrs. Harrison's at noon, if you should want me. The automatic lunch timer will go off at 12:15, eat, both of you! At one o'clock do your musical tapes with the violin and piano. I've written the schedule on the electric board—

PETER: Sure, mom, sure—

LYDIA: Have fun, and don't forget Bombay, India, while you're at it!

(She exits and is hardly gone when: a thunderous roar ensues. Peter, throwing out one hand, pointing at the walls, has given a shout.)

PETER: All right! Now! Now! Now!

(An unseen avalanche thunders down a vast mountain in torrents of destruction. Wendy seizes Peter's arm.)

WENDY: Peter!

PETER: Now! More! More!

WENDY: Peter, stop it!

(The avalanche filters away to dust and silence.)

What are you doing? What was that?

PETER: *(Looks at her strangely)* Why, an avalanche, of course. I made an avalanche come down a mountain, a hundred thousand tons of stone and rocks. An avalanche.

WENDY: *(Looking about)* You filled the lake. It's gone. The boat's gone. You and dad are gone.

PETER: Did I? Is it? Are they? *(Awed)* Yeah . . . sure . . . that's right. Hey, this is . . . *fun* . . . *(He accents this last word oddly.)* *You* try something now, Wendy.

WENDY: I—London Bridge. Let me see—London Bridge.

(The shadows spin slowly. Peter and Wendy stand, watching.)

PETER: You're stupid. That's no fun. Think, girl, think! Now!

Let's see. *(A beat)* Let there be darkness! Let there be—night!

(Blackout.

The lights come up. We hear a helicopter come down, fly away. George enters, stage left.)

GEORGE: Hi! I'm home!

(In a small alcove, which represents only a section of the kitchen, far stage right, Lydia is seated staring at a machine

that is mixing something for her.
George *advances across the stage.)*
Hi! How goes it?

LYDIA: *(Looking up)* Oh, hello. Fine.

GEORGE: Perfect, you mean. Flying home just now I thought, Good Lord, what a house! We've lived in it since the kids were born, never lacked for a thing. A great life. Incredible.

LYDIA: It's incredible, all right, but—

GEORGE: But what?

LYDIA: This kitchen. I don't know. It's—*selfish.* Sometimes I think it'd be happy if I just stayed out, stayed away completely, and let it work. *(She tries to smile.)* Aren't I silly?

GEORGE: You are indeed. All these time-saving devices; no one on the block has half as many.

LYDIA: *(Unconvinced)* You're right, of course. *(She pauses.)* George . . . I want you to look at the playroom.

GEORGE: Look at it? Is it broken? Good Lord, we've only had it eight weeks.

LYDIA: No, not broken, exactly. Well, see it first, then you tell *me.*

(She starts leading him across the stage.)

GEORGE: Fair enough. Lead on, Macduff.

LYDIA: I first noticed this "thing" I'm going to show you about four weeks ago. Then it kept reoccurring. I didn't want to worry you, but now, with the thing happening all the time— well—*here.*

(She opens the playroom door. George steps in and looks as across a great distance, silently.)

GEORGE: Lord, but it's quiet.

LYDIA: Too quiet, yes.

GEORGE: Don't tell me. I know right off. This is—Africa.

LYDIA: Africa.

GEORGE: Good Lord, is there a child in the world hasn't wanted to go to Africa? Is there one exists who can't close his eyes and paint the whole thing on his inner lids? High blue deep warm sky. Horizons a billion miles off in the dust that smells like pulverized honeybees and old manuscripts and cloves and cinnamon. Boma-trees, veldtland. And a lush smell. Smell it?

LYDIA: Yes.

GEORGE: That must mean a water hole nearby, bwana. *(Laughs)* Oh, Lydia, it's perfect, perfect! But—the sun—damn hot. Look, a perfect necklace of sweat right off the brow!

(Shows her) But I've lost the point. You brought me here be-
cause you were worried. Well—I see nothing to worry about.
LYDIA: Wait a moment. Let it sink in.
GEORGE: Let *what* sink in? I—
*(Shadows flick over their faces. He looks quizzically up. She
does, too, with distaste. We hear a dry rustling leathery sound
from above; distant strange bird cries.)*
LYDIA: Filthy things.
GEORGE: *(Looking up, following the circling birds)* What? Vul-
tures? Yes, God made his ugliest kites on the day he sent
those things sailing. Is *that* what worries you?
LYDIA: That's only part of it. Look around.
*(George turns slowly. There is a heavy, rich purring rumble
from off to the right. George blinks and smiles.)*
GEORGE: It couldn't be—the lions?
LYDIA: I think so, yes. I don't like—having lions in the house.
GEORGE: *(Amused)* Well, they're not exactly in the house, dear.
There! Look at that big male. Face like a blast furnace at high
noon, and a mane like a field of wheat. Burns your eyes to
look at him. There's another—a female—and another, a
whole pride—isn't that a fine word? A pride—a regular tapes-
try of lions woven of gold thread and sunlight. *(An after-
thought)* What are they up to?
*(He turns to Lydia, who is watching the unseen beasts,
disquieted.)*
LYDIA: I think they're—feeding.
GEORGE: On what? *(Squints)* Zebra or baby giraffe, I imagine.
LYDIA: Are you certain?
GEORGE: *(Shielding his eyes)* Well, it's a bit late to be certain of
anything. They've been lunching quite some time. No—lunch
is over. There they go toward the water hole! *(He follows
with his eyes.)*
LYDIA: George? On our way down the hall just now . . . did you
. . . hear a scream from in here?
GEORGE: *(Glances at her)* A scream? No. For God's sake—
LYDIA: All right. Forget it. It's just, the lions won't go away.
GEORGE: What do you mean? Won't go?
LYDIA: Nor will Africa, either. George, the fact is, the room has
stayed that way for 31 days. Every day that same yellow sun
in the sky. Every day the lions with teeth like daggers dusting
their pelts out there, killing, slavering on the red-hot meat,
printing their bloody tracks through the trees, killing, gorging,

over and over, no day different, no hour any change. Doesn't it strike you as odd that the children never ask for a different locale?

GEORGE: No! They must love Africa as all kids do. The smell of violence. Life stark, raw, visceral. Here, you, hey! Hey!
(He snaps his fingers, points, snaps his fingers again. He turns smiling to Lydia.)
You see, they come to pay their respects.

LYDIA: *(Nervously; gasps)* Oh, George, not so close!
(The rumbling of the lions is very loud now, to the right, we feel the approach of the beasts. The light from the right side of the room becomes more brightly yellow.)

GEORGE: Lydia, you're not afraid?

LYDIA: No, no, it's just—don't you *feel* it? It's almost as if they can see us!

GEORGE: Yes, the illusion is three-dimensional. Pure fire, isn't he? There. There. *(Holds out his hands)* You can warm yourself at a hearth like that. Listen to him breathe, it's like a beehive swarming with yellow.
(He stretches one hand further out.)
You feel you could just—reach—and run your hand over the bronze, the gold—

LYDIA: *(Screams)* Look out!
(There is a fearful snarling roar. The shadows race in the room. Lydia falls back, runs, George, startled, cannot stop her, so follows. She slams the door and falls against it. He is laughing. She is almost in tears.)

GEORGE: Lydia, dear Lydia!

LYDIA: George, they almost—

GEORGE: Almost what? It's machinery, electronics, sonics, visuals!

LYDIA: No, *more!* Much more! Now listen to me, I insist, I insist, do you hear, that you warn the children this playing in Africa must cease!

GEORGE: *(Comforting, kissing her)* OK, I'll talk to them.

LYDIA: Talk to them, no; lay down the law. Every day for a month I've tried to get their attention. But they just stroll off under that damned hot African sky! Do you remember that night three weeks ago when you switched the whole room off for 24 hours to punish the children?

GEORGE: *(Laughing quietly)* Oh, how they hated me for that. It's a great threat. If they misbehave I'll shut it off again.

LYDIA: And they'll hate you again.

GEORGE: Let them. It's perfectly natural to hate your father when he punishes you.

LYDIA: Yes, but they don't say a word. They just look at you. And day by day, the playroom gets hotter, the veldtland wider and more desolate, and the lions grow big as the sun.

(There is an awkward moment. Then a buzzer rings, loudly. George presses a panel in the wall. A loudspeaker bell sounds, there is a faint crackle and:)

PETER'S VOICE: Mom, we won't be home for supper.

WENDY'S VOICE: We're at the automation show across town, OK?

GEORGE: I think that—

PETER'S VOICE: Swell!

WENDY'S VOICE: Keen!

(Buzz ding! Silence. Lydia stares at the ceiling from which the voices came.)

LYDIA: No hellos, no good-byes, no pleases, no thank-yous.

(George takes her hand.)

GEORGE: Lydia, you've been working too hard.

LYDIA: Have I really! Then why is something wrong with the room, and the house and the four people who live in the house?

(She touches the playroom door.)

Feel? It trembles as if a huge bake oven were breathing against it.

(She takes her hand off, burnt.)

The lions—they can't come out, can they? They can't?

(George smiles, shakes his head. She hurries off.)

GEORGE: Where are you going?

(She pauses near the door.)

LYDIA: Just to press the button . . . that will make us our dinner.

(She touches the wall panel. The lights go out. End of scene.)

(In the dark, music. As the light comes up dimly again we find George in his easy chair, smoking his pipe, glancing at his watch, listening to the hi-fi system. After a moment, impatiently, he gets up and switches off the music. He moves next to the radio, switches it on, listens to a moment of news:)

WEATHER VOICE: Weather in the city tomorrow will be 66 in the morning, 70 in the afternoon, with some chance of rain.

(He cuts this off, too, checking his watch. Next he switches on a TV screen to one side, its face away from us. For a moment, the ghostly pallor of the screen fills the room. He winces, shuts it

off. He lights his pipe. There is a bell sound.)
LYDIA'S VOICE: George, are you in the living room?
GEORGE: I couldn't sleep.
LYDIA: The children *are* home, aren't they?
GEORGE: I waited up for them — *(Finishes lamely)* Not yet.
LYDIA: But it's midnight! I'll be down in a minute —
GEORGE: Don't bother —
(But the bell has rung. Lydia has cut off. George paces the floor, taps out his pipe, starts to reload it, looks at the play-room door, decides against it, looks again, and finally approaches it. He turns the knob and lets it drift open. Inside the room it is darker. George is surprised.)
Hello, what? Is the veldt gone? Wait — no. The sun's gone down. The vultures have flown into the trees far over there. Twilight. Bird cries. Stars coming out. There's the crescent moon. But where — ? So you're *still* there, are you?
(There is a faint purring.)
What are you waiting for, eh? Why don't you want to go away? Paris, Cairo, Stockholm, London, they and all their millions of people swarmed out of this room when told to leave. So why not you? *(Snaps his fingers)* Go!
(The purring continues.)
A new scene, new place, new animals, people! Let's have Ali Baba and the Forty Thieves! The Leaning Tower of Pisa! I demand it, room! *Now!*
(A jackal laughs off in the darkness.)
Shut up, shut up, shut up! Change, change, now! *(His voice fades.)* . . . now . . .
(The lions rumble. Monkeys gibber from distant trees. An elephant trumpets in the dusk. George backs off out the door. Slowly he shuts the door, as Lydia enters stage left.)
You're right . . . the fool room's out of order. It won't obey.
LYDIA: Won't, or *can't?*
(She lights a candle on a table to one side.)
GEORGE: Turn on the light. Why do you fuss with candles like that?
(She looks at the flame as she lights a second and a third candle.)
LYDIA: I rather like candles. There's always the chance they will blow out and then I can light them again. Gives me something to do. Anything else in the house goes wrong, electronic doors don't slide or the garbage disposal clogs, I'm helpless

and must call an engineer or a photoelectric brain surgeon to put it right. So, as I think I said, I like candles.
(George *has seated himself.* Lydia *turns to come to him now.*)
George, is it possible that since the children have thought and thought about Africa and lions and those terrible vultures day after day, the room has developed a psychological "set"?
GEORGE: I'll call a repair man in the morning.
LYDIA: No. Call our psychiatrist.
(George *looks at her in amazement.*)
GEORGE: David Maclean?
LYDIA: *(Steadily)* Yes, David Maclean.
(*The front door springs open,* Peter *and* Wendy *run in laughing.*)
PETER: Last one there's an old maid in a clock factory!
WENDY: Not me, not me!
GEORGE: Children!
(*The children freeze.*)
Do you know what time it is?
PETER: Why, it's midnight, of course.
GEORGE: Of course? Are you in the habit of coming in this late?
PETER: Sometimes, yes. Just last month, remember, you had some friends over, drinking, and we came in and you didn't kick up a fuss, so—
GEORGE: Enough of that! We'll go into this late-hour business again. Right now I want to talk about Africa! The playroom . . .
(*The children blink . . . *)
PETER: The playroom. . .?
(Lydia *tries to do this lightly.*)
LYDIA: Your father and I were just traveling through African veldtland; lion grass, water holes, vultures, all that.
PETER: I don't remember any Africa in the playroom. Do you, Wendy?
WENDY: No . . .
(*They look at each other earnestly.*)
PETER: Run see and come tell.
(Wendy *bolts.* George *thrusts out his hand.*)
GEORGE: Wendy!
(*But she is gone through the door of the playroom.* George *leaps up.* Peter *faces him calmly.*)
PETER: It's all right, George. She'll look and give us a report.
GEORGE: I don't want a report. I've seen! And stop calling me George!

PETER: *(Serenely)* All right—father.
GEORGE: Now get out of the way! Wendy!
(Wendy runs back out.)
WENDY: It's not Africa at *all!*
(George stares, astonished at her nerve.)
GEORGE: We'll see about that!
  (He thrusts the playroom door wide and steps through, startled.
  Lush green garden colors surround him in the playroom. Robins, orioles, bluebirds sing in choirs, tree shadows blow on a bright wind over shimmering banks of flower colors.
  Butterfly shadows tatter the air about George's face which, surprised, grows dark as he turns to:
  The smiling children; they stop smiling.)
  You—
LYDIA: George!
GEORGE: She changed it from Africa to *this!*
(He jerks his hand at the tranquil, beautiful scene.)
WENDY: Father, it's only Apple Valley in April—
GEORGE: Don't lie to me! You changed it! Go to bed!
(Peter takes Wendy's hand and backs out of the room. Their parents watch them go, then turn to be surrounded again by green leaf colors, butterfly shadows, and the singing of the birds.)
LYDIA: George, are you sure you didn't change the scene yourself, accidentally?
GEORGE: It wouldn't change for me or you. The children have spent so much time here, it only obeys them.
LYDIA: Oh, God, I'm sorry, sorry, sorry you had this room built!
(He gazes around at the green shadows, the lovely flecks of spring light.)
GEORGE: No. No, I see now, that in the long run, it may help us in a roundabout way, to see our children clearly. I'll call our psychiatrist first thing tomorrow.
LYDIA: *(Relieved)* Good, oh good . . .
(They start to move from the room. Lydia stops and bends to pick something from the floor.)
  Wait a moment.
GEORGE: What is it?
LYDIA: I don't know. What does it look like, to you?
GEORGE: *(Touches it)* Leather. Why, it must be—my old wallet!
LYDIA: What's happened to it?

GEORGE: Looks like it's been run through a machine.
LYDIA: Or else — it's been chewed. Look, all the teethmarks!
GEORGE: Teethmarks, hell! The marks of cogs and wheels.
LYDIA: And this?
(They turn the wallet between them.)
GEORGE: The dark stuff? Chocolate, I think.
LYDIA: Do you?
(He sniffs the leather, touches it, sniffs again.)
GEORGE: Blood.
*(The room is green spring around and behind them. The birds
sing louder now, in the silence that follows the one word he has
pronounced. George and Lydia look around at the innocent
colors, at the simple and lovely view.*

*Far away, after a moment, we hear the faint trailing off of one
scream, or perhaps two. We are not quite certain. George
quickens.)*
LYDIA: There! You heard it! This time, you *did!*
GEORGE: No.
LYDIA: You did. I know you did!
GEORGE: I heard nothing, nothing at all! Good Lord, it's late, let's
get to bed!
(He throws the wallet down, and hurries out.

*After he is gone, Lydia picks up the shapeless wallet, turns it
in her hands, and looks through the door of the playroom.*

*There the birds sing, the green-yellow shadows stir in leaf pat-
terns everywhere, softly whispering. She describes it to herself.)*
LYDIA: . . . flowering apple tree . . . peach blossoms . . . so
white . . .
*(Behind her, in the living room, George blows out one
candle.)*
. . . so lovely . . .
(He blows out the other candle. Darkness.
The scene is ended.)

*(After a moment of silence and darkness, we hear a helicopter
thunder down outside the house. A door opens. When it shuts,
the lights come on, and George is leading David Maclean on.)*
GEORGE: Awfully nice of you to come by so early, David.
DAVID: No bother, really, if you'll give me my breakfast.
GEORGE: I'll fix it myself — or — rather — almost fix it myself. The
room's there. I'm sure you'll want to examine it alone,
anyway.

DAVID: I would.

GEORGE: It's nothing, of course. In the light of day, I see that. But—go ahead. I'll be right back.

(George exits. Maclean, who is carrying what looks like a medical kit, puts it down and takes out some tools. Small, delicate tools of the sort used to repair TV sets, unorthodox equipment for a psychiatrist. He opens a panel in the wall. We see intricate film spools, lights, lenses there, revealed for the first time. Maclean is checking it when the playroom door opens and Peter comes out. The boy stops when he sees Maclean.)

PETER: Hello, who are you?

DAVID: David Maclean.

PETER: Electronics repair?

DAVID: Not exactly.

PETER: David Maclean. I know. You read the bumps on people's heads.

DAVID: I wish it were that simple. Right now I've come to see what you and your sister have written on the walls of this room.

PETER: We haven't written—oh, I see what you mean. Are you always this honest?

DAVID: People know when you lie.

PETER: But they don't! And you know why? They're not listening. They're tuned to themselves. So you might as well lie, since, in the end, you're the only one awake.

DAVID: Do you really believe that?

PETER: *(Truly amazed)* I thought everyone did!

(He grabs the playroom door as if to go back in.)

DAVID: Please.

PETER: I must clean the room.

(David steps between him and the door.)

DAVID: If you don't mind, I'd *prefer* it untidy.

(Peter hesitates. They stare each other down.)

PETER: All right. It doesn't matter. Go ahead.

(Peter walks off, circling once, then runs, gone.

Maclean *looks after the boy, then turns to the door of the playroom, and slowly opens it. From the color of the light inside the room we can sense that it is Africa again. We hear faint lion sounds, far off, and the distant leather flapping of wings.* Maclean *looks around for only a moment, then kneels on the floor of the room where he opens a trapdoor and looks down at intricate flickering machineries where firefly lights wink and*

*glow and where there is oiled secretive motion. He touches this
button, that switch, that bit of film, this sprocket, that dial.*

*In obedience to this, the light within the room gets fierce,
oven-white, blinding as an atomic explosion, the screams get a
bit louder, the roaring of the lions louder.*

Maclean *touches into the paneling again.*

*The roars get very loud, the screams very high and shrill, over
and over, over and over as if repeated on a broken phonograph
record.* Maclean *stands riven. There is a tremendous rustling of
wings. The lion rumble fades. And as silence falls, the color of
the walls of the room is stained by crimson flowing red until all
is redness within the room, all is bleeding sunset light upon
which, slowly, slowly, with grim thoughtfulness,* David Maclean
closes the trapdoor and backs out into the living room area.

Lydia *enters with a tray on which is breakfast coffee and
toast.*

When she sees that Maclean *is deep in thought, she says nothing, puts down the tray, pours coffee for three, at which point*
George *enters and frowns when he sees* Maclean's *deep concern. The husband and wife look at each other, and wait.* Maclean *at last comes over, picks up his coffee, sips it thoughtfully,
and at last speaks.)*

MACLEAN: George . . . Lydia . . .

(He hesitates a moment, drinks more coffee, prepares himself.)
When I gave my approval of your building that playroom it
was because the record in the past with such playrooms has
been exceptionally good. They not only provide imaginative
atmospheres wherein children can implement their desires and
dreams, they also give us, if we wish, as parents, teachers and
psychiatrists, the opportunity to study the patterns left on the
walls by the children's minds. Road maps, as it were, which
we can look at in our leisure time to see where our children
are going and how we can help them on their way. We humans are mostly inarticulate, there is so much we wish to say
we cannot say, so the rooms, and the walls of such rooms,
offered a way of speaking out with the silent tongue of the
mind. In 99 cases out of 100, it works. Children use the
rooms, parents observe the blueprints marked on the walls of
the rooms, and everyone is happy. But in this case — *(He
stops.)*

LYDIA: This case?

MACLEAN: I'm afraid the room has become a channel *toward*

destructive thoughts rather than a release away from them.
George . . . Lydia . . . why do your children hate you so
much?

LYDIA: *(Surprised)* Hate us? They don't hate us!

GEORGE: We're their parents!

MACLEAN: Are you really? Let's see.

(Maclean paces the room, pointing out this door, indicating that machine panel, or another here or there.)
What kind of life do you lead? Machines make your bed,
shine your shoes, blow your noses for you. Machines listen
for you, learn for you, speak for you. Machines ventilate your
house, drive you down the street at ninety miles an hour, or
lift you straight up into the sky, always away and away from
your home. I call on the phone and another machine answers,
pre-recorded, and says you're not here. How long has it been
since you got out of your car and walked with your children
to find your *own* air, which means air no one else has
breathed, outside of town? How long since you flew a kite or
picked do-it-yourself wild strawberries? How long? How
long? How long?

(Maclean sits. The parents are silent. Unnoticed, Peter *and*
Wendy *have come into the door at the far side of the room.*
Maclean *drinks his coffee and finishes, as quietly as possible,*
thus:)
You haven't been around. And since you haven't been around,
this house and its machines, that playroom have become the
only available garden where your children can take root. But
when you force-grow flowers in a mechanical greenhouse,
don't be surprised if you wind up with exotic orchids, strange
tiger-lilies or Venus's fly-traps.

GEORGE: What must we do?

MACLEAN: Now, very late, after playing an idiot Father Christmas
for years, I'm going to ask you to play what will seem like
Ebenezer Scrooge to your children.

(George rises up and turns toward the playroom door.)

GEORGE: You want me to switch off the room?

MACLEAN: The room, the house, the damned "sprinklers" in the
lawn! Get out, stay out, get away; send the kids to me for
treatment, but better yet, treat them yourselves. Look at them
with your eyes, show them your faces, talk to them not on
the intercom, but let them feel your warm breath in their
ears, comb their hair with your fingers, wash their backs with

your hands, sing to them, run with them a little way before they run so far ahead they run out of your lives.

(George *moves toward the door.*)

GEORGE: But if I switch off the room, the shock —

MACLEAN: Better a clean, hard shock now than letting the kids get any further from reality.

GEORGE: Yes . . . yes . . .

(*He opens the door of the room. Crimson light pours out. The walls inside bleed with running color. Reacting to this,* George *kneels to the panel in the floor and tears at it.*

Suddenly, Peter *stands out from the door.*)

PETER: George! No!

(Maclean *and* Lydia *are on their feet at this.*)

MACLEAN: Hold on, George. Not with the children here.

(George *whips the panel open.* Peter *leaps forward and slams it shut.*)

PETER: No, George, no, no!

MACLEAN: Listen to me — wait!

GEORGE: Get out of the way.

PETER: George!

GEORGE: (*Evenly*) Don't call me George.

(*He thrusts the boy aside, gets the panel open, but the boy is scrabbling now. Screams well out the walls of the scarlet room in a tidal blast.* Maclean *and* Lydia *freeze as the boy and* George *fight over the switches. Heat shimmers, animal heartbeats ricochet from walls, avalanches of zebras panic away with okapi, gazelle, and wildebeest, thundering, shrieking.*

George *knocks* Peter's *hands off, twists and shoves him, and hits all the switches at once.*

There are great elephant trumpetings, a final cry from many creatures now struck by electronic death, dying . . . The sounds run down like a phonograph record. In a flush of red light, all the colors of the room dissolve like oil down the walls into the floor as blood might be let from a flask. Silence. The room shadows into darkness. George *slams the trap and locks it with his key and stands on it. The only sound is* Peter's *sobbing and crying, slumped by* George.)

PETER: You! You!

GEORGE: (*To himself*) Yes . . . me . . . me!

PETER: (*Rising*) You killed them! You killed them! I hate you! I wish you were dead! I wish you were dead!

(George *slaps his face.*

Peter *holds his cheek, startled, then jumps and runs from the room.* Wendy, *bewildered, at the door, follows.*

George *holds out a key to no one in particular.)*

GEORGE: *(Barely audible)* Lock the door.

(Lydia does so. George *holds out other keys.)*

Now . . . turn off the stoves, the voice clocks, the talking books, the TVs, the telephones, the body scrubbers, the bed-makers, turn off everything!

(Lydia takes the keys, looks at George's *face, and hurries away.* Maclean *looks after her.)*

MACLEAN: No, George. That was badly handled. Brutal . . . brutal!

(Maclean hurries off after Lydia.

George, *alone, rests his head against the playroom door, listening, eyes closed.)*

GEORGE: *(To himself)* Brutal? Yes, but dead! Are you dead in there?! Good. *(Tiredly)* Good . . .

(He moves away across the room, exhausted, and at the door turns to look back at the door.)

I wonder . . . does the room hate me, too? Yes . . . it must. Nothing ever likes to die. Even a machine.

(He exits.

Blackout.

Music in darkness.

A small bedlight comes slowly up after half a minute. We see Lydia *in bed at the front of the stage. A dark scrim has come down between the bed and the set in back, so we do this scene in-one.* Lydia *rouses.)*

LYDIA: George?

(She sees him to stage left now, back turned, in his dressing robe, looking out an imaginary window, smoking.)

Can't sleep?

GEORGE: Who can?

LYDIA: Not me, anyway.

GEORGE: It's after midnight.

LYDIA: Yes. Listen. The house is so still. *(She sits up, listening.)* It used to hum all the time, under its breath . . . I never quite guessed the tune . . . though I listened for years and tried to hum the same way, I never learned. . . .

GEORGE: Thank God for small favors. Good Lord, it was strange, walking around, shutting off all the heaters and scrubbers and polishers, and washers. For an hour there, the house felt like a cemetery, and me its keeper. That's past now. I'm adjusting.

LYDIA: The children will, too. They cried themselves to sleep, but they will forgive us.
(She sits up listening as if she had heard something.)
There's no way for them to—tamper—with the room, is there?
GEORGE: Tamper?
LYDIA: I just don't want them doing anything down there, messing about, rearranging things—they couldn't do anything to the room, could they?
GEORGE: *To* the room? What would they want to do *to* the room? Anyway, there's a lot of electricity in those walls with all the machinery. They know better than to mess, and get a nasty shock.
(She listens again, and breaks up her own mood by trying to be jocular.)
LYDIA: Oh, I'm glad we're leaving tomorrow, mountains, fishing, everything out in the open again after years.
GEORGE: Dave said he'd bring his helicopter round after breakfast and take us to the lake himself. Good old Dave!
(George comes back to sit on the edge of his wife's bed.)
Lydia?
LYDIA: Yes?
(He takes her hand. He kisses her on the cheek. She jerks away suddenly.)
GEORGE: What is it?
LYDIA: Oh, listen, listen!
(Far away, the sound of running antelope, the roar of lions.)
WENDY and PETER: *(Very remote)* Help! Mother! Father! Help! Help!
LYDIA: The children!
GEORGE: The playroom! They must have broken into it!
PETER and WENDY: *(Remote)* Mother! Father, help, oh, help!
LYDIA: Peter! Wendy!
GEORGE: Kids! Kids! We're coming! We're coming!
(The parents rush off into darkness, as the lights go off over the bed.
In the dark the voices continue.)
PETER: Father, father, quick! Quick!
GEORGE: Peter, Wendy!
LYDIA: Children, where are you?
WENDY: Here, oh, here!
(The lights flash on; George and Lydia rush in through the playroom door.)

GEORGE: They're in the playroom!

LYDIA: Peter! Wendy!

(Once inside the door they peer around.)

That's strange . . .

GEORGE: I'd have sworn —

(They look about to left and right and straight ahead through the fourth wall, at the audience.)

LYDIA: George, it's — Africa again, the sun, the veldt, the vultures . . .

(She backs off. George half turns and as he does so, the door slams shut behind them. George leaps toward it.)

GEORGE: Damn door. A draft must have —

(Locks click outside.

George *tries the lock, beats at the door.)*

It's locked!

LYDIA: It can't be! There's no way for it to lock itself!

GEORGE: *(Thinking)* No . . . no . . . Peter? Wendy?

LYDIA: George, over there, under the trees . . .

GEORGE: Kids, open up . . . I know you're out there.

LYDIA: The lions . . . they're walking out into the sun . . .

GEORGE: *(Shaking the door)* Peter, Wendy, now don't be ridiculous. Unlock this door!

(The light is getting brighter in the room, the sun is blazing from above. The sound of the rustling vulture wings grows louder. Shadows flash across the faces of George *and* Lydia. *The rumbling of the lions is nearer.)*

LYDIA: George, the lions, they're running toward us!

(George looks out through the fourth wall, grows uneasy, somewhat panicky, and bangs at the door.)

GEORGE: It's all right, Lydia. Children, damn you, you're frightening your mother, open up! You hear?

LYDIA: Running! Running! Near! Near!

GEORGE: Peter!

LYDIA: Oh, George, the screams, the screams. I know now what I never said . . . the screams were familiar . . . the voices . . . because the voices, the screams were us, you and me, George, you and me . . .

GEORGE: No! Kids! Hear me!

(He bangs the door, turns, freezes, horrified.)

LYDIA: George, stop them running, stop them, stop, stop!

(She throws up her hands to guard her face, sinks to her knees.)

They're going to jump! Stop, stop!

GEORGE: No, they can't, they can't! No! No!

(The light blazes, the lions roar! A great shadow rushes from the audience, as if the lions, in a solid pack, were engulfing the stage in darkness!

Swallowing blackness takes all light away.

In the darkness, Lydia *and* George *scream and scream. Then abrupt silence, the roar, the rumbling purr of the yellow beasts fading away.*

After a long while of silence, a helicopter lands nearby. We hear David Maclean *calling in the darkness.)*

MACLEAN: *(Easily)* George! Lydia! I'm here! George? Lydia?

(The lights come slowly up. We are still inside the playroom. Seated facing the audience on two corduroy pillows are Peter *and* Wendy, *their faces impassive, as if they had gone through all that life might ever do to them and were beyond hearing, seeing, feeling. On a pillow between them are small cups and saucers, a sugar and creamer set, and a porcelain pot.* Wendy *holds one cup and saucer in her frozen hands, as does* Peter.

The door to the playroom opens. Maclean *peers in, does not see the children immediately.)*

George —

(He stops, peering off into the distance, as across a veldt. We hear the faint roar of lions. He hears the flap of vulture wings sailing down the sky, and looks up into the burning sun, protecting his eyes. Then at last he looks over at the children, sees them, and in his face is the beginning of realization, of horror, of insight into what they have done.)

(Slowly) Peter? . . . Wendy . . . ?

(Peter turns his head slowly to look beyond the man.)

PETER: Mr. Maclean.

(Wendy turns more slowly, in shock, to hold out before her the small cup, her eyes blind to any sight, her voice toneless.)

WENDY: A cup of tea?

(Blackout.)

AFTERWORD

1. You are the director of *The Veldt*. What characteristics would you want the actors playing George and Lydia to emphasize? Think of two movie or TV actors who would be well suited to these roles. Compare notes with one or two classmates.

2. George uses the word "perfect" several times to describe his life. With a partner, roleplay a short dialogue between George and a colleague of his, in which George talks about why he thinks his life is perfect. Share your roleplay with a small group or the rest of the class.

3. a) Much of the play takes place in the Happylife Electrodynamic Playroom. In a group, discuss the techniques Bradbury uses to bring this room to life.

b) Dramatize one of the scenes that occurs in the playroom. Try to follow the stage directions as closely as possible. It may be necessary to modify the lighting and sound effects to accommodate the resources available to your group. Ask your audience to evaluate how well you captured the mood of the scene.

4. Locate the scene in which Lydia shows George the Africa that the children have created. Divide the lines among the members of your group, and read the scene aloud. Discuss what Africa seems to mean to George, to Lydia, and to the children. Present your ideas to the class in the form of a chart.

5. The Veldt ends just as Maclean sees the children. In your group, discuss what might happen next, and then create a script that continues the play for another two or three minutes. When your script is complete, ask another group to evaluate how effective it is and to suggest improvements. You might wish to dramatize your script for the class.

6. The Happylife Electrodynamic Playroom has just been installed in your home. What place would you ask it to recreate? What would you do there? Write a story telling about a day in the Playroom.
OR
You are a newspaper reporter who is concerned about the dangers of the Happylife Electrodynamic Playroom. Write the feature article in which you inform the public about the Playroom's potential harmful effects.

7. David Maclean says, "We humans are mostly inarticulate, there is so much we wish to say we cannot say . . ." Recall an occasion at home or at school when you wanted to talk about something, but did not. Describe the incident in a journal entry. If a similar occasion occurred today, how would you handle it?

8. Ray Bradbury has always loved comics, and some of his own stories have been made into comic strips. Pick a segment from *The Veldt*, and create a comic strip version of it. You might work alone or with other writers and illustrators.

   Each frame of a comic strip is like one frame of a video. Artists often use dramatic "camera angles" and other special effects to keep comics interesting. Before you begin, you should look at some comic strips in newspapers or comic books. Consider these questions:
   • How much action and dialogue can one frame contain?
   • How does the artist show what the characters are saying and thinking?
   • Is there a narrator? How is the narrator's voice presented? Is the narrator a character in the comic?
   • Does the comic feature different styles of lettering for dialogue and sound effects?
   • Are the frames all the same size or do they change?
   • Does the artist use different angles and points of view to keep the reader interested?
   Display the comic strips on a "Veldt" bulletin board.

9. The following excerpt is the opening scene from Ray Bradbury's short story *The Veldt*.

   Read through the excerpt and then reread the opening scene from the play. In your group, discuss which opening is more effective. Keep in mind that opening scenes are supposed to capture the audience's attention, introduce the major characters, and provide clues about what the central conflict will be. Write a letter to Ray Bradbury indicating which opener you think works better and why.

   "George, I wish you'd look at the nursery."
   "What's wrong with it?"
   "I don't know."
   "Well, then."
   "I just want you to look at it, is all, or call a psychologist in to look at it."

"What would a psychologist want with a nursery?"

"You know very well what he'd want." His wife paused in the middle of the kitchen and watched the stove busy humming to itself, making supper for four.

They walked down the hall of their sound proofed Happy-life Home, which had cost them thirty thousand dollars installed, this house which clothed and fed and rocked them to sleep and played and sang and was good to them. Their approach sensitized a switch somewhere and the nursery light flicked on when they came within ten feet of it. Similarly, behind them, in the halls, lights want on and off as they left them behind, with a soft automaticity.

"Well," said George Hadley.

They stood on the thatched floor of the nursery. It was forty feet across by forty feet long and thirty feet high; it had cost half again as much as the rest of the house. "But nothing's too good for our children," George had said.

The nursery was silent. It was empty as a jungle glade at hot high noon. The walls were blank and two-dimensional. Now, as George and Lydia Hadley stood in the center of the room, the walls began to purr and recede into crystalline distance, it seemed, and presently an African veldt appeared, in three dimensions; on all sides, in colors reproduced to the final pebble and bit of straw. The ceiling above became a deep sky with a hot yellow sun.

George Hadley felt the perspiration start on his brow.

"Let's get out of the sun," he said. "This is a little real. But I don't see anything wrong."

"Wait a moment, you'll see," said his wife.

Now the hidden odorphonics were beginning to blow a wind of odor at the two people in the middle of the baked veltland. The hot straw smell of lion grass, the cool green smell of the hidden waterhole, the great rust smell of animals, the smell of dust like a red paprika in the hot air. And now the sounds: the thump of distant antelope feet on grassy sod, the papery rustling of vultures. A shadow passed through the sky. The shadow flickered on George Hadley's upturned, sweating face.

A Storm in Summer

Rod Serling

"You always have to compromise lest somebody—a sponsor, a pressure group, a network censor—gets upset. Result is that you settle for second best. It's a crime, but scripts with social significance can't get done on TV."
Rod Serling

fter forty rejections, Rod Serling sold his first television play in 1950 and never looked back. Over his lifetime, he wrote hundreds of scripts for television, including *Requiem for a Heavyweight*, later made into a feature film. Serling is probably best known as the creator, writer, and host of one of the most popular TV series of the 1960s, "The Twilight Zone."

Serling's commitment to socially relevant drama thrust him into conflict with TV sponsors and network managers, who regularly attempted to censor his work. The teleplay in this anthology is a prime example of the kind of script that Serling fought so hard to get on the air.

A Storm in Summer takes place during the Vietnamese War. The echoes of that conflict can be heard even in the peaceful little town where Herman Washington and Abel Shaddick accidentally meet one hot summer day.

G E T T I N G   S T A R T E D

1. Abel Shaddick is an elderly Jewish shopkeeper, Herman Washington is a small black boy, and Gloria Ross is a white society woman. Using the title *A Storm in Summer* and these brief descriptions of the characters as clues, write down the ideas or themes you think this teleplay might focus on. Compare notes with a few classmates.

2. With a partner, talk about the ways in which a death in the family can affect the surviving family members. Can a death in the family *permanently* change the way another family member thinks or feels?

3. *a)* In a small group, brainstorm four reasons why an elderly person might have a lonely life. Next, brainstorm four reasons why a child might feel isolated.

   b) Write a journal entry about a time when you were lonely. What did you do to make yourself feel better?

4. "It's a crime, but scripts with social significance can't get done on TV." Do a quick survey of your class to find out how many people agree or disagree with Serling's statement. After the survey, have a class discussion to discover the reasons behind the different points of view.

▼ ▼ ▼ *TELEPLAY*

A Storm in Summer

Rod Serling

CHARACTERS

ABEL SHADDICK – *an elderly shopkeeper in a small town in upstate New York*

STANLEY BANNER – *his fast-talking and unreliable nephew*

HERMAN WASHINGTON – *a black boy from a New York City ghetto*

GLORIA ROSS – *a society woman who spends her summers in the town*

HARRIET – *her friend*

MRS. GOLD – *one of Shaddick's customers*

TWO HOT RODDERS – *two local teenage bullies*

MAITRE D' – *at Gloria's country club*

MRS. PARKER – *a conservative member of Gloria's country club*

POLICEMAN

OFFSTAGE VOICES

TEASER

(Shaddick, inside his delicatessen, is just in the process of putting away the various items for the night — chickens, trays of cold cuts, and so on. He then moves out through the front door and starts to crank up the awning.

A police car pulls up and a Policeman *gets out, checks the store alongside, then notices* Shaddick.)

POLICEMAN: How are you tonight, Mr. Shaddick?

SHADDICK: A day older since you last asked me.

POLICEMAN: Another hot one, huh?

SHADDICK: Why not? You wanna know something? *(He jerks his thumb skyward.)* Up there — in the Kingdom of Heaven — is a special department. A Celestial Bureau dedicated to the harassment of Abel Shaddick. It is staffed by a hundred fallen angels, blue-printing my ultimate destruction.

POLICEMAN: *(Grins)* Somebody up there doesn't like you much, huh?

SHADDICK: I can see the staff meetings now. Monday, we'll give him prickly heat. Tuesday, two bum cheques he'll get and a breakdown in the refrigeration. On Wednesday, the bank will call one of his notes and on Thursday, his nephew Stanley will come to stay with him. And on Friday — which is today — they'll send down a heat wave — with humidity, yet — so he'll have insomnia and have to lie in bed all night worrying about something worse than Friday.

POLICEMAN: *(Grins)* What's worse than Friday?

SHADDICK: Saturday!

ACT ONE

(It is a bright sunny morning. Shaddick *starts to lower very old awning, letting it squeak slowly down. At one point while he's turning handle it sticks — this is obviously an everyday occurrence. He gives handle a slap with his hand to free it, then awning continues down into place.*

The scene changes to inside the deli. Shaddick *enters with some crates.)*

SHADDICK: Morning, Benjy.

(The phone rings and Shaddick *puts down crates to answer it.)*
Yes?
(Takes pencil and pad of paper)
One pint pickled herrings. Yes. Loaf of corn rye. You want that sliced? All right. *(Pause)* Yes, lady — I'm writing it down!
(Continues to scribble down order)
Yes. Two dozen eggs. That it? *(Pause)* No, lady — I don't deliver. I'm too poor for a truck and too old for a bicycle!
(Pause, then he furiously scratches out everything he's written.)
So suit yourself. You wanna come in and pick it up — come in and pick it up. *(Pause)* That's right, lady — independent!
(He slams down phone, stares at it, shakes his head, then aloud to himself.)
Deliveries yet. Food stamps. Lucky numbers. Name the president. Hit . . . the jackpot. A black year on the twentieth century!
(He goes behind counter, moves over to picture of his son, looks at it.)

So, Benjy—the hot spell continues. Your cousin Stanley has been here for six days—oh, I told you yesterday. And your cousin Stanley, as I also told you, has all the charm of an untipped waiter. He commutes between his mattress and the country club. And should I have failed to mention it, Benjy—your cousin Stanley is not my glass of tea.
(A Cadillac convertible pulls up in front of the deli. An attractive woman, Gloria Ross, gets out of car, looks a little dubiously at store front, and then enters. As she opens the door, a bell rings.)
Can I help you, lady?
GLORIA: *(Brittle smile—half nervous, half condescending)* Good morning . . . does a Mr. Banner live here?
SHADDICK: Mr. Banner? Oh, yes, Mr. Banner. Formerly Mr. "Bloom." Strictly speaking, he doesn't *live* here. He just drops in on occasion in between his big deals. Mr. Banner, formerly Mr. Bloom, is my nephew.
GLORIA: *(Smile persists)* You must be Mr. Shaddick.
SHADDICK: I must be . . . Now what can I get you?
(She removes papers from her purse.)
GLORIA: I'm Gloria Ross, Mr. Shaddick. I met your nephew at the club last night.
(Slight pause as Shaddick glares at her. Her smile fades slightly.)
The country club. Perhaps Mr . . . Mr. Banner mentioned it.
SHADDICK: By the time my nephew with the new name returned to his mattress early this morning, I'd already had five hours of sleep and two sizable nightmares—one having to do with an avenging angel knocking on my door and telling me that Stanley Banner, formerly Bloom, would live with me for the rest of his life. *(Pause)* No, lady—I have not talked to my nephew since early yesterday.
(The bell rings again as a little old lady enters. She is Mrs. Gold, a "professional shopper," a chicken feeler, pickle analyst, an all-around pain.)
MRS. GOLD: Morning, Shaddick.
(Shaddick mumbles. Mrs. Gold starts feeling vegetables, then heads toward a hanging line of plucked, scrawny chickens and immediately begins to feel them, one by one. Shaddick throws her one icy look, then turns back toward Gloria. Her smile persists but it's wearing around the edges.)
GLORIA: You've no doubt heard of the Fresh Air Vacation Plan—

SHADDICK: *(Another look at* Mrs. Gold *fingering chickens.)* The Fresh Air Vacation Plan.

GLORIA: *(Eagerly)* We bring children in from the city to spend two weeks here with families in the community.

(Shaddick *mumbles.)*

But of course . . . well . . . we make it a policy to check on the nature of the homes that the children are entering. It's just a . . . a standard procedure. You know, just to make certain of . . . of compatibility.

SHADDICK: So how much does my nephew Stanley owe for the raffle tickets?

GLORIA: *(Frowning a little)* No, there aren't any raffle tickets, Mr. Shaddick. You see, when a family volunteers to take a child—

SHADDICK: *(Interrupting by turning away, pointing toward* Mrs. Gold) Mrs. Gold—you here to purchase or just fondle?

MRS. GOLD: *(Coldly)* I don't buy anything but the fresh. *(Pointing to chickens)* These are fresh?

SHADDICK: They were until you played with them.

MRS. GOLD: You want my business or don't you, Mr. Shaddick?

SHADDICK: Your business I would welcome, Mrs. Gold—but your daily rubdown of my poultry I can do without.

MRS. GOLD: I'll take this one.

(She brings it to Shaddick.)

SHADDICK: A prize winner . . . lucky chicken . . . I found a home for you.

(He throws it on scale. Mrs. Gold *peers over counter to check weight.)*

MRS. GOLD: Just the chicken, Mr. Shaddick—I'm not buying your thumb.

(Shaddick throws her an icy look, scoops chicken off scale, tosses it on some brown paper, wraps it up, ties it up, bites off string, tosses it on counter.)

SHADDICK: A dollar ninety-one.

(Mrs. Gold laboriously counts out change, puts it on counter, takes chicken, stares back at Shaddick.)

MRS. GOLD: If it's no good, you'll hear from me.

SHADDICK: *(Nodding)* I won't sleep until your decision is handed down.

(Mrs. Gold walks haughtily toward door, mumbling, moves out, slamming it behind her.)

(Nodding, hot with anger, tightlipped) Some way to start a day—protecting the honour of a plucked chicken.

(Turns to Gloria*)* Nu.

(Gloria *is nervous, flustered, ill at ease.)*

GLORIA: Do you think I could speak to Stanley—?

SHADDICK: The big shot? Like I told you—he's in bed.

GLORIA: *(Taking the bit in her teeth)* The child is supposed to arrive today, Mr. Shaddick—

SHADDICK: What child?

GLORIA: I've been trying to explain it to you. Mr. Banner—Mr. Bloom—your nephew Stanley—he volunteered—

SHADDICK: *(Interrupting her)* He volunteered? A child is coming here because my nephew Stanley volunteered?

GLORIA: You still don't understand, Mr. Shaddick.

SHADDICK: *(Throwing up his hands, his voice loud)* What, what, what? Tell me. What don't I understand?

GLORIA: *(Almost recoiling)* The idea was that you'd be, in a sense, cosponsors of the child. Stanley assured us that he'd be staying with you through the summer—

(He *whirls around, picks up a cleaver off chopping block.* Gloria *hurriedly moves back.* Shaddick *whirls around toward her, holding cleaver.)*

SHADDICK: Lady from the country club—do yourself a favour! The next time my bigshot nephew shows up at one of your pishy-poshy Junior League affairs, just show him the door.

GLORIA: Really, Mr. Shaddick—

SHADDICK: *(Overlapping her)* That way you'll save yourself embarrassment and very likely a bum cheque. Good-bye, lady.

(The woman stands there, blinking, and it takes a moment for anything to come out.)

GLORIA: What . . . what about the boy? He's probably on a train by now.

SHADDICK: Then take him *off* the train.

(For the first time, anger overcomes fear on Gloria's *face.)*

GLORIA: Mr. Shaddick, a little child is coming here out of the slums—

SHADDICK: *(Disgusted)* Please, lady—that's where *I* came from and I still don't get enough fresh air.

(Jerks his thumb in direction of stairway.)

All I got is that freeloader in the summer tuxedo up there—half-sponge, half-mouth!

GLORIA: Mr. Shaddick . . .

SHADDICK: You go back and tell your members that I got no time for children, no sympathy for their social charities, and no place for my nephew Stanley Banner! This is my final word! Again — good-bye, lady!

(Turns his back on her, walks away.)

GLORIA: You've put me in a dreadful position, Mr. Shaddick. I'm going to be on the phone half the day trying to . . .

SHADDICK: Lady, please, enough already.

(He stands there listening to her footsteps as she leaves. We hear the bell on the door ring and then the door closing.

Gloria *exits from the delicatessen and walks over to her convertible. Another debutante-type,* Harriet, *sits alongside driver's seat. She looks expectantly toward* Gloria, *who comes around and enters through driver's door. We then see* Gloria *and* Harriet *in car.)*

HARRIET: What's he like?

(Gloria turns on ignition.)

GLORIA: Scrooge! *(Throws car into gear)* You put some poor unsuspecting little kid in with that old goat, he'd be scarred for life.

HARRIET: That kid may be on a train now.

GLORIA: I'll put in a call to New York.

(Harriet takes piece of paper out of purse, looks up.)

HARRIET: The kid's name is Washington.

GLORIA: As in George.

(Harriet with a little smile, shakes her head.)

HARRIET: Not according to this. As in Booker T.

(Car zooms away from curb.

We move back inside the deli. Stanley *starts down the steps. He is a smooth manipulator. He comes down the steps imitating Fred Astaire, singing and finger snapping — and once down, moving over to the hotplate and a mug of coffee. The dance steps and the singing continue.* Shaddick *looks skyward at the invisible God.)*

STANLEY: Morning, Unc . . .

SHADDICK: *(To himself)* Tell me something — I deserve this?

STANLEY: Nice affair at the club last night.

(Shaddick just glares at him, then turns his back.)

Gonna be hot today. New York'll be murder. *(Pause)* I gotta be there by lunchtime.

(Another pause. Still no response from Shaddick.)

Guy I know got a discotheque in Atlantic City. He's looking for a manager. Could be three hundred a week. Listen, I could be gone for quite some time —

SHADDICK: I'm very upset.

(Stanley *shakes his head, grins at him.*)

STANLEY: I'll bet. Well, I'll send you a post card from Atlantic City —

SHADDICK: I already know Atlantic City. And your post cards usually cost me two cents to cover the insufficient postage. Do me a favour, Stanley — if by some miracle you get the job and the three hundred a week, and you find yourself with an extra ten bucks, please use 'em to buy some flowers for your mama's grave.

(Stanley *looks at him, smile fading.*)

STANLEY: You got a thing about death, don't you, Unc?

SHADDICK: You don't, huh, Stanley? You're immortal. You don't die.

(Stanley *tilts his head at him — half bewildered, half not really liking the old man or understanding him.*)

STANLEY: How long has Ben been gone? Nineteen forty-four, wasn't it? That's almost twenty-five years ago. You keep his picture around . . . his effects . . . like he was killed on Thursday.

SHADDICK: Mr. Bloom — son of my late sister — my bed you can borrow. My telephone you can use. My food, feel free to eat . . . but how I mourn my child . . . and for how long . . . that's *my* business. Understand?

STANLEY: *(With exaggerated shrug)* All right, all right! *(Looks at his watch, whistles)* Oh, look at the time! I wanna catch the eleven o'clock train. *(Pause)* Stay loose, Unc.

(He *starts through door. Shaddick holds up a hand.*)

SHADDICK: A moment, please, Mr. Rockefeller. An item of unfinished business. Namely, your last philanthropy.

(Stanley *turns to him from door and frowns.*)

STANLEY: What're you talking about?

SHADDICK: The slum child you're going to entertain for two weeks. A lady was here earlier. Miss Ross.

(Stanley *slaps his palm against his forehead.*)

STANLEY: I forgot all about that. *(Pause)* I'll call her from the station.

SHADDICK: You do that, Stanley. Your bad debts I'll meet — your indiscriminate charities . . . no!

STANLEY: Relax! Will you relax? *(Thin little smile)* I had a little too much to drink last night. They had this booth where they were signing up kids — they had one more to place — well, you know how it is.

SHADDICK: *(Not smiling)* I know how it is with you. A good deed must be accompanied by a brass section and a photographer!

STANLEY: How is it with you, Unc?

SHADDICK: Yeah . . . explain the question.

STANLEY: I don't know how you survive.

SHADDICK: I manage.

STANLEY: What do you manage? Seven days a week, hating everything you do and doing the same thing. Up at eight, open the cases, hang up the chickens, scream at somebody on the phone. Nine o'clock at night you lock it all up and next morning you start all over again.

SHADDICK: In the language of the time, Stanley, that's what's known as making a living. Easy it's not. Enjoyable it's not. But it's what ancient idiots like me do to say alive. I wouldn't expect *you* to understand it. Anyone who could change a name like they change their shirt—this kind of person wants the rose without the thorn. Life isn't like that! Life is misery. But *I* made a pact with it.

STANLEY: You made a pact with it, you love it. Because that's the way you're built, Unc. You'd rather be caught dead than smiling.

SHADDICK: You wanna see me smile, Stanley? In heaven, you'll see me smile. When they read out my will and they get to that part where it says how much I leave to my nephew, Stanley Banner. One blank page.

(Stanley *shakes his head back and forth and has to smile.*)

STANLEY: I can't top you, Unc. I'll go pack. *(Starts toward stairs)* Wish me luck.

SHADDICK: *(Shrugs)* What I wish for you, I apologize to God for. *(The scene changes to the town's small train station. Train is just pulling out. Room is mobbed with fresh-air kids, all tagged and identified, and one by one being led away by waiting foster parents. Herman Washington sits by himself. He is a grim little gnome—a tiny man-child. Stanley enters, moves over to ticket cage, buys ticket, turns, spots Herman sitting alone. He moves to Herman, looks briefly at name tag, and sees his own name underneath.)*

STANLEY: Whadd'ya say?

(Herman *looks at him very soberly.*)

HERMAN: You the man what they call the sponsor?

STANLEY: *(Wetting his lips a little nervously)* I'm Stan Banner.

You're . . . *(Reads from tag)* . . . Herman Washington.
(Herman nods.)
HERMAN: Where we goin'?
STANLEY: *(Nervous laugh)* We got a little problem —
(Herman waits patiently.)
Like here I've been waiting for you all along — and suddenly I
get this special hurry-up call to get to New York.
(Herman again just waits and doesn't respond.)
But I tell you what you do. You go down to the delicates-
sen — it's just down the street — turn right out there and you'll
run right into it. A little tiny place on the other side of the
street. My uncle's there. He'll look after you until I get back.
LOUDSPEAKER VOICE: Eleven-oh-eight to New York now arriving.
STANLEY: That's my train, kid. *(Sticks out his hand)* You have a
ball, Herm. I'll be seeing you later.
*(Herman looks at hand, then very slowly lets his eyes rise up
to Stanley's face, making his own very special judgment. Stanley moves to ticket window.)*
New York . . . *(Turns to Herman)* Don't let my . . . my uncle
turn you off. He's not a bad egg. Just a little . . . a little old
and . . . set in his ways . . . But you go over there and tell him
who you are.
*(Herman picks up his battered suitcase, looks toward door,
then back to Stanley. Stanley is hung-up, guilty, and anxious.)*
I'm awful sorry I gotta cut out on you like this, Herm. I
mean it.
HERMAN: Your uncle like you?
STANLEY: *(Blinks)* You don't dig me?
HERMAN: *(After slow head shake)* You talk too much and you talk
too loud.
*(Herman turns and moves to door, leaving Stanley there just
blinking at him. He leaves the station and starts a slow walk
down sidewalk toward heart of town.*

*The scene changes to inside the deli. Shaddick finishes arrang-
ing trays inside display case, then looks up toward window.
Standing on sidewalk, staring back at him, is Herman — the un-
dersized black militant with a grim, set, determined, challenging
look on his face.*

*There is no question that he's right out of a ghetto. This mo-
ment finds him out of it for the first time. He has to exercise his
own special brand of courage to combat his little-boy fear. After
a moment he straightens his little bony shoulders, moves into*

delicatessen, reading from paper in his hand as he does so.
Shaddick at this point doesn't make the connection at all be-
tween his nephew and the child.)
SHADDICK: *(After long, waiting pause)* Nu?
(Herman blinks, frowns, looks down at himself.)
HERMAN: You mean the suit?
SHADDICK: I mean—what can I get you?
(Herman puts down suitcase.)
HERMAN: What do you got?
(Shaddick studies him for a moment.)
SHADDICK: What do you want?
HERMAN: Got a Coca Cola?
SHADDICK: For a Coca Cola, you go to the drugstore.
HERMAN: I'll take a glass of water.
SHADDICK: A glass of water.
   (He shrugs, moves over to sink, rinses out glass, fills it, carries
   it back over to counter, puts glass on top of it.)
   With customers like you I could go bankrupt in a week. Here
   you are . . .
(Herman reaches up for glass, takes it, drinks it thirstily, returns
glass to top of counter, stands there, unsure of himself for a
moment, then fingers large hand-painted badge on his lapel
which reads "Herman D. Washington.")
HERMAN: I'm Herman D. Washington.
SHADDICK: I'm Abel Shaddick . . .
HERMAN: I come on the train. Just a coupla minutes ago.
(Shaddick scratches his head, leans on counter.)
SHADDICK: I came on a boat fifty-five years ago. So what else
   should we talk about?
HERMAN: This here is the address I was supposed to go to, so I'm
   your kid.
SHADDICK: Mr. Washington, do you get the same impression that I
   do—that there is occurring a breakdown in our communication?
HERMAN: *(Studying him)* Don't you dig, man? *(Pause)* I'm sup-
   posed to stay here two weeks.
(He looks down at piece of paper.)
Stanley Banner. *(He looks up.)* He's what they call my spon-
sor. He was at the train station. He sent me here.
(Shaddick begins to understand.)
My Gramma got this phone call late last night. Lady say I
should be on the train at eight o'clock. So that's what I do.
(He holds up paper in his hand.)

And they give me this here thing to tell me who was gonna meet me. And where I was supposed to go. *(Pause)* That Stanley cat—the one I met—he say I should come over here and see you.

SHADDICK: *(Hesitates)* Mr. Washington . . . the man you accurately described as the Stanley cat, Mr. Banner, has left town and in the process left both of us on a limb. I'm afraid that . . . that . . . well, there is nobody here to look after you.

(Herman nods. His brief eight years have obviously been a parade of disappointments. He absorbs them like food. He reaches into his pocket, his little face sober, takes out a train ticket, puts it on counter.)

HERMAN: Is this what I use to go back to New York?

(Shaddick turns it around and looks at it, nods.)

SHADDICK: That's right. It's the return part of your ticket. Don't lose that now. *(Looks up at clock on wall)* The next train is about three hours from now. You've missed the eleven o'clock.

HERMAN: Okay. *(He looks fascinated at counter.)*

SHADDICK: *(Very reluctantly)* You want some breakfast? *(Pause)* I asked you a question. Do you want some breakfast? You want something to eat?

(Herman, after studying Shaddick with his own special intensity, shakes his head.)

HERMAN: I jus' go back on the train. I don't wanna stay here.

(Shaddick shrugs. He's vaguely disturbed. He's not sure why.)

SHADDICK: So go back on the train. But first—the least I could do is offer you something to eat. *(Pause)* See anything you like?

(Herman takes a slow walk down length of counter, looking into display case.)

HERMAN: *(Pointing)* What's that there?

SHADDICK: Show me . . . That's pastrami. You want a nice pastrami sandwich?

HERMAN: What's pastrami?

SHADDICK: It's corned beef. Highly seasoned. It's . . . it's Jewish.

(Herman looks up at him with his sombre little face.)

HERMAN: You Jewish? Guy who own our building—he Jewish. Man, he pretty bad cat. Nobody likes him. I ain't hungry.

(Turns toward door)

SHADDICK: So where are you going?

HERMAN: To the train station.

SHADDICK: You got a three-hour wait. You might as well stay here.

(Herman *shakes his head.*)
Why not?

HERMAN: 'Cause I don't like you.

(Shaddick *again has the sense of being disturbed and again is unable to put his finger on why.*)

SHADDICK: So you don't like me. So go sit in a hot train station and broil for three hours.

HERMAN: What you care?

SHADDICK: I don't care. I really don't care. Between a bankrupt business and bum nephew, I don't need a three-foot-tall black kid! You, I don't need.

(He *deliberately turns his back on boy.* Herman *looks through glass of display case to a tray of fish.* Shaddick *turns toward him.*)
Nu? What keeps you?

HERMAN: (*Pointing toward fish*) Them are fish.

SHADDICK: That's what them are.

HERMAN: (*Looks up at him*) I never been fishin'. They told me that's one of the things you done when you got sponsored. People take you fishin'. (*Looks down at fish*) I ain't never been fishin'.

(Shaddick *moves down counter, leans on it, looking across and down at boy.*)

SHADDICK: Where do you live?

HERMAN: Hundred Thirty-Sixth Street.

SHADDICK: (*Softly*) No lakes on Hundred Thirty-Sixth Street, huh?

(Herman *shakes his head, then looks up.*)

HERMAN: You got a lake here?

SHADDICK: Yeah, I got a small lake.

HERMAN: You ever fish in it?

SHADDICK: My son and I used to. My son. Now there was a fisherman.

(Moves over to picture, holds it up)
That's him there . . . Benjy.

HERMAN: Soldier.

SHADDICK: Second lieutenant. A bombardier.

HERMAN: Where is he now?

SHADDICK: (*With a soft little smile*) He was killed on a raid over a place called Stuttgart.

HERMAN: I got a brother. His name's Bill. He's in Vietnam. A sergeant. Man, he's a tiger. He sent me a picture of him carryin' a gun. He's a real tiger.

(Looks intently at picture, then into Shaddick's *face)*
You say he's dead?

SHADDICK: *(Nods)* He was nineteen. *(Looks at picture)* This was twenty-four years ago.

HERMAN: What about your mama? *(Then frowning)* I mean, *his* mama.

SHADDICK: His mama died many years ago, when he was a baby. I raised him.

HERMAN: *(Studies* Shaddick *intently)* Who is this cat, Stanley?

SHADDICK: Don't ask.

(Looks long at the boy)
Thanks to him you took a train ride for nothing.

HERMAN: Where this here lake?

SHADDICK: You want to see the lake? It's one mile south. You take a left on Main Street. Lake Wanateeshie.

HERMAN: *(Repeating it but stumbling)* Wana-tee-shie. *(Frowns)* That Jewish?

SHADDICK: Jewish — Indian. While you're gone I'll call the lady here in town who's responsible for you. She can phone your grandmother.
(Turns away, busying himself behind counter)
All right, go along then and . . . don't drown.

HERMAN: When my brother come back — he gonna take me fishin'. He promise me. My brother — when he say somethin', you gotta believe him.

SHADDICK: *(Nods)* Without question. It's a trait that runs in your family. Honour and invincibility.
*(Herman *remains standing there. There is a pause.)*
So what do you wait for now — the Messiah?

HERMAN: This here lake I'm goin' to — nobody give me trouble . . . will they? I mean . . . I mean . . . I black.

SHADDICK: Who could give you trouble? Who would dare? You're the only ten-year-old kid on earth who sounds like Humphrey Bogart.
(Then he turns to Herman, *who still stands there, unsure, irresolute.)*
Now what?

HERMAN: Nothin'.

SHADDICK: Nothin'. That means *something.*

HERMAN: That mean *nothin'.*

SHADDICK: You're afraid to tell me?

HERMAN: Afraid? No way, baby. No how.

SHADDICK: Then speak your mind, why don't you?
(Pause)
HERMAN: Don't you ever go fishin'?
SHADDICK: Not since my Benjy was killed have I put a worm to hook. *(Pause)* Why?
HERMAN: Nothin'.
SHADDICK: Nothing, meaning why don't you and I go fishing?
(Herman shrugs but doesn't say anything. Shaddick looks at Benjy's photo.)
Benjy . . . an inspiration!
(He whirls around, pounds a fish on cash register to ring up a "NO SALE.")
Since the first of the month I haven't taken in enough to pay the electric bill — and this fisherman from a Hundred Thirty-Sixth Street thinks I got nothing better in life to do than play Huckleberry Finn.
(Herman stares at him. Shaddick returns the look.)
HERMAN: What that thing you say goes runnin' in the family?
SHADDICK: *(Frowning)* A trait.
HERMAN: *(Nods)* Whatever you call it. You got the same thing goin' between Stanley and you.
SHADDICK: *(Mockingly)* The philosopher. So tell me. What is the trait that binds me with my nephew Stanley?
HERMAN: *(Emotionlessly)* You're the same kinda cats. He get on a train. You hide behind the pastrami.
(Shaddick gnaws slightly on his lower lip, studying the boy, then the delicatessen, then he looks up toward the clock.)
SHADDICK: You know what an Achilles heel is?
(Herman shakes his head.)
It's an infected boil on the soul.
(Again he looks up toward clock. He starts to remove apron.)
For maybe an hour I'll go with you. But for no longer than an hour.
HERMAN: Maybe we catch some big fish, then you can sell 'em.
SHADDICK: Mr. Washington . . . with my luck I will catch one minnow, one sunstroke, and a summons from the game warden.
(He heaves a gigantic sigh, moves to door, opens it, and hangs "CLOSED" sign on door. Herman stands in door holding his suitcase.)
A question: in your luggage there — you got worms?
(Herman shakes his head.)

Then why are you taking it with us?
(Herman *leaves suitcase inside by door.* Shaddick *looks down at* Herman, *who gives him a quizzical look.)*
Nu? You got something to say?
HERMAN: You forgot somethin'.
SHADDICK: Enlighten me.
HERMAN: Fishin' poles. We ain't got no fishin' poles. When you go fishin' you gotta have fishin' poles.
(Shaddick *nods seriously, as if responding to some incredibly deep philosophy.)*
SHADDICK: I give you this, Herman. You have all the gaiety of an undertaker— but you are a very discerning boy. Very discerning. So you know what we'll have to do? We'll have to stop at the hardware store, and we'll buy—what was it?
HERMAN: Fishing poles.
(We next see the two of them walking down the street. Every now and then *Herman* looks a little secretively at *Shaddick. They stop at a light before crossing the street.)*
SHADDICK: Ah . . . I need this.
(Shaddick *reaches down to take the boy's hand.* Herman *pulls it away.)*
That's to cross the street.
HERMAN: *(Quite seriously)* I been crossin' streets since I was two years old.
SHADDICK: *(Looks down at him)* I don't suppose it ever occurred to you that maybe *I* needed help crossing the street?
HERMAN: *(Nods very seriously)* That's different, man.
(He looks up at *Shaddick's hand, frowns with that intense, inquisitive little look.)*
What you say your name was?
SHADDICK: Shaddick. Abel Shaddick.
(Herman *looks very thoughtful.)*
You don't like it?
HERMAN: *(Shrugs)* Make no difference to me what they call you.
(The signal light turns green. *Herman* reaches up, takes *Shaddick's hand.)*
Let's go, Shaddick.
SHADDICK: *(For first time smiling)* I'm right with you, Washington.
(They *walk across the street, hand in hand.)*
Fade out.

ACT TWO
(Shaddick and Herman *are perched on large, jutting rock that overhangs a small lake shaded by a couple of giant elms. They both have fishing poles.* Shaddick *is explaining how to use them.)*

SHADDICK: Now this is what you have to do, Herman. Keep your eye on that bobbin. The bait we are using, Herman, is what the fish want.

HERMAN: Why?

SHADDICK: *(Blinks at him for a moment)* Because . . . because a wise fish knows what he wants. Every once in a while give the line a little pull.

HERMAN: *(Imitating him)* Like this?

SHADDICK: Just a little bit . . . that's it. If we're lucky, this will attract their attention. Now when the fish nibbles, the bobbin will begin to shake. And when that happens don't get excited. When he's got the hook in his mouth he'll pull the bobbin way underwater. Then you give it a good tug and that sets the hook. You understand me?
(Herman nods. Both of them sit on rock with lines.)
Now I, myself, have conquered this thing only in theory. But my son, Benjy . . . there was a fisherman. He had a nose for it.

HERMAN: A nose?

SHADDICK: An instinct.
(He shakes his head back and forth.)
Right from the start I never had to teach Benjy anything.
(During this speech the camera moves to Herman, *whose eyes suddenly go wide. He's not listening to* Shaddick, *he's just watching.* Shaddick *continues to talk, unaware of what's going on.)*
I remember one summer — lessee — it must have been around '37, '38 . . . in that area but a little further down . . . Benjy caught a bass at this very lake . . .
(Herman tugs at him.)
Such a bass —
(Pauses, shuts his eyes, still oblivious to boy tugging at him)
All I know is that this was a fish among fish —
(Herman is tugging. A fish is hooked on Shaddick's *line.* Shaddick *is completely unaware of it.)*

HERMAN: *(Exploding)* You got somethin', man! You got a fish! Somethin's pullin' —

SHADDICK: What did I tell you to do?! Remind me!
(*Shaddick is suddenly aware of what is going on, rises, and topples forward with a yell into shallow water below. He sits in water, drenched—water up around his neck.*
Herman *has gotten his own bite and is pulling furiously on line, reeling in as he pulls. A large bass emerges on* Herman's *line—he pulls it off hook and then holds it, squirming, in his hand.*)
HERMAN: Look! Look! I gotta fish! Look at this one! This here is a fish! And I got it! Look at this fish!
(*The camera moves back to* Shaddick *sitting in water, his rod and reel floating nearby. He looks up at* Herman *on rock, wipes his wet face with a sleeve—tries to interrupt* Herman.)
SHADDICK: I see the fish . . . Mr. Washington—a favour?
(Herman, *still clutching fish, looks down at him.*)
You have one more minute to exult in pulling in the fish. After that, be so kind as to pull in this ancient mariner.
(Herman *carefully puts fish in cheap basket alongside him, then climbs down from rock, wades out to where* Shaddick *is, and helps the old man to shore.*
The scene changes to the delicatessen. The clock on the wall reads 7:30. Shaddick *enters from bedroom.* Herman *is asleep on the bed, dead to the world. Also visible is a plate of partially eaten food and an empty glass.* Shaddick *picks up plate and glass, turns, and walks out of room with them.* Shaddick *starts to wash dishes, looks at picture.*)
SHADDICK: Benjy—today, a revelation! I now know what ultimately destroys old men. It is not hardening of the arteries, as has been thought—but a softening of the brain. Inside my bedroom, sleeping, is a small, dark shadow with a chip on his shoulder the size of a loaf of pumpernickel! And you know what I've been doing today, Benjy! I've been fishing on the lake with this boy. Where you and I used to go. Five and a half hours in the hot sun—much of it spent underwater—because your cousin Stanley has got a mouth like a whale and the instincts of a shark!
(*He turns as we hear a car coming to a stop. Through window we see* Gloria Ross *get out of convertible, leaving an attractive young man on front seat. She walks toward door, opens it. The bell on the door rings.*)
GLORIA: I received a message you'd called, Mr. Shaddick—
SHADDICK: It was so long ago, I'd forgotten.

GLORIA: *(With courteous apology)* I'm so sorry. It was the golf tournament—

SHADDICK: Miss Ross, for each day of your life I wish you a hole in one. But at the moment, I've got a few problems of my own.

GLORIA: I understand from your message that the little boy arrived and he's here with you.

SHADDICK: *(With a jerk of his thumb toward bedroom)* He's asleep.

GLORIA: Didn't your nephew—

SHADDICK: *(Interrupting)* Don't mention that name, please. Now did you find someone else in town who can take the child off my hands?

GLORIA: That's why I'm here, Mr. Shaddick. I'm going to have to take the child myself.

SHADDICK: He'll make a good caddy.

GLORIA: Well, he obviously can't stay here.

SHADDICK: For once, we're in agreement. Between a seventy-two-year-old Jew and a ten-year-old black boy, Miss Ross, there is not what you would call a mutuality of interest.

GLORIA: He can stay with me tonight and I'll arrange to send him home in the morning.

SHADDICK: Home? Are you telling me that on the membership rolls of that pishy-poshy club of yours, isn't there one lousy family willing to take him?

GLORIA: Given time, we'd find many. *(An apologetic smile)* But we want the boy to feel comfortable. And under the circumstances—well . . . you know—

SHADDICK: *(Intensely)* Enlighten me.

GLORIA: Well, for a black child to move into—

SHADDICK: A black child.

GLORIA: Now wait a minute . . .

SHADDICK: The cardinal sin.

GLORIA: *(Tightly)* Don't make me out a bigot—

SHADDICK: *(Overlapping her speech)* Then don't make *me* out an idiot! I'm a long time on this earth, lady—and I'm an expert on bigotry.

GLORIA: *(Struggling for composure and patience)* Mr. Shaddick, I want that little boy to enjoy himself. I don't care what colour he is. But you don't take a child off a Harlem street, stick him in the swimming pool at the country club, and expect him to make an adjustment between breakfast and lunch!

SHADDICK: Since when is swimming such an adjustment?

GLORIA: This is a sociological problem.

SHADDICK: Mazeltov to all the sociological problems in the world. I got a feeling about you, Miss Ross . . . you'll forgive me in advance . . . that you dabble in good deeds the way a person would reach for a pickle in a barrel. Tentatively and gingerly.

GLORIA: I think that will be quite enough, Mr. Shaddick.

SHADDICK: Not quite. You're a little like my nephew. You're so busy dressing up for the charity ball—you forget what the charity is! An act of kindness, Miss Ross, is not such a big deal when it comes in fashionable spasms during the social season! You understand?!

GLORIA: I'll take the boy now, Mr. Shaddick.

SHADDICK: Miss Ross, you shouldn't give yourself such trouble. The boy . . . stays here. Maybe two days . . . maybe a week.

GLORIA: *(Letting it all out)* That's very nice, Mr. Shaddick. Well, let me tell you something. You don't like my good deeds—I don't like yours. They're grudging, rotten-tempered after-thoughts, using a child you couldn't care less about as a gesture to those of us you loathe. And I gather you loathe a lot of us, Mr. Shaddick.

SHADDICK: Which is my right, Miss Ross?

GLORIA: Yes, it is, Mr. Shaddick. And it proves the point. You don't have to go to a country club to find a bigot—sometimes they're in delicatessens.

(Shaddick's *head goes down for a moment as the words hit him; then he looks up, half smiles.*)

SHADDICK: So we each drew a little blood—Miss Ross?

(*He pauses, then looks back toward curtained partition, then back to* Gloria.)

But the boy stays here . . . and we'll do a little fishing . . . a little hiking . . . maybe even compare notes on ghettos. I am not the most gracious of men, Miss Ross—as you have pointed out. But in my life I have made some friends.

(Pause)

GLORIA: Good night, Mr. Shaddick.

(*She nods, turns, moves to door, and exits; the door slams and the bell tinkles loudly.*

Herman *enters through the curtained partition, rubbing his eyes with one hand, holding the fish in the other.*)

SHADDICK: Nu? *(Points to fish)* You got plans for that?

HERMAN: *(Nods)* What did the lady want?

SHADDICK: She wanted to divest herself of responsibility. This is the national pastime, Herman. The great American sport. This year's slogan: "Let George do it."

HERMAN: Who's George?

SHADDICK: George. Tom, Dick, and Harry. Somebody else. The other guy. I play the game too.

HERMAN: *(Cocking his head at him)* You sure do talk funny. *(Pause)*

SHADDICK: What are you going to do with that?

HERMAN: I gonna get it stuffed. And then I gonna put one of them metal things with writing on it underneath—

SHADDICK: A plaque.

HERMAN: *(Delighted)* Yeah, a plaque. And I gonna say on it, "This fish caught by Herman D. Washington in honour of his brother, Bill, Sergeant in the Green Berets . . . with love from his brother, Herman D. Washington." *(Looks up, suddenly concerned)* Can I get that all in there?

SHADDICK: In small print.

HERMAN: *(Holds up fish)* Big, ain't she?

SHADDICK: Enormous.

(Moves over to fish, takes it from Herman.)

But we'll put it on ice so that by the time it reaches your brother he'll be able to stand close enough to read the small print.

(Shaddick carries fish to cooler, opens it, puts fish on shelf, looks at boy.)

Herman—I want to ask you something. You have a choice. You can leave on the train tomorrow morning or you can stay here with me for a few days.

HERMAN: Why?

SHADDICK: What do you mean, why?

HERMAN: Why you want me to stay?

SHADDICK: Did I say I wanted you to stay? I gave you a choice. I said you could stay if you wanted to or you could go home tomorrow.

(Herman, as always, is analysing in his little-old-man way— and dead serious.)

HERMAN: I stay a coupla days.

SHADDICK: *(With a gesture)* I'm overwhelmed. *(Pause)* Now go wash your face and hands in that sink there . . . been touching fish. . . .Then we'll go see what's playing at the movies. And then after that we'll have a soda. And after that we'll come back here and I'll lie awake half the night wondering why I'm going to all the trouble.

(There is a pause. Shaddick *watches* Herman, *amused.)*

HERMAN: *(Looking at* Shaddick*)* You lookin' at me all smiley. Why you look at me smiley?

SHADDICK: You prefer rage?

HERMAN: You know what my brother Bill say? He say he don't care if Mister Charlie hates him . . . and he sure don't care if Mister Charlie likes him. He say that Mister Charlie should just get his foot offa him. That what my brother Bill say.

SHADDICK: *(Reacting)* Have I put my foot on you?

HERMAN: I just wanted to tell you. I'm stayin' because it hot in New York. And here I can go fishin'. That why I'm stayin'. *(Herman moves to bedroom.* Shaddick *follows him.)* Too bad you ain't black.

SHADDICK: Why?

HERMAN: I seen all the people lookin' at us this afternoon while we was fishin'.

SHADDICK: So they looked at us.

HERMAN: I know what they thinkin'.

SHADDICK: Enlighten me.

HERMAN: They thinkin' . . . they thinkin', "What that li'l black boy doin' with the old Jew?"

*(*Shaddick's *face turns grim and cold. He walks over to* Herman.*)*

SHADDICK: Listen, as one former ghetto dweller to another — a lesson maybe both of us should learn, Herman. Once two people go fishing together . . . or to the movies . . . all they should care about is that they enjoy. This is fundamental.

HERMAN: *(Looks up at him)* We equal, huh?

SHADDICK: More than we both realize.

HERMAN: There's rats where I live. Great big ones. And the johns stink. You smell 'em all over the building. If we equal — how come I gotta live there?

(Again his little mind obviously gallops ahead.)

When my brother come back, we gonna move outta there. We gonna move out to the country.

(Herman stares straight at Shaddick.*)*

And we gonna spit right in that landlord's eye.

*(*Shaddick *winces at this.)*

SHADDICK: *(Voice soft, almost a whisper)* Mazeltov. But for the time being . . . with *this* Jew . . . you'll go to the movies.

HERMAN: *(Shrugs)* Okay.

SHADDICK: The good fortune of Abel Shaddick. A hundred and seventy million people I could have as a house guest . . . and I get him!
(Herman *follows* Shaddick *to door. Shaddick flicks a light switch, then opens door.* Herman *goes out.* Herman *reaches for "CLOSED" sign, hangs it on doorknob outside.* Shaddick *closes door and locks it.*

The scene changes to an ice-cream parlour, later that night. Through front window we're looking at Shaddick *and* Herman *sitting in a near-empty room, finishing up two sodas. The camera's point of view then moves inside the ice-cream parlour.* Herman's *piping little voice is continuous as we move in toward table.)*

HERMAN: . . . but when the cat with the machine gun give it to that other bad cat, how come the FBI leave the back door open and them other two bad cats able to get out? Man, anybody know you gotta guard the back door when you got two bad cats up in a building and you know they got tommy-guns too.
(Shaddick *finishes last slurp of his soda, pushes it aside.)*

SHADDICK: Herman, there are multiple areas which I know nothing about. One is tommy-guns, the other is bad cats, and still another is the FBI.

HERMAN: But they crazy not to guard the back door.

SHADDICK: Are they . . . yes, I agree.
(Waitress *hands* Shaddick *check.)*
Thanks . . .
(He points to Herman's *soda.)*
You finished?

HERMAN: *(Nods)* If it was me, man, I'd'a guarded that back door—

SHADDICK: So we'll write to Hollywood and we'll put the question to them? Would that satisfy you?

HERMAN: *(Scratches his head, continues to sit there)* Maybe we do that. I'll give you the words—what do they call that?

SHADDICK: *(Taking some money out of his pocket.)* You'll dictate the letter. *(He rises from table.)*

HERMAN: Yeah, I think I do that.

SHADDICK: *(Mumbles)* . . . back door . . .
(Shaddick *pays* Cashier. Herman *moves past him, exits.*
Out in the street Herman *meets two* Hot Rodders, *who block his path.)*

HOT RODDER NO. 1: Jus' don't stand there, baby . . . aren't you gonna get outta the way of two big dudes like us?

HOT RODDER NO. 2: Yeah, kid, let's see you do it.

(Shaddick *comes out, stands alongside* Herman. *The* Hot Rodder *sticks an unlit cigarette in his mouth, lounges against car. He points at* Shaddick.)

Get a load of this . . . what a combination. Whadda ya say, old man?

(Shaddick, *taking* Herman's *arm, starts to move down sidewalk.* Shaddick *faces* Hot Rodders, *who block his path.*)

SHADDICK: The name is Shaddick.

(*Nods toward* Herman)

That name is Washington. What's the matter, cowboys? You bored . . . is that it? You got to go after an old man and a little boy . . . is that it?

(Shaddick *backs away to stand next to* Herman *and looks warily from one to the other.*)

You know who these are . . . two night crawlers in search of proof of manhood!

HOT RODDER NO. 2: Manhood!

SHADDICK: Such courage, Herman, such courtesy.

(At this point Hot Rodder No. 2 *advances on* Shaddick, *lashes out, pushing him against the wall of the building, holding up one clenched fist as if to strike.* Herman *takes a knife out of his pocket and starts to run toward them.* Hot Rodder No. 1 *sticks out his foot, tripping* Herman. *The knife falls to the sidewalk.*)

HERMAN: *(Shouting)* Get the knife, Shaddick! Use the knife!

(Herman *moves toward it on his hands and knees, scrabbling for it as* Hot Rodder No. 1 *pulls him back by the legs. He is screaming now.*)

Use the knife, Shaddick!

(Suddenly the whole scene is engulfed in light as a police prowl car comes around corner—a spotlight alongside driver's seat is aimed at them. Car moves over to scene—two Policemen get out.)

POLICEMAN: What's the trouble here?

HOT RODDER NO. 1: No trouble, man . . . no trouble at all. We're just on our way out.

POLICEMAN: Hold it.

(*He moves over to* Shaddick.)

Mr. Shaddick. You okay?

SHADDICK: In the pink.

POLICEMAN: *(To* Hot Rodders*)* Take off.
(Hot Rodders *get in car, drive off.)*
You want a ride home?
SHADDICK: My friend and I will walk.
(The Policeman *looks from one to the other, then suddenly sees the knife still on sidewalk, walks over to it, picks it up, closes blade, then pops it open.)*
POLICEMAN: Who belongs to this?
SHADDICK: *(Quickly)* That's mine.
POLICEMAN: Yours?
SHADDICK: Definitely mine.
(The Policeman *closes blade again, moves over to Shaddick, hands it to him.)*
POLICEMAN: That's quite a weapon, Mr. Shaddick. Be careful with it. *(Pause)* Give a yell if we're needed. Good night.
(He turns, moves back into police car, guns the engine. The car pulls away.
Shaddick *turns to look at the boy, then looks down at the knife in his hand. He hands it to* Herman.*)*
SHADDICK: Good night. *(Very softly)* Put this in your pants and don't let me see it again.
(Boy soberly takes knife, looks at it briefly, puts it in his pants pocket. Then the two of them exchange a look.)
If it ever reaches a point where I must cut into another man's stomach, I will have lived too long.
(Again, here we get a reading into the incredible telescoped maturity of the kid.)
HERMAN: Where you been? You let some cat back you up against a wall and you don't do nothin' about it—you ain't gonna live long *enough!*
SHADDICK: *(After a pause)* You'd have used it?
HERMAN: *(Nods)* If I had to.
SHADDICK: *(Looks off thoughtfully down empty street)* Which is perhaps the worst thing about prejudice, Herman. The haters turn the victims into haters. You line up the two teams . . . and who's to tell them apart. *(Pause)* So let's go home.
(The scene changes to the delicatessen. Herman *and* Shaddick *enter.)*
SHADDICK: *(With look at clock on wall)* Look at the time. Past midnight. *(He locks the door.)* You got a toothbrush? All right . . . go.
*(Herman *nods, moves toward bedroom.)*

Herman . . . an invitation from Miss Ross for you to swim in the country-club swimming pool. Reeking of perfume . . . and misplaced contrition.

(He sticks invitation under Herman's *nose.* Herman *moves away.)*

HERMAN: You talkin' crazy again.

SHADDICK: Want to go swimming . . . shall we accept?

HERMAN: Yeah.

SHADDICK: Sure . . . All right, go to bed now.

(Herman moves into bedroom. Shaddick *follows him.)*

HERMAN: What you do before I come here?

SHADDICK: What did I do?

HERMAN: I mean . . . you don't go fishing. You don't go to the movies. You don't drink no sodas.

(Shaddick looks off thoughtfully.)

SHADDICK: You know . . . you're right. This is the first movie I've seen since Myrna Loy. I used to love Myrna Loy. And I'd forgotten how good a soda could taste.

(Looks at the little boy)

At the risk of leaning on you, Herman — you seem to have opened up my life a little bit.

HERMAN: *(Very tightly)* You make a mistake if you lean on anybody. That what Bill say. He say never count on the other guy and don't ever turn your back. That what it all about.

SHADDICK: And if someone leans on you?

HERMAN: *(Very simply)* Break his arm.

(Shaddick, after a long silence, walks to Herman, *looks deep into the little boy's face.)*

SHADDICK: Listen, my little boychik — even if you think it — don't say it — all right? I have tasted more hate in my lifetime than I have wine.

HERMAN: *(Softly)* Man — don't you think I ain't?

(Shaddick turns, goes through partition into the other room, goes to coffee pot and begins cleaning it. After a moment the curtain parts a little and the little boy is standing there.)

Shaddick?

(Shaddick turns to him.)

It don't make no difference — but you ain't chicken.

SHADDICK: I'm not?

HERMAN: No. You're a tiger.

SHADDICK: Then you tell me something. Why is my mouth dry and my heart still beating like it had been trying to get across the road ahead of me?

HERMAN: *(With a little shrug)* You an *old* tiger.

SHADDICK: *(With a smile)* Old tiger . . . You remind me of that the next time I go crazy and think I'm Moyshe Dayan.

HERMAN: *(Shaking his head)* Maybe you not crazy—but you talk crazy.

(Shaddick waves him off. He disappears into the curtained room again. Shaddick moves around counter, pausing by photograph of his son, looks at it.)

SHADDICK: Good night, Benjy.

(He takes a slow, shuffling walk to stairway, flicks light, and starts to move upstairs.)

Fade out.

ACT THREE

(The scene is the dining room in the country club. Herman and Shaddick enter, go to table. They look out window from table.)

SHADDICK: See Miss Ross?

(Mrs. Parker, a formidable dowager at another table, calls over Maitre D', whispers to him. He casts glances toward Shaddick, listens to woman, and walks to Shaddick's table.)

HERMAN: Next time I'm gonna go off that high board feet first . . .

MAITRE D': Excuse me, sir . . . I didn't see you come in.

SHADDICK: You're forgiven.

HERMAN: But I ain't gonna hold my nose or anything like that.

SHADDICK: He is available for lifeguard duties after lunch. Please inform the members.

MAITRE D': *(A little nervously)* The . . . ah . . . the pool and club house are open only to members and guests.

(Shaddick looks at him.)

SHADDICK: A fact?

MAITRE D': I'm afraid so.

SHADDICK: We are guests of a member.

MAITRE D': A member?

SHADDICK: Miss Gloria Ross.

MAITRE D': I see. Well . . . thank you very much. *(Pause)*

SHADDICK: *(To Herman)* Do you see anything you like?

(The Maitre D' turns and moves back over to the table where Mrs. Parker is staring at them with a cold, arrogant hostility; then he turns back toward Shaddick.)

MAITRE D': I wonder if I might have your name, sir.

SHADDICK: Shaddick. Abel Shaddick. And Herman D. Washington.

MAITRE D': I'll take your order in just a minute, sir.
(The Maitre D' *nods and continues over to* Mrs. Parker's *table. We see them gesturing.* Shaddick *studies this scene for a moment, then looks at* Herman.*)*
SHADDICK: Our enemies are multiplying, Herman.
HERMAN: *(Looks up, reading from the menu)* Hey, Shaddick— what's "ground steak garnished with delicacies, served in sizzling splendour"?
SHADDICK: Hamburger . . . overpriced!
(Again he looks toward the woman beyond them who is staring at them with explicit displeasure. Shaddick *leans over toward* Herman, *his voice lower.)*
Herman—I got an idea! Let's go fishing at the lake. On the way is a diner where hamburgers are hamburgers and they cost a quarter.
*(*Herman *studies him for a moment, quickly looks toward* Mrs. Parker.*)*
HERMAN: She's gettin' to you?
SHADDICK: I'm afraid we're getting to her.
*(*Herman *shrugs, rises.)*
HERMAN: I get my clothes from the locker.
*(*Herman *exits.*
Gloria *enters from another room, moves toward* Shaddick's *table.* Mrs. Parker *approaches her.)*
MRS. PARKER: Gloria? *(*Gloria *stops.)* Are they your guests?
GLORIA: They're my guests.
MRS. PARKER: Well, my dear, I don't want to start anything . . .
GLORIA: Then don't.
*(*Gloria *continues over to* Shaddick's *table.)*
SHADDICK: Ah . . . Miss Ross . . .
GLORIA: How are you, Mr. Shaddick?
SHADDICK: Fine, thank you. And appreciative of the invitation. Herman enjoyed his swim—
GLORIA: You're not leaving?
SHADDICK: *(With a look toward* Mrs. Parker*)* We're going to the lake to fish. Here it is a little difficult to breathe.
*(*Maitre D' *approaches* Gloria.*)*
MAITRE D': Telephone call for you, Miss Ross . . . long distance.
GLORIA: I'll be right there. Please wait—please . . .
(She goes to the telephone and speaks into it.)
Yes! *(She frowns.)* Who? I'm afraid I don't hear you. Could you speak louder? Who? *(Pause)* Mrs. Washington?

Mrs. Washington — could you . . . could you control yourself?
I don't understand you. *(Pause)* That's right. Please. *(Pause)*
Now tell me that again, would you?
(The camera moves in on a closer shot of her face. She speaks into phone, very softly.)
I see. I'm . . . I'm terribly sorry. Do you . . . do you want us to tell the boy? *(Pause)* All right. Will you be there the rest of the afternoon? I'll see that somebody gets on the train with him back to New York. *(Pause)* Yes, I'll call you later and tell you what train. That's all right. *(Pause)* And Mrs. Washington — I'm . . . I'm truly very sorry.
(She puts the receiver down, walks across the room over to the door where Shaddick is just about to walk out.)
Mr. Shaddick — that call was from Herman's grandmother.
SHADDICK: Oh . . .
GLORIA: *(A pause as she struggles a little)* It seems he had a brother in Vietnam.
SHADDICK: *(Smiles)* You should hear Herman talk about that brother! Lawrence of Arabia and Joe Louis rolled into one.
GLORIA: *(Softly)* He's dead, Mr. Shaddick. The grandmother just received the telegram. He was killed on Monday.
(Shaddick stands motionless. His eyes close for a moment, his head goes down. Then he looks up, tears in his eyes. He nods, gnaws on his lip, and just nods.
Through the window we see Herman walking along the pool, now clothed in shorts and T-shirt, with his bathing suit wrapped in a towel.)
SHADDICK: *(Turning to Gloria)* Who tells him?
GLORIA: His grandmother suggested that we do.
SHADDICK: We do?
(He takes a deep breath, closes his eyes again.)
We do.
GLORIA: I . . . I don't know how.
SHADDICK: It's very easy. *(Pause)* You just stick a hole in the little boy's heart, and then you stand back and watch him bleed.
GLORIA: *(Her eyes glistening)* What can I do, Mr. Shaddick?
(Shaddick shrugs.)
SHADDICK: What can any of us do . . .
(He looks toward the window.)
. . . except to start the bleeding process and then . . . then hope that there's enough iron in that little black frame to withstand the blow.

GLORIA: Are you going to tell him now?

SHADDICK: No . . . no . . . not here.

(They stand there waiting as Herman *enters.)*

HERMAN: *(To* Gloria*)* Thanks for letting me swim.

GLORIA: That's all right, Herman.

HERMAN: *(To Shaddick)* You sick?

SHADDICK: No, Herman, I'm not sick.

HERMAN: We goin' to the lake now?

SHADDICK: Why not?

HERMAN: We gotta stop at the delicatessen and get the fishin' poles.

SHADDICK: If that's what you want.

HERMAN: *(Looks at him)* You sure you ain't sick?

SHADDICK: No . . . perhaps just a little.

GLORIA: I'll see you both later . . .

(Shaddick and Herman *move toward door.* Herman *carefully eyes her.)*

HERMAN: Bye. *(To* Shaddick*)* She looks a little sick, too.

*(Gloria *stands there silently and motionlessly for a moment after they leave.* Mrs. Parker *rises, moves over to Gloria.)*

MRS. PARKER: Gloria, my dear — I don't want to make a thing about this — and this is hardly personal.

GLORIA: *(In a soft, whispered voice)* Isn't it?

MRS. PARKER: There are certain lines that have to be drawn. I mean . . . to invite that old man —

*(Gloria's *face freezes, and it's the look on her face that stops* Mrs. Parker *cold.)*

GLORIA: That old man and that soon-to-be wounded little boy . . . are the only honest-to-God human beings anywhere near this swimming pool. And that, Mrs. Parker, is meant to be extremely personal.

(The scene changes to the lake. Herman *and* Shaddick *are on the rock, fishing. There's a dead silence —* Herman *engrossed in his fishing,* Shaddick *looking pale and old and waiting for the right moment. And finally, because he can wait no longer, he turns to the boy.)*

SHADDICK: Herman . . . I have something to tell you now. Something . . . something very serious.

HERMAN: *(Without looking at him)* What?

SHADDICK: Look at me, Herman.

(The camera shows us Herman's *face as he turns to look at* Shaddick.*)*

SHADDICK'S VOICE: There was a call from your grandmother. It's about your brother Bill.

(At this point bobbin is suddenly grabbed by a fish and pulled under the water. We watch it spiral in descent down into the depths, carrying a fishing pole with it. A pan back over to the rock. Shaddick *is there alone, looking after a running little boy.*

The scene changes to the front of the delicatessen. The bright afternoon has turned into a cloud-laced sky, darkening by the moment, the sound of distant rolling thunder, and after a moment heavy drops of rain.

Shaddick *walks slowly toward the delicatessen. He stops for a moment, reacts, then continues to walk.*

Herman *stands by the front door of the delicatessen.* Shaddick *moves to him, says nothing—just inserts the key in the lock, opens the door.* Herman *enters, walks the length of the counter, and disappears into the bedroom.* Shaddick *stands near the front door, then closes it.*

Inside the store, Shaddick *pauses for a moment, then walks slowly over to the bedroom, stands at the curtains, then calls out.)*

SHADDICK: *(Calling)* Herman? May I come in?

(There is a silence. Shaddick *parts the curtains, moves into the bedroom.*

Herman *has his suitcase on the bed and is thrusting in the few tiny remnants of what he owns.* Shaddick *takes his suit off the hanger, lays it on the bed along with a shirt and tie. We hear distant thunder.)*

The train leaves in about an hour. We have plenty of time.

(Herman nods, finishes jamming the stuff into the suitcase, starts to close it, turns, looks up at Shaddick.)

HERMAN: You know the fish?

SHADDICK: The enormous one.

HERMAN: You keep it. Eat it or sell it. I ain't gonna need it.

SHADDICK: What if I . . . what if I had it mounted? On a gold plaque? Your name on it?

(Herman shakes his head.)

HERMAN: Don't want it. I caught it for Bill.

(With the speaking of the name, the cold-steel defence of the boy gets dented. He lets out one tiny sob that catches in his throat. Shaddick sits at table, hands folded in front of him.)

SHADDICK: If I said something, Herman . . . would you listen?

(Herman nods.)

A long time ago — almost twenty-five years ago — in this very room — I got a telegram. You know, Herman — the telegrams don't change. The wars change. The enemy changes. But the words used to tell the living about the dead . . . they don't change. *(Pause)* "We regret to inform you that your son, Second Lieutenant Benjamin Shaddick, was killed in action, June 14th, 1944, while on a bombing mission over Stuttgart, Germany." *(Pause)* I read that telegram, Herman, maybe a hundred times. I read it until the words seemed to float in the air in front of my eyes.

(He reaches across the bed to touch Herman's *hand.)*

Do you know what I thought then, Herman? I thought my life had ended. I thought there had been stripped from me some . . . some vital part of my body — that from that moment on I would never again be able to smile . . . to laugh . . . to enjoy anything on earth. I felt as you must feel now.

(All of what the old man is saying does not reach Herman, *but something of its truth and its understanding does reach him.)*

You think at the time that the sorrow and the anguish is unbearable . . . and that the tears will never stop. But Herman . . . the tears do stop. Somehow . . . some way . . . there is an end to the crying.

HERMAN: *(Very softly, thoughtfully)* One time . . . long time ago . . . I jus' a li'l kid then. I got roller skates, see? And I start down the steps . . . and I fall. And man, it hurt real bad. And Bill come out and he go down the steps and he pick me up and he look at me and he say, "Hermie . . . Hermie — don't you cry." *(Pause)* I don't cry, Shaddick. Not me. I never gonna cry.

(Shaddick rises from the bed, moves to the curtained partition, his back to the boy.)

SHADDICK: You are a very brave boy, Herman. You are really incredibly brave. *(Pause)* You stay here . . . go on with your packing. I'll call you when it's time to go.

(He comes out through the curtains, walks behind the counter, stops, his head down. Softly, under his breath, he speaks.)

Let this old Jew cry, Herman. I'll cry for the two of us.

(Shaddick moves to the window. The rain now comes down in torrents against the pane. The camera shows Shaddick's face — the tears roll down the ancient, lined cheeks much as the rain drops on the window.

Herman *comes into the room carrying his suitcase. He moves to* Shaddick. Shaddick *turns to him, wiping his face.)*

HERMAN: Why you cry? He nothin' to you. You never even know my brother. So why you cry, man?

SHADDICK: *(Very softly)* I cry because I'm an old man, Herman. And sometimes . . . that's all that's left to old men. They cry at the irony of things. That the fine young men die . . . and the old men go on.

(Gloria's *car pulls up outside.* Gloria *gets out, rushes through the rain to the front door, and enters.)*

GLORIA: I thought I'd drive Herman to New York, Mr. Shaddick.

(Shaddick *looks at* Herman.*)*

SHADDICK: It's for him to decide. The weather is so bad . . .

GLORIA: It's begun to rain. I'll drive you, Herman. Is that all right?

(Herman *nods silently, unemotionally.)*

HERMAN: That all right.

GLORIA: Herman . . . I'm truly sorry.

(Herman *again nods but says nothing.)*

SHADDICK: Do you want me to drive in with you, Herman?

(Herman *turns to him. There is a moment's pause.)*

HERMAN: No. No, you stay here. *(He picks up his suitcase.)* I ready.

(Gloria *opens the door, steps aside to let him pass.* Herman *moves to the door, then turns very slowly to look at* Shaddick. *He speaks very directly and with no emotion.)*
G'bye.

(Shaddick *takes a step toward the boy, wanting to say more, do more, show more, but he can't bring himself to try to scale the fortress that surrounds this kid. He puts his hand up in the way of a wave.* Herman *turns, follows* Gloria *out and into the car.*

The engine starts, then suddenly the passenger's door opens. Herman *comes out, runs through the rain to the front door of the delicatessen, and then enters. He moves very close to the old man and looks up at him, then very slowly reaches up.* Shaddick *puts out his own hand and the two of them clasp.)*
I jus' wanna say somethin' to you—Don't you cry no more. Understand?

(The camera shows us Herman's *little face, and for the first time we see tears.)*
We gonna make out. You'n me. We gonna make out—

(And then he starts to cry. Shaddick *takes the little boy to him, hugs him fiercely, protectively, then very slowly they separate.)*

SHADDICK: When you come back we can go fishing again.

HERMAN: I come back. I really gonna come back.

(Herman turns, moves out the door and into the car. The car door closes and the car pulls away.

Shaddick *turns from the window, moves down the length of the counter, pausing—just to stand there, looking at nothing.)*

SHADDICK: Benjy . . .

(The phone rings. Shaddick *turns, moves toward the phone, picks it up as if it were a heavy weight.)*

Yes? *(Pause)* Who? *(Pause)* A collect call. A collect call from who—I shouldn't ask. *(He closes his eyes, nods.)* Mr. Banner. All right, I'll take it.

(We hear a torrential pouring of words at the other end of the receiver. Shaddick *simply stands there, shoulders bent, eyes half closed. He waits for the outpouring of words to dry up.)*

Hello, Stanley . . . what—I am sorry that the thing blew up. Yeah, you, you may come back and stay for as long as you want.

(Another outpouring of words, then Shaddick *looks up, studies the curtained room.)*

No . . . not there. That room is reserved, for Herman. *(Pause)* That's right—Herman Washington. He's a friend of mine. A very close and personal friend. That room will be saved for him. Upstairs, Stanley. *(Pause)* Think nothing of it, Stanley . . . bye.

(He replaces the receiver, looks briefly toward the curtained room again, then takes a slow walk over to the counter and moves behind it to look down at the picture of his dead son.)

The dead, my son, come in all colours. You must know this. We, unfortunately, are still learning.

(He turns and looks down the length of the counter toward the window.)

It's raining quite hard, Benjy. A real summer storm. And this, I guess, will end the heat. End the heat . . . and cleanse the earth.

(A silence; he closes his eyes tightly.)

How we need it!

(He moves down the length of the counter back to the window to look out at the falling rain.)

Fade out.

AFTERWORD

1. In Act One, Gloria Ross tells her friend Harriet: "You put some poor unsuspecting little kid in with that old goat, he'd be scarred for life." By the end of the play, Gloria knows more about Shaddick. With a partner, roleplay a brief dialogue between Gloria and Harriet after Gloria's return from New York City. What would Gloria say about Shaddick?

2. As a talent scout, your job is to find the right actor to play Herman Washington. You prepare by
   - rereading the stage directions for Herman's dialogue and jotting down the words and phrases that seem to describe him best;
   - listing any of your own conclusions about Herman's character.
   In a group, compare the notes you made. Do the members of your group have similar views about Herman's character? Think of two or three actors who might play this role effectively.

3. In Act Two, Herman says to Shaddick, "We equal, huh?" and Shaddick answers, "More than we both realize." In what ways do you think Herman and Shaddick are equal? In your journal, describe one of your own friends. How is your friend different from you? Are the two of you equal in any ways?

4. What do you think Shaddick means when he says to Herman, "The haters turn the victims into haters. You line up the two teams . . . and who's to tell them apart"? Write a letter to Shaddick in which you tell him why you either agree or disagree about his views on hatred.

5. At the end of Act Three, Shaddick tries to say something comforting to Herman about his brother's death. In your journal, write what you might say to try to help someone who has just experienced the death of a close friend or relative.

6. At the beginning of the play, Gloria, Herman, and Shaddick do not trust one another. With a group, discuss how these characters stereotype others. How do *you* feel about the three characters? Are they merely stereotypes? After your discussion, present your conclusions to the class. If different groups have opposite opinions, you might arrange an informal debate to explore the various viewpoints.

7. You have joined an actor's workshop and your task is to perform Shaddick's monologue that ends *A Storm in Summer*. You begin by creating an actor's notebook.

Prepare the monologue as a double-spaced script, including the stage directions. Write your interpretation for each line of what the words mean to Shaddick. On your script, make notes about the *subtext* of the lines by determining what attitudes and emotions lie behind the words.

Make notes on how you will say the lines: the words you will emphasize, where you will pause, how quickly you will speak, and the mood you want to convey. If you decide to use gestures and facial expressions, make notes about these as well.

Rehearse your monologue and perform it for a partner. Add your partner's suggestions to your notebook. Watch your partner's monologue and offer your feedback. Exchange notebooks with your partner and compare your approaches.

Actor's Notebook: for the speech Romeo makes about Juliet in Act 2, Scene 2, *Romeo and Juliet*. He is looking up at her balcony on the left hand of the stage and sees her in the light of her window.

Romeo:
It is my lady, O, it is my love!
O, that she knew she were!
She speaks, yet she says nothing; what of that?
Her eye discourses; I will answer it.
I am too bold, 'tis not to me she speaks.
Two of the fairest stars in all the heaven,
Having some business, do entreat her eyes
To twinkle in their spheres till they return.
What if her eyes were there, they in her head?
The brightness of her cheek would shame those stars,
As daylight doth a lamp; her eyes in heaven
Would through the airy region stream so bright
That birds would sing and think it were not night.
See, how she leans her cheek upon her hand!
O, that I were a glove upon that hand,
That I might touch that cheek!

Handwritten annotations:

pause

move to centre stage.
look to window.
Say with great longing in voice.

Look at audience.
Say "to me" with emphasis.

pause

pause

Move toward balcony.
Look to sky
Then look to audience.

Hold out hand and put it to cheek.
Say in longing voice.

Look to window.
Say lovingly.

▼ ▼ ▼ *INTRODUCTION TO:*

The Dream and the Triumph

Transcript by Jim Purdy
Based on the short story by Ernest Buckler

" . . . if writing is hell, not writing is worse."
Ernest Buckler

he well-known Canadian novelist Ernest Buckler was born in Nova Scotia in 1908 and educated at Dalhousie University and the University of Toronto. After a brief stint as an actuary in Toronto, he returned to the family farm near Annapolis Royal where he remained for the rest of his life. He once described himself as "a farmer who writes, not a writer who farms."

Buckler began his career by writing sketches and short stories. Like his later work, these stories are deeply rooted in rural Nova Scotia. This teleplay is an adaptation of a short story in the collection entitled *The Rebellion of Young David and Other Stories.* It is about a young man who is forced to leave college and help his grandmother run the family farm when his grandfather dies. He dreams of what life might have held for him if he had been able to finish school and become an engineer.

GETTING STARTED

1. In your journal, write about a time when you or someone you know said something in anger that you (or the person) felt sorry about later. What, if anything, was done to try to set things right? If you had the chance to relive your experience, what would you do differently?

2. What are three advantages of living in the country and three advantages of living in the city? Where would you prefer to live? Share your responses with a group. If your group is divided in opinion, hold a quick debate on the advantages of country versus city living.

3. What do you think the saying "It is better to give than to receive" means? With a partner, roleplay the giving of an expensive gift. The recipient is embarrassed about taking it, while the giver tries to convince the recipient to accept. Compare your roleplay with another group's. How is their roleplay similar to yours? How is it different?

TELEPLAY

The Dream and the Triumph

Transcript by Jim Purdy
Based on the short story by Ernest Buckler

CHARACTERS

CHRIS REDMOND — *an elderly man and a farmer in an isolated community*

MARY REDMOND — *an elderly woman, married to Chris*

PAUL REDMOND — *their nineteen-year-old grandson, a student in a distant city*

DR. KEY — *a surgeon*

Fade in:

1. INT. MASTER BEDROOM, FARMHOUSE. DAY.
(Extreme closeup on Chris. He is an old man, his face not just wrinkled but also very weary, weak. He stares blankly into space and there is a vagueness to his speech. He is lost in his own world and is obviously dying.)
CHRIS: D'ya mind the time he lost that new wallet? Christmas, wasn't it? He was still just a boy. His first wallet. And he lost it. And you went and bought him another one. Just like it. But you pretended you'd found it. Where he'd gone tobogganing, wasn't it? *(Pause)* And you never let on. Don't think he ever knew the difference. *(Pause)* Must ask him about that . . . When he gets back home here.
(He falls silent and just stares blankly as we hear a voice speaking over:)
PAUL: *(VO)* I was on my way as soon as Gram wrote me. A fork tine in his heel when he was bedding the horses. Tetanus.
Fade to black.

2. EXT/INT. COUNTRYSIDE/TRAIN. DAY.
(Titles begin over.
POV of rural countryside seen through the window of a moving train. Pan to discover the reflection in the glass of a young man — Paul — staring glumly out the window. He glances down to the floor where his ice skates and a small trunk sit at his feet as we hear over:)
PAUL: *(VO)* All I could think about on the train was how bedding the horses had always been my job and if only I'd been at home . . .
(Paul picks up a letter and stares at it.)
(VO) They'd raised me after my mother and father died, both in the same week, of the black diphtheria. I was ten at the time. They'd worked hard so I could go to college.

3. INT. KITCHEN, FARMHOUSE. DAY.
(Titles continue over.
An elderly lady — Mary — sits alone in the kitchen.)
PAUL: *(VO)* I don't think they really understood what going to college or being an engineer meant. But it had always been my dream. And so it became their dream.

4. EXT. COUNTRY ROAD/FARM. DAY.
(Titles continue over.
A truck circa late 1940s pulls away leaving Paul standing alone on the dusty road, his trunk and skates by his side. He is nineteen years old and dressed in early 1950s fashion.
He walks up the driveway to the house.)
PAUL: *(VO)* Walking up the road to the house that first day back, I felt my nerves tauten. Everything that was so familiar was also coated with dread.

5. INT. KITCHEN, FARMHOUSE. DAY.
(Paul stands with Mary.)
PAUL: I'm sorry Gram. I should've come home sooner.
MARY: No, no. It was a long time coming.
(Tilt down to closeup on Mary's eyeglasses on the table in the foreground.)
PAUL: *(VO)* Dear old Gram. Now alone after all those years.

6. EXT. CHURCH CEMETERY. DAY.
(Paul and Mary stand by Chris's tombstone.)

PAUL: *(VO)* Her thoughts creeping back into her mind from the touch of table and chair which need two faces in the room in order to have a face of their own.

7. INT. KITCHEN, FARMHOUSE. DAY.
(Paul *stokes the fire in the woodstove. He glances up to* Mary *who places two dinners at the table.*
Paul *rises and moves to the table, uncertain as to what to do or say. He then sits opposite her.*
They sit eating in silence for a moment. Then Mary *looks across to him.)*
MARY: What made you bring everything home with you? Your books and everything?
(Paul *says nothing; the reason he brought them home is clear.)*
You can't stay here. There's nothing here for you.
PAUL: Gram . . .
MARY: No, Paul. I mean it. I'll manage.
(Paul *shakes his head — that option is unacceptable.)*
Then we can sell this place and I could . . .
PAUL: Gram, you're not selling the place.
MARY: You've got to go back to the city. To your studies.
(Paul *simply looks at her again. He knows he cannot escape the inevitable.*
Mary *looks at him in regret. She cannot argue back; for her too it is inevitable.*
They sit eating in silence as:)
PAUL: *(VO)* "Sell this place". I knew what it had cost her to pronounce those words.

8. INT. PAUL'S BEDROOM, FARMHOUSE. NIGHT.
(Pan *over the school pennant, the textbooks, skates, typewriter.)*
PAUL: *(VO)* I could no more leave her and this place than she could have left me when I was orphaned at ten years old.
(Come to Paul *sitting on his bed. He slams shut a book, rises and moves to the window. He looks back over his books.)*
(VO) But still, it hung over me. What kind, what better kind, of someone else might I have been? If I could go back there. Instead of being stuck here. In this place.
(He *stares out the window.)*

9. EXT. FARM FIELD. DAY.
(Paul *walks through the mud in the field.)*

PAUL: *(VO)* With the fences to mend and the wood to chop and the cows to milk. It didn't take long for my hands to be hard and toughened again. As if the axe and the plough were the only tools scaled to them.
(End in closeup on Paul.)

10. *INT. KITCHEN, FARMHOUSE. DAY.*
(Mary makes tea while Paul sits at the table half-heartedly perusing the local farm paper. He looks up, watching her thoughtfully.)
PAUL: *(VO)* And she knew. She knew exactly how I felt. I was restless and she was beholden. That was always there. And it became an area of constraint as tender and diffused as a boil.
(She pours tea and they exchange silent looks.)

11. *EXT. FIELD. DAY.*
(Long shot of Paul hammering the fence post.)
PAUL: *(VO)* And the days wore on, one after the other, leading nowhere. And I tried to lose myself in the fence posts and the feed supplies and in the cattle, especially in a sick cow named Betty.
Fade to:

12. *INT. KITCHEN, FARMHOUSE. DAY.*
(Sound of heavy footsteps running down the stairs.
Paul *thunders down the stairs into the kitchen where* Mary *sits reading a newspaper with a magnifying glass. He storms across the room to the back door, pulling on his jacket and boots. She rises and moves to the stove to prepare him breakfast.)*
PAUL: Why didn't ya wake me up?
MARY: You've been working so hard, I thought . . .
PAUL: I don't have time for breakfast now.
MARY: But, Paul, you have to eat.
PAUL: Pete's due today, right?
MARY: Uh . . . What day is it?
PAUL: Tuesday. He still comes on Tuesdays, right?
MARY: Tuesday. Yes, Tuesday.
PAUL: Lunchtime?
MARY: Uh . . . Yes.
PAUL: Good. I'll be in the back lot. But I'll be here by lunch. So make sure he waits. I've got to talk to him about Betty. Her heifer's due soon and she's not at all well.

(He pushes his way out the door.)
MARY: I'll tell him, Paul.
(Mary stands alone not quite sure what she did wrong.)

13. EXT. FIELD. DAY.
(Paul hammers a fencepost into the ground, slamming the post with all the frustration at the turn his life has taken.
    He pauses to pull out his pocket watch and check the time. He is puzzled at the early hour. He puts the watch to his ear and is shocked when he hears nothing. He shakes it in anger but it has stopped.
    He wheels around and dashes for the car, cursing in rage.)

14. INT. KITCHEN, FARMHOUSE. DAY.
(Paul bursts into the kitchen breathless.
    Mary *is busy at the table and looks up at* Paul *in surprise.)*
MARY: Where were you?
PAUL: Is he gone?
MARY: Why didn't you come home? Did you forget he was coming . . . ?
PAUL: Is he gone?!
MARY: He was here. He sat here and waited. I kept him here as long as I could.
    (Paul groans and angrily removes his boots.)
I told him you wanted to talk to him. But finally, when you didn't come, he just had to . . .
PAUL: It doesn't matter.
MARY: What happened? Why didn't you come home . . . ?
PAUL: *(Exploding as he rips off his coat)* I said it doesn't matter! It doesn't make any difference! How could it? In this damn backwater. Nothing ever goes right.
    (He stops short, realizing he's gone too far.
    She stands there staring at him in shock and hurt.)
I'm sorry, Gram. It's just . . .
(He leaves the room. She is alone.)
PAUL: *(VO)* I don't know where the words came from. How they slipped out.

15. INT. KITCHEN, FARMHOUSE. EVENING.
(Angle on: Paul *and* Mary *sitting at the table for dinner, a terrible silence between them.)*
PAUL: *(VO)* There is nothing so terrible as the silence in a country

kitchen after words like that. There is nothing as terrible as sitting at the table and swallowing your food after a silence like that.

16. EXT. MAILBOX BY ROAD. DAY.

(Paul *removes a wad of mail and the newspaper from the mailbox by the road at the end of the farm's driveway. He examines the mail and notices an envelope addressed to him.*)

PAUL: *(VO)* Then, as if to seal my fate, a letter from the college refunding my tuition. I felt robbed.

(*Closeup on the letter with engineering college letterhead:* "Dear Mr. Redmond: Please find enclosed the refund due to you on your tuition and residency fees . . .")

I'd never have what I once worked so hard for.

(*Angle on:* Paul *looking out across the landscape in despair.*)

17. INT. KITCHEN, FARMHOUSE. DAY.

(Paul *enters from outside, removing his boots and calling.*)

PAUL: Gram?! . . . Gram! Where's the bandages?

(*He removes his coat and crosses to the sink.*
Mary *hurries into the room.*)

MARY: What's wrong?

PAUL: *(Washing his hands)* Nothing. I just caught my finger in the gate.

MARY: *(Crossing to him)* Let's see.

PAUL: It's alright. Just a little gash.

(*She takes his hand to look at it, squinting to see clearly.*)

I can look after it. Just tell me where the bandages are.

MARY: *(Letting go of his hand)* Wash it well.

(*She reaches up to the shelves and pulls down an old shoebox which she rummages through for a bandage.*)

PAUL: Yeah, yeah . . .

MARY: Get all the dirt out. You'll get infection.

PAUL: It's just a small cut.

(*She pulls a roll of bandage from the box.*)

MARY: *(Asking for his hand)* Here.

PAUL: I can do it.

(*She takes his hand and carefully wraps the bandage around his finger.*)

MARY: Your grandfather wouldn't listen to me. I don't want anything happening to you.

(*He watches her closely as she cuts off the bandage and*

secures it to his finger.)
PAUL: What I said the other day. I didn't mean it. It just . . . I
don't know . . .
MARY: What's said is said.
*(She finishes wrapping his finger in silence. He glances down at
the shoebox where something catches his eye.*
*His POV: Closeup on the debris in the box, particularly a
yellowed newspaper clipping: "Operation Restores Sight to 90-
Year-Old Woman".*
*She finishes with the bandage and notices Paul looking at the
clipping.)*
There, that should be alright now.
PAUL: *(VO)* Until that moment, I hadn't noticed. It was her
eyesight.
*(She turns to the shoebox and quickly gathers up the debris, in-
cluding the clipping.)*
MARY: Should clean all this trash out of here.
(She scrunches up the clipping and returns the box to the shelf.
*Paul watches her silently while she crosses to the woodstove
and tosses the clipping into the flames.)*
Be more careful next time. You're not as used to things
around here anymore like you used to be.
PAUL: *(VO)* I wanted to say something, but how, after what had
happened between us?
(She turns and moves out of the room.
Hold on Paul as he ponders the situation.)

18. INT. STAIRWAY/LIVING ROOM, FARMHOUSE. DAY.
*(Paul is repairing one of the steps near the bottom of the stairs
leading to the second floor. He hammers the step securely into
place, tests it and is satisfied that it is now fixed. He then looks
into the living room.*
*His POV: Mary sits on the couch, some old clothes and sew-
ing equipment laid out before her, struggling vainly to thread a
needle.*
*He watches her a moment, then rises and moves to her while
she continues to try to thread the needle.)*
PAUL: Here, let me help you.
*(She surrenders the needle and thread to him, not really want-
ing to but recognizing she has no choice.)*
(As he threads the needle) Why don't you go see the doctor
about your eyes? Those old glasses must be . . .

MARY: I did.

PAUL: What did he say?

MARY: Oh, nothing very different. He gave me some drops. They didn't do any good. It's just . . . getting old, that's all. *(He finishes threading the needle and hands it back to her.)* Old people just have to keep on living till they die. *(He looks at her.)*

19. INT/EXT. KITCHEN/FARMYARD. DAY.

(POV through the kitchen window to the chicken coop where Mary *is feeding the hens.* Paul's *voice is heard offscreen.)*

PAUL: *(OS)* And an operation is the only thing . . . ?

(Angle on: Paul *in the kitchen on the phone keeping an eye on* Mary *outside.)*

Yeah . . . That much? . . . No. You know her. She wouldn't spend that much on herself. Even if she did have it . . . No, she'd never take it from anyone else . . . Yeah, well . . . Thanks, Doctor.

(He hangs up and continues to watch Mary.*)*

PAUL: *(VO)* Was it her fault that she was old and got half angry at anything that might be considered pity?

20. INT. KITCHEN, FARMHOUSE. NIGHT.

(Paul is at the table reading the local paper. Mary *stands at the sink, her back to him, doing the dishes.)*

PAUL: *(VO)* But I'd failed her and only wanted to undo the damage. Then a sudden wild notion hit me.

PAUL: *(Referring to the paper)* Did you see this? *(Reading)* "The Oddest Thing That Ever Happened to Me".

MARY: What's that?

PAUL: *(Reading)* "Write about the strangest or funniest event that ever occurred to you and win five brand-new one-hundred-dollar bills."

MARY: So?

PAUL: What about you trying it?

MARY: Don't be silly.

PAUL: No. You've told me all kinds of funny things that happened to you.

MARY: I've never won anything in my life.

PAUL: You can tell it to me and I'll write it down for you.

(She does not answer and continues the dishes in silence. After a moment, Paul *returns to his paper.)*

21. EXT. FRONT DRIVE, FARMHOUSE. DAY.
(Pete's *dairy truck is pulling away as* Paul *and* Mary *stand by watching.)*
MARY: That's good news about Betty.
PAUL: Yeah. A relief.
MARY: Pete said you looked after her real well.
PAUL: Well, wouldn't want to lose a cow and her heifer.
MARY: You know, that reminds me . . . *(Stops short)*
PAUL: What?
MARY: *(Turning towards the house)* Oh, nothing.
PAUL: What does it remind you of? Something strange? Funny?
(She glances back at Paul.
He smiles at her.)*

22. INT. KITCHEN, FARMHOUSE. NIGHT.
(Pan over memorabilia: old snapshots, letters, newspaper clippings spanning the years from the nineteen-twenties to the postwar years. Featured are photos of a young Mary *and* Chris; *their children; a young* Paul, *first with his parents,* Mary's *daughter, then with just* Mary *and* Chris. *Included is a notice of* Paul's *parents' deaths in the same week of black diphtheria.*
Offscreen is heard:)
PAUL: *(OS)* Well, have you decided?
MARY: *(OS)* I never realized there was so much. But I can re-member it all so . . .
(Angle on: Mary *sitting at the kitchen table with the memo-rabilia spread out before her and* Paul, *pen and paper in hand, sitting opposite her.)*
Yet, I can't remember what happened two days ago.
*(*Paul *watches her perusing through the stuff.)*
PAUL: *(VO)* It was curiously hurting to see her so unsuspectingly serious over choosing a favourite memory. That she really did hope she might win the five-hundred dollars.
MARY: I don't even know how to get started.
PAUL: Just the same way you used to tell me all those stories. About you and Gramp. And mom and dad.
MARY: That was different.
PAUL: What's different?
MARY: Those stories were 'specially for you.
PAUL: So? I'm the only one here. Make this one for me.
(She cannot help but smile.)
MARY: Alright. You ready?

PAUL: All set.

MARY: Well, um . . . *(Dictating)* "Chris was working away the day I . . ." *(Stops short)* Oh, wait, they don't know who Chris is. I better say "my husband", don't you think?

PAUL: Good idea.

(She starts slowly, uncertainly but gradually gets caught up in her memories, allowing them to flood back and then out in a torrent of words.

Paul *writes all this very diligently.)*

MARY: *(Dictating)* "I hated to tell him when he came home. I mean, that ring had cost twenty dollars." *(Stopping and addressing* Paul*)* That was an awful lot more money back then, let me tell you. *(Resumes dictating)* "Well, I was pretty sure I had lost it in the barn. But we couldn't find it. Well, he had a heifer he was raising for an extra cow. So one day he said, 'I think I'll beef that heifer.' And I thought, now he's going to beef that heifer and sell her and buy me another ring. But I didn't dare tell him not to in case that wasn't what he had in mind."

(She continues to narrate the story over the following scenes.)

23. INT. BANK. DAY.

(Mary's voiceover continues.

Paul *stands before a teller's wicket.)*

MARY: *(VO)* "Anyway, they killed the heifer and when they cut her open, there was the ring, in her stomach. It must have gotten into her feedbox and she'd swallowed it. Well, I remember the look on his face when he came in with his fist stuck out."

(Closeup on five one-hundred-dollar bills being counted out.)

24. INT. PAUL'S BEDROOM. NIGHT.

(Mary's voiceover continues.

Paul *sits at a typewriter typing. He finishes a one-page letter, pulls it out of the typewriter and then stops abruptly, as if he's heard something. He turns toward his closed door and listens a moment. Satisfied no one is there, he folds the letter, picks up an envelope and puts the letter into it.*

Closeup on the envelope addressed to "Mrs. Mary Redmond RR #2 Middleton Nova Scotia".)*

MARY: *(VO)* "And when he spread his fingers open and there was the ring in the palm of his hand. And I remember what he said when he slipped it on my finger again: 'This should be a lesson.' "

25. EXT. MAILBOX BY ROAD. DAY.

(Mary's *voiceover continues.*

Paul *removes the mail from the mailbox, then reaches into his coat and pulls out the envelope he has typed for* Mary *and adds it to the mail.)*

MARY: *(VO)* "'We must never be afraid to part with something we need to buy something we . . .' He didn't finish, but I knew what he meant. And we never were."

(Paul *heads to the house as we hear over:)*

PAUL: *(VO)* It was important that she never find out what I was doing.

26. INT. KITCHEN, FARMHOUSE. DAY.

(Mary *is in the kitchen as* Paul *enters with the mail.)*

PAUL: *(VO)* It was the only way I could help her without seeming to help her.

(Paul *moves to her with the mail.)*

PAUL: There's some mail for you here. From that newspaper contest.

(He hands it to her but she just stares at him in surprise.)

Well, come on. Open it.

(She nervously opens the envelope, then stops.)

MARY: Paul, I can't.

PAUL: Just open it and find out what it says.

MARY: I can't read it anyway.

PAUL: Just open it.

(She pulls a folded sheet of paper from the envelope and as she unfolds it, the hundred-dollar bills slip out onto the table. She sits there staring at them in stunned silence.

Paul *picks up the sheet of paper and reads it.)*

Gram, you won. You won!

MARY: Oh, Paul! . . . I never dreamed . . . Did you?

PAUL: There it is. You won.

MARY: *(Starting to cry)* I can't help it . . . I'm such a fool when anything like this . . . Oh, Paul . . . I can't believe it . . .

(He sits down opposite her and looks her in the eye.)

PAUL: And Gram. This money. You and I will go to the city. To the hospital. And get your eyes seen to.

MARY: Oh, no. There's so many other things we need . . .

PAUL: Gram, this is your money. You won it. So for once in your life, you use it for yourself.
MARY: I can't. Not when we could . . .
PAUL: Gram. Remember what Gramp said? About what you need and what you . . . ?
(She just looks at him, emotion welling up inside her.)
PAUL: *(VO)* She had to try hard, not to cry again.

27. EXT. FARM. DAY.
(Pan over the house, barns and fields.)
PAUL: *(VO)* The way it is when some affliction borne silently and without hope suddenly seems almost like a friend, now that a miraculous way is open to release from it.

28. INT. HALLWAY, FARMHOUSE. DAY.
(Mary, dressed in a coat, looks into the mirror adjusting her hat.)
PAUL: *(VO)* She put up no real resistance to any of the things I'd expected her to resist. The new clothes, the trip . . .

29. EXT. HOSPITAL. DAY.
(Long shot of Paul and Mary entering the hospital.)
PAUL: *(VO)* . . . the hospital.

30. INT. HOSPITAL ROOM. DAY.
(Mary has moved into her hospital room and is sitting up in bed dressed in a hospital gown.
Doctor Key sits at her bedside talking with her. Paul stands beside them.)
DR. KEY: There's a very good chance, yes. But I have to be honest with you. With someone your age, we can't be absolutely sure.
MARY: And if I don't have the operation?
DR. KEY: The pressure in your eyes will get worse and more painful. And you will eventually go blind.
(Pause. Doctor Key looks at her sympathetically, letting her make her own decision.
She looks to Paul.
He gives her a smile of reassurance.
She looks to Doctor Key.)
MARY: Well, I haven't come all this way not to give it a try.
(Doctor Key smiles at her and clasps her hand.)

DR. KEY: *(Rising)* I'll check in with you later and let you know when it's been scheduled.

MARY: Thank you.

DR. KEY: And get some rest in the meantime, okay? *(To Paul)* Nice meeting you.

PAUL: Thank you, Doctor.

(Doctor Key moves out of the room. Paul sits down on the bed with Mary. They look at one another, both recognizing what's at stake. She feels strengthened by his presence; he feels proud of her courage.)

MARY: If it works and I can see again, I was thinking that . . . You wouldn't have to come back to the farm. You could stay here. Go back to university.

PAUL: Gram, don't talk like that . . .

MARY: No. It's what you want, isn't it?

(He looks at her.)

And it's what I want for you.

31. EXT. CITY COLLEGE. DAY.

(Angle on: an old, ivied college building.

Paul *sits on a bench looking at it. A couple of students pass him by chatting, satchels of books under their arms. He watches them as we hear over:)*

PAUL: *(VO)* She'd seen right into me. More than I'd seen into myself. Back in the city again, the old restlessness came over me.

32. INT. LECTURE HALL, COLLEGE. DAY.

(An empty lecture hall—rows and rows of seats facing a lectern and blackboard.

Paul *moves down the aisle, looking about, soaking up the atmosphere.*

Various notations are scrawled over the board.

He stares at them with fascination. This is where he belongs; this is where he feels at home.)

PAUL: *(VO)* I was face to face with the ghost of that other possible life. Would I have to do battle all over again with my old dreams when I got back to the farm?

33. INT. HOSPITAL ROOM. DAY.

(Angle on: a medical eye chart in a darkened hospital room as light from the window begins to increase on it.

Angle on: the nurse *at the window slowly opening the venetian blinds.)*

PAUL: *(VO)* Or maybe, as Gram suggested, was this another chance for me too?

(Closeup on Mary, *the light increasing on her face, her eyes squinting in an effort to see.*

   Angle on: Paul, *very tense.)*

DR. KEY: Take your time. Let your eyes adjust to the light.

MARY: *(Squinting)* I can see the "E".

DR. KEY: *(Pointing to the second row of letters on the chart)* What about here?

MARY: *(Straining to see)* "D" . . . "T" . . .

(Closeup on Doctor Key's *pencil pointing to each letter as* Mary *correctly identifies each one.)*

MARY: *(OS)* "P" . . . "S" . . . "J" . . .

   (Paul watches in earnest.

   Closeup on Mary.)

   (Hesitates) "Q" . . . "B" . . . "O" . . .

(Closeup on Paul, *relieved, exultant.*

   Doctor Key *stops and looks at* Mary *with a warm smile.)*

DR. KEY: Well, Mrs. Redmond. When do you feel like going home?

(She turns to Paul, *tears in her eyes.*

   He smiles at her.)

MARY: It's like being reborn. It really is.

   (Paul moves to the bed and sits with her.)

   I guess for you too. You can move back here now. Go back to university like you want to.

(Paul looks at her in uncertainty.)

---

34. EXT/INT. COUNTRYSIDE/TRAIN. DAY.

(Pan over the countryside moving past the train window. Mary's *voice is heard offscreen.)*

MARY: *(OS)* It's like someone lifted the window shade and let the light in for me. And I can see inside and outside. For the first time in a long time. Beautiful, isn't it?

(Pan to Paul *sitting beside* Mary *on the train looking out the window.)*

PAUL: Sure is, Gram. Good to be getting back home, too.

(They stare out the window.)

PAUL: *(VO)* What I hadn't expected was how homesick the city had made me for the farm. It was as simple as that.

35. EXT. FARM DRIVEWAY. DAY.
(Long shot of Paul *and* Mary *walking up the roadway to the house.)*
MARY: Paul.
PAUL: Yeah?
MARY: Do you remember that wallet you got that Christmas? I think you were eight. And you lost it?
PAUL: Yeah.
MARY: Then I found it where you'd gone tobogganing and gave it to you? You remember that?
PAUL: Yeah.
MARY: Did you ever figure out that I didn't find it? That I really bought another one and just pretended to find it.
(Paul stops and looks at her.
She smiles mishievously at him.)
PAUL: *(VO)* She didn't actually mention the contest, but the way she smiled at me, with a kind of wink. And I had a wonderful feeling when it suddenly dawns on you that you really love someone, the feeling that, between you, an insight into everything is possible.

(Dissolve to:
Tail credits over:
Snapshot of Paul *in the field with the fenceposts.*

Dissolve to:
Snapshot of Paul *with his bride on their wedding day.*

Dissolve to:
Snapshot of Paul *and his wife posing with a newborn infant.*

Dissolve to:
Snapshot of Mary *proudly holding a baby.*

Dissolve to:
Snapshot of Paul *with a very young boy on the farm.*

Dissolve to:
Snapshot of Mary *playing with the young boy.*

Dissolve to:
Snapshot of Paul, *his wife, an older boy with a new heifer.*
End tail credits.)

Fade out.

AFTERWORD

1. Paul's dream was to finish college and become an engineer. Write a journal entry about your dreams for the future. How might you feel if for some reason you couldn't realize your dream? In your journal, describe what might block the achievement of your dreams, and suggest ways of responding to these problems.

2. Imagine that you are Paul and that you have to decide whether to live on the farm or go back to school. Create a chart to help you make your decision. On the chart, list the pros and cons of both options. Looking at your chart, what decision would you make? Did Paul make the same decision? Compare your chart with a partner's.

3. This play was adapted from a short story by Ernest Buckler. Read the following excerpt from Buckler's story and compare it to the same moment in the play (see page 282).

> Finally, as it was bound to, there came the afternoon when the blighting accusation was spoken and the indelible response was put into words.
>
> It had been for Paul one of those days of clenched, grinding mood which everyone knows occasionally. When there is a conspiracy among even trifles to frustrate you.
>
> He had overslept. The single gust of wind that morning came at the very second the butt of the big spruce was severed, and took it into the thicket. He couldn't have found a rock in that part of the woods if he'd searched for one, but his axe found one all right. His watch stopped and tricked him into arriving home just too late to catch the dairyman he'd been waiting weeks to see . . . .
>
> When he stepped into the kitchen half an hour past dinnertime, Mary said to him, "I thought you were coming home early, Paul. The dairyman stopped in to see you, but he couldn't wait."
>
> "What the hell difference does it make?" he flashed out at her. "Anyone buried in this damn . . . all his life . . . poor as a church mouse . . . working your heart out for a few dollars . . . ."
>
> He didn't know where the false words came from, how they slipped past his guard. They made no sense as an answer to her question.

Mary caught her breath. "Well, Paul," she said, "old people have to live till they die. Do you ever stop to think what it's like for me? You'll be old some day."

They turned away from each other's face, and each looked as if he wished he could turn away from his own. There is nothing so terrible as the silence after words like that in a country kitchen . . . .

In a group, discuss how the two versions of Buckler's story are alike, and how they are different. Which do you think is more effective, and why? Present your ideas to the class.

4. As Mary, write a diary entry about what the future holds for you now that your sight has returned and Paul wants to stay on the farm.

5. With a partner, roleplay a scene that takes place eight years after the end of the play, in which Mary tells her great-grandson the story about Paul and the writing contest. Share your roleplay with a small group or the rest of the class.

6. This teleplay ends with a "photomontage." The camera films a sequence of still photographs that combine to suggest a theme or establish a mood. As the director of the teleplay, what do you want the photos to suggest about Paul's decision to stay on the farm? What mood do you want the photos to convey? Write a memo to the cameraperson explaining how you want the photomontage to be filmed.

7. A photomontage can be filmed, or it can be presented as a display. Using photographs of your own or from magazines, newspapers, or other sources, create a photomontage display to convey a particular mood. On the back of your display or on a separate piece of paper, create a key to your work. It might consist of a poem, a sentence, a paragraph, or a web of words related to your theme. Display your photomontage and have members of the class guess what mood you are trying to convey. Afterwards, show them your key, and answer any questions they might have about your display.

▼ ▼ ▼ *INTRODUCTION TO:*

The Hangashore

Ted Russell

"You might be interested in knowing that the summoning of a magistrate to handle a matter of two stolen holes actually occurred. I was that magistrate! When I eventually arrived at the settlement in question (when the spring ice had moved off, making travel by boat possible), the "evidence" had, of course, disappeared. The matter didn't come to court, but I often imagine what might have happened if it had. The story in this play is the result."
Ted Russell

ed Russell was born in 1904 in a village in Conception Bay, Newfoundland called Coley's Point. At the age of sixteen he became a school teacher and spent most of his life working as a teacher and magistrate in towns and villages across Newfoundland.

After Newfoundland joined Confederation in 1949, Russell knew that the social and economic changes would threaten the traditional outport way of life. He wrote short stories and radio plays in the 1950s to record life in the outports as he had known it.

This is how Russell described the connections between the Newfoundland that he knew so well and the imaginary outport in *The Hangashore*:

"*The Hangashore* is set in Pigeon Inlet. Now, Pigeon Inlet is not an actual place; you will not find it on any map of Newfoundland. Rather it is representative of many outports that existed in the first half of this century. It is very much like places where I lived and worked: Coley's Point, Pass Island, Harbour Breton, Fogo. Its inhabitants, too, are fictitious, yet they are the types of people who were an integral part of the outport way of life. Many readers may think that my play is a bit nostalgic or even that it tells of a world that never existed. All I can do is assure such people that there were places like Pigeon Inlet; that characters like Uncle Ben, Solomon Noddy and Magistrate Kettle did exist. I wrote as honestly as I could about the outports as I knew them."

GETTING STARTED

1. Describe a time when someone played a trick on you. Did you think about taking revenge? What was the final outcome? Share your experience with a group. Could one of the experiences be the basis of a short radio play? Which details would you emphasize or change if you were preparing a script?

2. Think of any personal stories, family histories, or stories about different ways of life that ought to be recorded before they are forgotten. You might wish to summarize a story in your journal.

3. With a partner, talk about the storytellers in your life. Who tells you about your family or about the "old days"? If you wanted to tape-record someone telling a story, who would you go to? Is there a particular story you would ask that person to tell?

4. Using your imagination, describe a place that is similar to one you knew well. Suggest three or four kinds of people who would be typical inhabitants of your imaginary place. Give your place an appropriate name, and then describe it to the rest of the class.

▼ ▼ ▼ *RADIO PLAY*

The Hangashore
Ted Russell

CHARACTERS
. . . .

GRAMPA WALCOTT – *a storyteller and resident of Pigeon Inlet, Newfoundland*

LIGE BARTLE – *a straightforward and honest fisherman*

SUSIE BARTLE – *a woman of great common sense, married to Lige*

SOLOMON NODDY – *a lazy and dishonest man, but very clever as well*

MAGISTRATE – *a judge who travels from outport to outport to hear disputes*

PHINEAS PRIOR – *a religious man, friend to Lige and Grampa*

TELEGRAPH OPERATOR

GRAMPA WALCOTT: Uncle Solomon Noddy was a hangashore if ever there was one. By that I mean he was too bad to be called a good-for-nothin' and not bad enough to be called a sleeveen. He was just . . . a hangashore.

You see, a good-for-nothin' might be no good in one place, but turn out alright in some other place. Like young Sim Briggs. He used to get seasick, almost die . . . every time they took him out to help haul the codtrap. His father, poor Skipper Tite Briggs, used to say that Sim was a waste of patience and good grub. Where's Sim now? He got a berth school teachin' and ended up a clergyman in Toronto.

Then . . . take Obadiah Mesher . . . a good-for-nothin'. Could never learn the compass, or set a salmon net. But still, when he was in his seventies, people used to come to him from all up and down the shore to get him to charm their toothache. And he could put away warts, just be countin' 'em.

As for sleeveens . . . look at old Marky Belcher . . . but that's

another story. Anyway, I'm not pretending that Uncle Solomon Noddy was as bad as old Marky. Like I've said, Uncle
Solomon was a hangashore. If you don't believe me wait 'till I
tell you about how he took the two holes in the ice from
Skipper Lige Bartle.

(*Music*)

Uncle Solomon's thievery led to court work in Pigeon Inlet,
a thing no respectable place likes. Worse than that, like the
Magistrate said, if Uncle Solomon could have afforded to
appeal his case to the Supreme Court, 'twould have been
one of the most talked-of cases in the world. And Pigeon Inlet
would've got a bad name, for sure.

It all started one day in March, forty-odd years ago, when
Skipper Lige Bartle came home from rabbit-catchin', tramped
into his back porch, opened his kitchen door and called out
to his wife.

LIGE: Soos, oh Soos.

SUSIE: *(Upstairs)* That you, Lige?

LIGE: Yes Soos. Come down and throw me out a pair of dry
cuffs. I'm in a hurry.

SUSIE: Never you mind dry cuffs. Come on in here and eat your
dinner. Get any rabbits?

LIGE: Naw. Just a brace.

SUSIE: Come on in. Your dinner is dryin' up in the oven. I've
been expectin' you home for two hours. Been worried to
death, thinkin' you fell through the ice. What kept you?

LIGE: I stopped on the way down the Inlet to cut two holes in
the ice. Goin' to put out a herrin' net to get some herrin' for
the dogs. Took me a long time to cut the holes. Ice is almost
two feet thick. Now, come on with the cuffs. I want to get
my herrin' net set and home again before dark.

SUSIE: Wait 'till tomorrow morning to set the net.

LIGE: No, the holes might get covered in with snow durin' the
night. Besides, someone else might see 'em there with no net
in 'em and might take 'em.

SUSIE: No one'd do a thing like that, would they? Take another
man's holes? Why, for a man to do that, he'd have to be a . . .
a . . . a . . . hangashore.

LIGE: There's some I know might do it if they got the chance.
There's that Solomon Noddy, I wouldn't trust him as far as
I'd throw him. Anyway, I won't give him the chance. Well,
I'm off. I'll be back before dark.

(Music, followed by sound of wind, ice, dogs, etc.)
Uncle Solomon . . . get that net outa my holes.
SOLOMON: Oh, good evenin', Skipper Lige. Nice sort of evenin', ain't it?
LIGE: Never mind the weather. Get that net outa my holes.
SOLOMON: Your holes? Yours? No. My holes. I found 'em.
LIGE: You found 'em. Why, you . . . you good-for-nothin'. I cut 'em.
SOLOMON: Oh, you cut 'em. I was wonderin' to myself only a few minutes ago . . . I said to myself, said I, "I wonder who cut these holes. Oh well," I said to myself. "Whoever cut 'em is all the same. It saves me the trouble of cuttin' 'em," says I. So 'twas you cut 'em, eh?
LIGE: Yes, I cut 'em. And I'm puttin' my herrin' net in 'em.
SOLOMON: Can't very well do that, can you? Everyone knows there's no room for two herrin' nets in the same two holes.
LIGE: Yours is comin' out. If you don't take it out, I will.
SOLOMON: You better not do that, Skipper Lige. After all, my net is my property. The law won't uphold a man for interferin' with another man's property.
LIGE: But what about my property? My holes?
SOLOMON: I'm not sure as how holes can be anybody's property. Anyway, how can they be your holes when I got my nets in 'em? Besides they was nobody's holes when I found 'em. How was I supposed to know who cut 'em?
LIGE: Look here, Uncle Solomon, I believe you watched me cut 'em, and then hurried out to claim 'em before I could get back, to save yourself the trouble of cuttin' your own holes. You . . . you lazy hangashore.
SOLOMON: Now, Skipper Lige, take it easy. That's hard talk. And the law won't uphold hard talk any more than it'll uphold interferin' with property.
LIGE: Then, you . . . you won't give up the holes?
SOLOMON: No. Don't see any reason why I should.
(Music
Sound: door slams, telegraph keys)
OPERATOR: Oh, good evening, Skipper Lige. Postage stamp?
LIGE: No miss. A telygram. Write it out for me.
OPERATOR: Yes, Skipper Lige. You want to send a telegram . . .
LIGE: To the Magistrate.
OPERATOR: The . . . the magistrate? Magistrate Kettle!
LIGE: Yes. Tell him . . . wait now . . . tell him "Come immediately

for court work. Solomon Noddy stole my holes in the ice," Signed Lige Bartle.

OPERATOR: *(Reads back)* . . . Yes, Mr. Bartle. That'll be thirty-one cents, please.

LIGE: Can't it go collect?

OPERATOR: Sorry, Mr. Bartle. Not to the Magistrate. Thirty-one cents, please.

LIGE: Oh, alright. Let me know as soon as a reply comes.

(Music

Sound of telegraph office)

OPERATOR: Your reply came in today, Mr. Bartle.

LIGE: What's it say? Will you read it, please?

OPERATOR: 'Regret travelling conditions make it impossible have court work in Pigeon Inlet until June. Signed, Magistrate Kettle.'

LIGE: Can't come 'till June, eh? Oh, well, better than never. I'll just have to wait until June then.

(Music

Sound: courtroom babble and gravel)

MAGISTRATE: Court'll come to order to try the case of Elijah Bartle versus Solomon Noddy. Bein' as how with no war on, the price of fish is what it is, we'll call it a pauper's case, and there'll be no court charges.
Solomon Noddy . . . you're charged with stealing the property of Elijah Bartle . . . to wit . . . two holes in the ice. Do you plead guilty or not guilty?

SOLOMON: Skipper Bob . . .

MAGISTRATE: Order. You must address me as 'Your Honour.'

SOLOMON: Well, Your Honour, could I just wait and hear Skipper Lige's story and then ask a question?

MAGISTRATE: Yes, Uncle Sol. That's your right as a British subject. Kiss the Book, Skipper Lige, and tell your story.

LIGE: Well, Skipper Bob . . . I mean Your Honour, it was this way. *(Slow fade)* Last winter when I went out on the ice I caught Uncle Solomon . . .

MAGISTRATE: Well, Solomon, did you hear Skipper Lige's story?

SOLOMON: Yes, Skipper . . . I mean, yes, Your Honour, but . . .

MAGISTRATE: Is his story true?

SOLOMON: Yes, Your Honour, as far as it goes, but . . .

MAGISTRATE: But what, Solomon?

SOLOMON: Your Honour, might I make so bold as to ask you a question?

MAGISTRATE: Yes, Solomon, of course. Go ahead.

SOLOMON: Your Honour, what's the law concernin' holes?

MAGISTRATE: The . . . the . . . law . . . concernin' *what*?

SOLOMON: Concernin' holes. Your Honour. What's the law concernin' holes?

MAGISTRATE: Oh yes, I see . . . concernin' holes. Well now, Solomon, that's not an easy question to answer. You see, there's
no special law about holes, any more than there's a special
law about pipes or tobacco, or . . . splitting knives. But there's
a law about stealing, and a man mustn't steal anything from
another man, including holes.

SOLOMON: But, Your Honour . . .

MAGISTRATE: Yes?

SOLOMON: How can a man steal a hole?

MAGISTRATE: What do you mean, how can a man steal a hole?

SOLOMON: I mean, Your Honour, a hole is nothin' . . . it's just . . .
well . . . it's just . . . a hole.

LIGE: Your Honour.

MAGISTRATE: Yes, Skipper Lige?

LIGE: He says a hole is nothin'.

MAGISTRATE: Yes, Skipper Lige?

LIGE: Well, Your Honour, I'm tellin' you he'd soon find out a
hole was something if he had to chop it, instead of takin'
someone else's . . . I'm tellin' you . . .

MAGISTRATE: Order, now. Uncle Solomon, I'm goin' to rule that a
hole is something, considering the fact that it took Skipper
Lige a long time to cut it. Any other questions?

SOLOMON: Why, yes, Your Honour. Why don't Skipper Lige produce the stolen goods . . . the goods he says were stolen?
Who's got 'em? I haven't got 'em.

(Music)

GRAMPA: Well, that started another argument, and Skipper Lige
had to be cautioned again not to lose his temper in Court.
Some of us began to get worried. There was Skipper Lige,
honest as the daylight, losin' his temper and makin' a bad
impression, while Uncle Solomon was lookin' as innercent as
a whitecoat.

Skipper Lige contended he couldn't produce the stolen
goods because they had gone out to sea when the ice broke
up and moved off.

Uncle Sol contended that the holes hadn't gone to sea. The
ice might've, but the holes hadn't. He argued that the holes

were only spots of open water, and that they were still up in the Inlet, exactly where Skipper Lige had cut 'em, although, as Uncle Sol was honest enough to admit . . .

(Sounds from courtroom)

SOLOMON: *(Pause)* 'Course, Your Honour, there's no ice around their edges, now.

(Music)

GRAMPA: Magistrate Kettle looked puzzled for a minute, but then he noticed it was half-past twelve, so he adjourned Court 'till two o'clock, and we went home to dinner. But, we . . . were . . . worried.

(Music)

Well, I gobbled my bite o'dinner in a hurry, and went over to Skipper Lige's, to give him a bit of encouragement. There were several fellows there, includin' Phineas Prior, the lay-reader in our church. Skipper Lige was too mad to eat his dinner.

SUSIE: Now, Lige, eat your dinner.

LIGE: No, Soos, I don't want dinner. I want my rights. Skipper Phineas, what in the world has come over Skipper Bob Kettle? By this time, he should've had Solomon Noddy sentenced to jail, or bound to the Peace, or something . . .

PHINEAS: Now, Lige, be patient. Skipper Bob is only doin' his duty. After all, Uncle Sol is a British subject, and the law's got to give him a chance to prove his point.

LIGE: His point! And what about me provin' my point?

SUSIE: Oh, you men! Always wantin' to prove your points. That's what's wrong with the world. Pig-headed men tryin' to prove their points. The Boers were tryin' to prove their point, and we were tryin' to prove our point. That's why we had that awful war. Eat your dinner, Lige.

PHINEAS: Right now, Solomon Noddy is like a Psalm says. He's flourishin' . . . flourishin' like the green bay-tree. But you watch how his leaf'll wither and his flower'll fade when Skipper Bob turns on him. In other words, Skipper Lige, you'll get to windard of him yet.

SUSIE: Finish your dinner Lige, it's time you were getting back to Court.

(Music
Sounds of courtroom)

MAGISTRATE: Order in the Court. Before we proceed, I want to say I've considered Uncle Solomon's last point, and I'm going to rule, that you can't have holes unless there's edges around them. Consequently, the holes we're talking about are no longer there. Proceed with your questions, Uncle Solomon.

SOLOMON: Your Honour, wasn't these holes abandoned?

MAGISTRATE: Were they, Skipper Lige?

LIGE: Abandoned. Why I didn't get a chance to abandon 'em. I didn't even get a chance to use 'em.

SOLOMON: How was I to know that?

LIGE: 'Twas easy for him to know the holes were fresh cut, Your Honour. Besides, there was the tobaccy stains around on the ice.

MAGISTRATE: Tobaccy stains?

LIGE: Yes, Your Honour.

MAGISTRATE: Rich, dark brown colours?

LIGE: That's right, Your Honour.

MAGISTRATE: I see, I see. Not faded and washed-out looking?

LIGE: No, Your Honour. Right fresh-lookin'.

MAGISTRATE: *(Up)* I think Skipper Lige is right on that point. I can't rule that the holes were abandoned.

SOLOMON: *(Pause)* Your Honour, I've got one more question.

MAGISTRATE: Yes, Uncle Solomon?

SOLOMON: Can a man steal anything if he don't move it from where he found it?

MAGISTRATE: Er . . . not very well.

SOLOMON: Well then, that clears me. I didn't shift those holes an inch from where I found them.

LIGE: You didn't shift 'em. You couldn't shift 'em. That's why you didn't shift 'em. If you could've, you'd have slung 'em over your shoulder and run off . . .

MAGISTRATE: Order, Skipper Lige . . .

SOLOMON: Your Honour, whether I didn't shift 'em because I couldn't or because I wouldn't, don't make a pin's worth of difference. Point is, I didn't shift 'em.

MAGISTRATE: Ah . . . Hmmmm . . . the court will now have a short recess, to consider judgement.

(Music
    Sounds of courtroom)

Order. The Court is now ready to give judgement. Solomon Noddy, stand up.

The court finds that what you did was wrong. But you did not steal the holes. You used them without having any right to, and so you committed a trespass. We could make another case of this, but it's a pauper's case anyway, with no court costs being charged to anyone. So while I'm here, I'll finish it. Solomon Noddy, you've committed a trespass on Skipper Lige's holes. What do you say for yourself?

SOLOMON: A trespass, Your Honour? Then, I can go free?

MAGISTRATE: What makes you think that?

SOLOMON: Well, Your Honour, Skipper Lige sets himself up as a God-fearin' man, I take it he'll "forgive those that trespass again' him."

MAGISTRATE: Will you do that, Skipper Lige?

LIGE: Do what, Your Honour?

MAGISTRATE: Forgive Uncle Sol that trespassed again' you?

LIGE: After he pays me damages, I'll forgive him.

SOLOMON: Can't get damages out of a man that can't pay, any more than you can get blood out of a turnip or a shirt off a naked man.

MAGISTRATE: Here's some damages you can pay, Solomon, and the Court orders you to cut two holes for Skipper Lige next winter in exactly the same place as you found his two holes. Is that clear?

SOLOMON: I have to cut two holes for Skipper Lige next winter in exactly the same place?

MAGISTRATE: Yes.

SOLOMON: Yes, Your Honour. Your Honour, may I make a charge against Skipper Lige?

MAGISTRATE: A charge? What for?

SOLOMON: He called me a hangashore.

MAGISTRATE: He had a very good reason to. Charge dismissed, and Court is closed.

SOLOMON: Your Honour, one more question. Nobody can say I stole the holes? Nobody can call me a thief? Eh?

MAGISTRATE: That's right, Uncle Sol. Nobody got the right to call you a thief.

LIGE: But there's one thing I will call him. Your Honour, I'll call him a hangashore.

MAGISTRATE: *(Fast)* Court's closed.

(Music)

GRAMPA: And so, that was the end of the court work, and the end of the trouble between Sol and Lige . . . for the time bein'. Skipper Lige went home figurin' he had proved his point, and he ate his warmed-over dinner with a good appetite, while as for the rest of us . . . opinions were divided. Some thought

Solomon Noddy got off too easy, while others figured there wasn't much else the Law could do. One thing we were all determined on, Solomon was goin' to cut them two holes next winter for Skipper Lige's herrin' net. And so, the summer passed . . . and the fall.

Then, along aroun' the middle of December, we had a frosty snap for about two days and the Inlet froze over, with between two and three inches of ice. Next mornin' it turned mild, and the ice thawed out and drove off-shore. That was the day Phineas Prior ran into Skipper Lige Bartle, and he was fit to be tied.

LIGE: Do you know what that hangashore has gone and done?

PHINEAS: What hangashore, Skipper Lige?

LIGE: Why, Solomon Noddy, that's who.

PHINEAS: What's he gone and done, this time?

LIGE: Why, yesterday, when the ice was just strong enough to bear him up, he went out on the Inlet and cut two holes, and had his boy Jethro with him for witness. Now he's braggin' that he's done all the Law ordered him to do and he's finished with it.

PHINEAS: Your two holes?

LIGE: Yes. My two holes.

PHINEAS: And now they're gone . . . melted?

LIGE: Yeah, gone.

PHINEAS: And what're you goin' to do, Skipper Lige? Are you goin' to have the law on him again?

LIGE: What's the use? No, I'm goin' to give it up for a bad job. I'm goin' to listen to Soos' advice for once in my life.

PHINEAS: Why? What does Soos say?

LIGE: Soos says, leave him alone, that not even the law can do anything to a hangashore.

GRAMPA: Well, perhaps Skipper Lige was right. Perhaps the law couldn't do anything with a hangashore like Uncle Solomon. But me and Phineas Prior thought different. Or anyway, we figured if the law couldn't do anything, we would. Uncle Sol'd do worse next time. But what could be done?

Well, about the middle of March when most people were puttin' out herrin' nets again, I got an idea, and over I went to put the proposition to Skipper Phineas. He heard me out. Then he said — kinda shocked . . .

PHINEAS: My goodness gracious, Skipper Ben. Surely you're not suggestin' I should help you in a scheme like that. Why —

'twould be — 'twould be agen' the law. Takin' Solomon
Noddy's net out of his net loft in the middle of the night.

GRAMPA: But fair exchange is no robbery, and we'd be puttin'
Skipper Lige's net in its place.

PHINEAS: Makes no difference, Skipper Ben. Uncle Sol is doin'
wrong, but it's not the likes of you and me to set it right.
Besides, like I've said before, "the ungodly shall fall into his
own pit."

GRAMPA: So he will, Skipper Phineas, so he will. But as long as
he's goin' to fall into the pit anyway, what's wrong with you
and me givin' him a — a bit of a push.

PHINEAS: *(Brightened)* Sounds reasonable enough. But I'm afraid I
can't do it. Awful thing if we were caught doin' it, especially
me — man in my position — you know — position — church — you
know . . .

GRAMPA: Not a chance in ten thousand of gettin' caught.

PHINEAS: Sure of that? Um! Alright, then. I'll help you. *(Chuckles)*
Givin' the ungodly a push. Christian duty — almost.

(Pause)

GRAMPA: So later that night me and Skipper Phineas took Uncle
Sol's herrin' net out of his net loft and put Skipper Lige's herrin' net in its place. Next mornin' we replaced Uncle Sol's net
and watched from the hill while Uncle Sol cut his holes and
set what he thought was his own net. Then we walked out
alongside him. I let Skipper Phineas do the talkin'.

PHINEAS: Good morning — good morning — Uncle Sol.

SOLOMON: Mornin'.

PHINEAS: Well, Uncle Sol, we're pleased to see you've obeyed the
law.

SOLOMON: Eh? What's that?

PHINEAS: You've done better than obey the law. You've done your
Christian duty. All the law said was to cut the holes — and
here you've gone and set Skipper Lige's net for him. Like the
Psalm says: "Skipper Lige's cup runneth over."

SOLOMON: Skipper Lige's net?

PHINEAS: Yes. Look at his initials on the buoy.

SOLOMON: Ye-es. So I see. Hey! Where's my net.

PHINEAS: Your *net*. Oh. Back in your net loft. We just saw it
there.

SOLOMON: You did eh? And what were you doing' in my net loft?

PHINEAS: Oh, nothin' special. Me and Skipper Ben here dropped
in to say good mornin', and I said to Skipper Ben — 'Skipper

Ben,' said I, 'Uncle Sol can't be gone to set his own herrin' net 'cause there it is.' And—there it was.

GRAMPA: Yep, there it was.

SOLOMON: Oh! And did you say to Skipper Ben or did Skipper Ben say to you just how Lige Bartle's net was the only net in my loft when I went there first thing this mornin'?

PHINEAS: Well no. But we must be goin' now. *(Fading)* We'll tell Skipper Lige you set his net for him.

SOLOMON: *(Up)* Yes, and you can tell him I'm goin' to unset it right now.

PHINEAS: *(Fade up)* Oh! Then me and Skipper Ben'll have to wait around.

SOLOMON: Wait around? What for?

GRAMPA: Because as respectable citizens—and as Christians, it's our duty to report breaches of the law.

SOLOMON: What breaches? What law?

PHINEAS: Law says Skipper Lige's holes. Initials says Skipper Lige's net. Breach of law for a man to take another man's net out of that other man's holes.

SOLOMON: I believe you two changed our nets last night. If I thought . . .

GRAMPA: Now, now, Uncle Sol. Serious charge against two men— and one of 'em a lay-reader. We might make you prove it. Something else you'd have to prove, too.

SOLOMON: Er—what?

PHINEAS: How come you have Skipper Lige's net in your possession?

SOLOMON: Yeah!

PHINEAS: Unless, of course, you took it to set for him.

SOLOMON: Yeah!

PHINEAS: It's like the Psalm says, Uncle Sol: "How often doth the wicked man get tangled in his own nets. The righteous man always ends up to wind'ard of the ungodly."

GRAMPA: And Uncle Sol turned and went home. I suppose deep inside he was just as bad as ever, but he had learned one lesson. It's easy to be a hangashore in a place like Pigeon Inlet, but it's hard to get away with it.

AFTERWORD

1. How would you explain the word "hangashore" to a friend? What current expressions have a similar meaning? Do you know someone who might be considered a hangashore? Describe that person to a partner.

2. The characters in this radio play are representative of people in the outports of Newfoundland more than fifty years ago. Write a character sketch of a typical resident of your community. The character might be real or imaginary, or a combination of both. You might include a drawing or cartoon of the character with your written description.

3. Newspaper headlines attempt to tell a story in one line. Create two newspaper headlines about the trial. One should be serious and the other amusing or sensational, as the headlines in tabloids often are. With a group, present a tableau to illustrate one of your headlines.

4. If you were the magistrate at the trial, what sentence would you hand down? Find specific lines in the play that lead you to your decision. Discuss your judgement with other members of your group. As a group, describe what sentence you think Solomon should be given, and write the magistrate's verdict.

5. a) Was Lige right to forget about Solomon's trick of cutting the new holes in thin ice? In a group, discuss whether it is better to ignore a trick or to respond in some way.

b) Susie says, "Oh, you men! Always wantin' to prove your points. That's what's wrong with the world. Pig-headed men tryin' to prove their points." What do you think she means? Do you agree with her? Explain your response to your group.

c) Summarize your group's conclusions and compare them with the conclusions reached by other groups.

6. What do you think Lige's reaction was when he heard about the trick that Grampa Walcott and Phineas played on Solomon? Improvise a scene in which Grampa Walcott and Phineas tell Lige about their trick.

7. In a group, select a scene or part of a scene to which you could add background sound effects. Decide what sound effects, including music, you think would work well in the scene. Rehearse the lines until you feel comfortable with them and then tape the scene, blending the dialogue and the sound effects. Play your tape and ask the audience to offer feedback on how successful you have been in conveying mood through sound effects.

8. Use the structure of *The Hangashore* as a model for dramatizing your own anecdote or joke. Be sure to select a story that can be told through dialogue between two or more characters. Introduce the story by using a narrator to establish the situation. The narrator might or might not be one of the actors in the drama.

9. Ted Russell wrote this play to record the way of life in the Newfoundland outports as it was in the first half of the 1900s. The newspaper clipping below describes the attempt of one woman, Wendy Wickwire, to preserve stories of the Similkameen Indians of British Columbia before they are lost forever.

Here's to You, Mr. Robinson
by Ian Robbins
She (Wickwire) was a young graduate student from Nova Scotia. He was an old native of the Similkameen Valley.

On August 24th, 1977, they met in the sweltering heat of Hedley, B.C. He started telling his stories; she started her Uher reel-to-reel tape recorder rolling.

"I tell stories for 21 hours or more when I get started," he told her, "Kind of hard to believe, but I do, because this [is] my job. I'm a storyteller."

Hundreds of stories later, Wendy Wickwire has transcribed 89-year-old Harry Robinson's stories in *Write It On Your Heart: The Epic World of An Okanagan Storyteller.*

Wendy Wickwire captured *oral history* — stories of the past as they were remembered and told by Harry Robinson. Create your own oral history: tape-record the memories of an older person who wants to talk about what life was like growing up in the first half of this century, or about moving to a new country. No rehearsal is necessary; just record the words as they are spoken. Your class may want to collect the stories together into an anthology on tape.

▼ ▼   *INTRODUCTION TO:*

Letters

Dennis Koenig
An episode from the M*A*S*H televison series

"In the beginning, not everyone knew what our show could
become. We came to tell jokes and stayed to touch the edges
of art."
Alan Alda

*A*S*H began as a bestselling novel by Richard
Hooker. It was transformed by filmmaker Robert
Altman into a blockbuster movie. Finally, it resur-
faced as an enormously popular CBS television series
that ran for eleven seasons and won hundreds of
awards and the hearts of millions of viewers around
the globe. When the final two-and-a-half-hour show
was aired on February 28, 1983, about seventy-five
percent of North Americans watching TV that night
were tuned to M*A*S*H.
   M*A*S*H dramatized the lives of people working in a Mobile
Army Surgical Hospital just miles from the front during the
Korean War. As one commentator put it, "M*A*S*H became
famous for its ability to deliver a laugh and a cry in the same
show, all the while convincing its audience that General William
Tecumseh Sherman was right all along: 'War is hell.' "
   Many different writers contributed episodes for M*A*S*H over
the years. *Letters* was written by Dennis Koenig, an executive
story editor for the television series.

GETTING STARTED

1. Imagine that you and a partner are doctors at a field hospital
in a war zone. How do you feel about the soldiers who are
brought to your hospital? What happens to the soldiers when
they are well enough to leave? Discuss these questions, and

then roleplay a conversation in which the two of you talk about your work.

2. Write one rule that you think people should use to guide their behaviour. Write a second rule that is exactly the opposite of the first. Share your rules with a group of classmates. Which rules are dramatized more often on television? Discuss whether television focuses mainly on positive or negative values.

3. If you received a letter from a grade four student asking you what it is like to be a teenager, what answer would you give? Make a list of incidents you could use to illustrate your answer; then draft a short reply to the student's letter.

4. What is your favourite half-hour sitcom? Why do you like it? How would you describe the kind of humour you find in the show? Survey your class to compile a Top Ten Sitcoms table. How many of the shows are current, and how many are reruns?

TELEVISION SCRIPT

Letters

Dennis Koenig
An episode from the M*A*S*H televison series

CHARACTERS

HAWKEYE—*a surgeon with a sharp sense of humour*
B.J.—*his best friend, also a surgeon*
CHARLES—*another surgeon, with a sour disposition*
POTTER—*the senior officer of the M*A*S*H unit, grumpy but soft-hearted*
HOT LIPS—*the chief of the nursing staff*
KLINGER—*Potter's administrative assistant*
MULCAHY—*a priest*
ROSIE—*a Korean woman who runs the camp's bar*
KO TOI—*an employee of Rosie's bar*
DR. BREUER—*the head of the local missionary school*
CAPTAIN WILLIAM BAINBRIDGE—*an Army lawyer*
SOLDIER—*a patient*
NURSE
KWAN LI—*an eight-year-old Korean girl*
OFFSTAGE VOICES

ACT ONE
Fade in
Under titles we see:

1. INT. MESS TENT. MORNING.
(The flaps are down. We hear rain outside. Various utensils are set up to catch water that leaks in. Two people enter wearing rain gear. They are wet and cold. They remove their hats, cross to the coffee, passing Hawkeye, B.J., Potter, Charles, Hot Lips *and* Mulcahy *sitting at a table bundled up. Their breakfasts are before them, but no one is eating much. Instead, all are visibly despondent.)*

HAWKEYE: *(Glumly)* I don't want to say it's wet outside but on my way over here I saw a duck carrying an umbrella.

B.J.: *(Shivering)* Must've been cold duck.

POTTER: Aw, four days of drizzles ain't diddly. One time in WW the First it poured cats and dachsunds for thirty-seven days straight. The whole platoon went skinny dippin' in the trenches.

CHARLES: Colonel, I find no humor in either abominable weather or abominable stories.

HOT LIPS: Everything stinks. That dismal grey sky is a perfect match for my mood . . . *(Pushing away her tray)* . . . and my breakfast.

MULCAHY: *(Angrily)* Especially the breakfast. Serving cold cuts in this weather is a devilish deed, indeed.

(Klinger enters carrying a large satchel. He's wet but cheerfully singing.)

KLINGER:

ZIPPITY DOO DAH,

ZIPPITY AAY

MY, OH, MY WHAT A WONDERFUL DAY

Ain't this weather aces? It reminds me of a summer Sunday in Toledo.

HOT LIPS: Stick it in your galoshes, tent nose.

HAWKEYE: Confucius say, 'Man who sings in the rain better be Gene Kelly.'

KLINGER: No need for rancid remarks. This is your wet letter day. *(Sets satchel on bench; opens it handing B.J. letter)* Captain Big Boots.

B.J.: *(Pleased)* From Mill Valley. Great, this'll make my day. *(He opens the letter and reads.)*

POTTER: Got anything for me, Klinger? Mildred promised to send me some Clovereen brand salve for these barkin' bunions.

KLINGER: Negative, Hoppy.

B.J.: *(Holding up his letter)* Wonderful, I have a dental checkup . . . yesterday.

KLINGER: And winner of this week's Truss Award is none other than our own eye of the Hawk.

(Klinger pulls a very large, very stuffed manila envelope out of his sack, hands it to Hawkeye.)

B.J.: Looks like a Dear John letter from the Rockettes.

HAWKEYE: *(Checks return address)* No, it's from Amy Clark. A friend of mine who's a teacher back in Crabapple Cove.

(He opens the envelope.)
CHARLES: Finishing fourth grade in your spare time?
(Hawkeye *is reading a letter.*)
HAWKEYE: *(Reading)* 'You said in your last letter how boring it can get there . . . So I thought it might be nice for my whole fourth grade class to write you.' *(Looks up)* We get to answer them.
MULCAHY: Well, well, this could be just the ticket out of our black and blue funk.
(Everyone but Charles *agrees, and* Hawkeye *begins passing out letters.)*
HAWKEYE: Okay, don't crowd, plenty for everybody. There must be forty letters here. Klinger, Margaret, Colonel . . .
POTTER: Mucho beaucoup.
HAWKEYE: Beej, Father, oh, here's one in crayon. Obviously for Charles.
CHARLES: Ah, you are a wag. But I do not need to write letters to communicate with children. I have you for that, Pierce.
(Charles *rises, turns to go.* Hawkeye *calls after.)*
HAWKEYE: That is an insult and you'll answer for it at recess.
(Hot Lips *is reading a letter. She laughs.)*
HOT LIPS: Oh, this is cute. Here's a boy who thinks MASH people sit around all day making potatoes.
KLINGER: *(Reading)* And this half-pint asks if all Army people have tattoos.
B.J.: You want to field that one, Margaret?
MULCAHY: *(Looks up from his letter)* Oh, dear. Here's a girl who wonders if I've saved many lives. A doctor should answer this.
HAWKEYE: Oh, no. My ground rules are no stealing, selling or swapping letters. You answer the ones you get.
MULCAHY: But I have never saved a life.
POTTER: Come on, Padre. Don't tell me you forgot about Irving.
MULCAHY: Irving? Oh, yes. *Irving.*
(Mulcahy *smiles. He takes a notebook and pencil from his pocket and begins to write.)*
MULCAHY: *(Voice over)* 'Dear Stacy, Although I am not a doctor, it can be truthfully said I did indeed save a life . . .'
Cut to:

2. *EXT. ROSIE'S BAR. DAY.*
(It is a bright, sunny day. Mulcahy *is walking up the road, passing Rosie's as he hears:)*

ROSIE: *(OS)* I've had it with you, Irving. This is a respectable place.
(Rosie throws back the drape and promptly 86's a small dog which lands at Mulcahy's feet.)
And *stay* out. *(Notices Mulcahy)* Oh, hello, Father.
MULCAHY: *(Surprised)* Hello, Rosie. Why are you giving this cute pup the bum's rush?
ROSIE: Because Irving is a lush.
MULCAHY: *(Surprised)* Oh? Yes, he does seem to be reeling a bit.
(Mulcahy kneels next to Irving, catches a whiff of his breath and recoils.)
And his breath is pure hellfire.
ROSIE: All the time he begs for booze. He climbs on the bar and licks it dry. And the worst thing, when he's really bombed, he starts singing.
MULCAHY: You know, we had a dog like this back at the seminary. My he could suck up that sacramental wine.
ROSIE: Irving will drink anything. Worst are martinis. He spits olive pits on the floor.
MULCAHY: Rose, bring me a bottle of whiskey and a bowl.
ROSIE: Wouldn't you rather have a glass?
MULCAHY: No. I'm going to cure Irving the same way we cured that dog at the seminary. By letting him drink bowl after bowl till he's sick.
ROSIE: I think your brain's stuck in first gear, Father. But okay.
(Calls out in Korean) Ko Toi, bring cheap booze and a bowl.
MULCAHY: *(Digs out money)* How much do I owe you?
ROSIE: Never mind. I'll just put it on Irving's tab.
(Ko Toi appears, hands Rosie a bottle and a bowl. Seeing the bottle, Irving barks eagerly.)
That dog has no pride.
(Mulcahy takes the bowl, sets it on the ground and pours booze into it.)
MULCAHY: There you are, Irving. Bottoms up.
(Irving eagerly starts drinking the booze.)
My, my, he is a little rummy, isn't he?
ROSIE: Yeah. Reminds me of my first husband.
Cut to:

3. EXT. COMPOUND DAY.
(We are on the faces of various M*A*S*H personnel as we hear Mulcahy speaking.)

MULCAHY: Yesterday, Irving drank till he got sick as a dog. And if all's gone well, he should have an intense aversion to alcohol, as well as one doozie of a hangover.
(During the above, we have widened to reveal they are looking at Mulcahy *who is kneeling next to* Irving. *He pours booze from a bottle into a bowl.)*
Actually, he's having a little of the hair of the man that bit him.
(He laughs and sets the bowl down. Irving *turns and runs away. All cheer.)*
Cut to:

4. INT. MESS TENT. DAY.
(As the rain continues, Mulcahy *writes in his notebook.)*
MULCAHY: *(Voice over)* . . . So, Irving was smart enough to go on the wagon for good, Stacy. If people only had the horse sense dogs do. Yours in Christ, Francis J. Mulcahy, S.J.
*(*Mulcahy *looks around. The Mess Tent is now empty. Suddenly a large drop of water splatters on his letter. As he looks up:)*
Cut to:

5. ANGLE ON A LEAK IN A CANVAS ROOF.
(As the camera tilts down, we reveal:)

6. INT. "THE SWAMP". DAY.
(Drops are falling into an inverted helmet placed next to Charles *who is reading a book.* Hawkeye *and* B.J. *are there discussing their letters. The flaps are down as the rain continues.)*
B.J.: *(Points to letter)* Oh, yeah? Well, my boy's gonna be a big league pitcher. Heck, just the other day he hurled a forty-eight hitter.
HAWKEYE: *(Points to letter)* That's nothing. My kid definitely has the makings of a U.S. Senator. This letter goes on for five pages and says absolutely nothing.
*(*Charles *looks up, irritated.)*
CHARLES: Gentlemen, while your stunted minds are understandably fascinated by prepubescent memoirs, I maintain that the people who put fences around playgrounds knew what they were doing. Pity they had to include gates.
HAWKEYE: The only thing Charles remembers fondly from his childhood is his hair.
*(*Hawkeye *turns to another letter and opens it.)*

B.J.: *(Opening another letter)* Come on, Chas baby, these are cute . . . listen . . . *(Reads)* 'Dear Doctors, you live a great life. I'm jealous of you.'

CHARLES: *(Sharply)* Jealous? He's jealous?

B.J.: *(Continuing to read)* 'You guys get to camp out every night and eat real Army food. Boy, you're lucky. I . . .'

CHARLES: *(Apoplectic)* Wha . . . I . . . give me that.
(Snaps his book shut and grabs the letter)
Camp out, eh?
(Grabs a pen and pad, begins writing)
My dear diminutive correspondent, Your misinformation is only exceeded by your . . . *(Glances at letter, squints)* . . . atrocious grammar.

B.J.: Leave it to Charles to be the world's first poison pen pal.
(Getting no reaction from Hawkeye, B.J. turns to him. Hawkeye is staring at a letter he is reading.)
Bad handwriting, Hawk?

HAWKEYE: *(Looks up)* No, it's all too clear. Listen. *(Reads)* 'Doctor, My brother was a soldier in Korea. He got hurt, but some doctors fixed him up so he could go back and fight some more. Then he got killed. Now I'll never see Keith again. You doctors just make people better so they can end up dead. I don't like you at all. Signed, Ronnie Hawkins.' *(Looks up)* What do I say to this kid?

B.J.: I don't know.

HAWKEYE: This isn't fiction. We've all sent kids back to the line and had them end up dead. What the hell do I say to this kid?
(Hawkeye stares at the letter.)
Cut to:

7. INT. KLINGER'S OFFICE. DAY.
(The rain still pours on, and we're aware of several leaks, with pots and assorted receptacles strategically placed to catch them. Klinger is at his typewriter, just finishing typing. We hear a clap of thunder.)

KLINGER: Ah, I'm so homesick.
(He pulls the paper out of the typewriter and begins to read what he's written. As his reading continues, he notices an additional leak above the file cabinet. During the following, he pulls the top drawer open, removes the folders and places them safely aside, and uses the open drawer to catch the rain, reading all the while.)

'Dear Freddie, I understand your problem and suggest in straight pool you always play safe on the first shot. As far as your question about Army pay, well, your Dad probably gives you a bigger allowance. In fact, I've always got my eye out for ways to supplement my income. For example . . .'
Cut to:

8. *EXT. KLINGER'S OFFICE. DAY.*
(Another sunny day. Potter *approaches the office, stops when he sees a large square container, covered by a sheet, next to the door. Chattering noises come from under the sheet. Puzzled,* Potter *removes the cloth to see a cage, on a stand. In the cage are two little furry animals.)*
POTTER: *(Screams)* Klinger!
(Klinger *rushes in.)*
KLINGER: You clamored, sir?
POTTER: Just uno questione, Soldierboy. *(Points to cage, yells)* What in the hell are these hairy rats doing here?
KLINGER: Sir, these are *not* rats. They are chinchillas. My key to a life of decadent riches. Surely you note the luxuriant pelts.
POTTER: Well, a rat's a rat, even if it's wearin' a fur coat. What're they doing in this neck of the war?
KLINGER: I ordered them by mail, sir, along with business cards and stationery for . . . Klinger's Chinchilla Villa Breeding Farms.
POTTER: *(Disbelieving)* Breeding farms? *(Puts his arm around* Klinger) Look, son, you haven't had any sudden falls lately, have you? Perhaps a stray anvil grazed the old noodle?
KLINGER: Sir, I am of sound mind and body, and I'll soon be of sound wallet. As these chinches multiply so does my bankroll, and they're *very* affectionate, if you get my drift.
POTTER: *(Sniffs)* I get their drift. You sure they're not part skunk?
KLINGER: Granted, they are aromatic, sir, probably eat a lot of garlic. That's why I ordered a large supply of . . . *(Holds up a can)* Chinchilla No-smell.
POTTER: Well, I'm warning you, if my brogans meet up with just one chinchilla chip, it's the hanging tree for the whole clan . . . now . . .
(Charles *approaches, eyeing the cage.)*
CHARLES: Well, well, what have we here, the world's smallest zoo?
POTTER: He calls 'em chinchillers.

KLINGER: I call them a gold mine. Now if you'll let me cover this cage, they're giving each other that look that only lovers share.

CHARLES: *(Peering into the cage)* Am I to understand you plan to breed these creatures, Klinger?

KLINGER: Well, you know, birds do it, etcetera. Wish I had a little soft music, for Romeo and Juliet.

CHARLES: Romeo and Mercutio's more like it.

KLINGER: Mercoosho. Who's she?

CHARLES: He, my dear fifteen-watt friend. Having done extensive lab work with rodents, I can state categorically these are two male 'chinchillers.'

KLINGER: Males?

(Klinger *is crestfallen.* Charles *and* Potter *both attempt to squelch a laugh, but failing, quickly walk off.* Klinger *peers into the cage, glumly.)*

(To the chincillas) Well, guys, let's go find us some good times.

Cut to:

9. INT. KLINGER'S OFFICE. DAY.

*(*Klinger *is back at the typewriter.)*

KLINGER: *(Voice over)* . . . But undaunted, I cut the letterhead off my Chinchilla Villa stationery and am now selling it dirt cheap . . .

(As a raindrop hits him, Klinger, *with great aplomb, reaches for an umbrella nearby, holds it over his head and goes back to typing with one hand.)*

. . . Maybe you'd be interested in some. It's perfectly square, you'll never write on the wrong end . . .

(He continues typing, as we:)

Cut to:

10. INT. HOT LIPS' TENT. CLOSE ON DOORWAY. DAY.

(Water is seeping through. Widen to reveal Hot Lips, *in robe and boots, putting a towel under the opening to keep water out. During the above, she is reading a letter she holds in her hand.)*

YOUNG BOY: *(Voice over)* 'Dear Masher, I just had my tonsils out which wasn't so bad because I got to eat a lot of ice cream. Anyway, I became good friends with the doctors and nurses. Do you ever make friends with the patients there?'

(Hot Lips *discontinues her towelling and thinks about this.*)
Cut to:

11. INT. PRE-OP. DAY.
(Hot Lips, *in fatigues, is talking to a nice-looking young* Soldier *who's lying on a table. She is smiling, holding his hand.*)
SOLDIER: And there's this great piece of land I've had my eye on since I was a kid. Sent my dad some money I saved and he put a down payment on it for me.
HOT LIPS: I'm sure you'll make a wonderful farmer, Frank.
SOLDIER: Yeah, and I'll get some chickens and goats, maybe a cow or two. I can hardly wait.
(*Another* Nurse *approaches.*)
NURSE: Dr. Pierce would like to talk to you, Major.
HOT LIPS: *(To* Soldier*)* I'll be right back.
SOLDIER: *(Kidding)* I'll be counting the minutes.
(Hot Lips *smiles, crosses to* Hawkeye *and* B.J. *who are conferring in the corner of the room.*)
HOT LIPS: What did you find out?
HAWKEYE: He's not gonna make it.
HOT LIPS: *(Shocked)* What? But he's feeling fine.
B.J.: Margaret, we just went over the X-rays. His spinal cord's severed, he can't feel a thing.
HAWKEYE: He's inoperable.
HOT LIPS: *(Softly)* Oh, no.
(*She looks back at the* Soldier.)
B.J.: He might last another few hours, but there's nothing we can do for him.
(Hot Lips *closes her eyes, trying to accept the thought.*)
HAWKEYE: I'm sorry, Margaret.
B.J.: You must be exhausted. Why don't you get some sleep?
HOT LIPS: *(Resolved)* No. I'll stay with him.
(Hot Lips *takes a deep breath, forces a smile on her face, turns and crosses back to the* Soldier. Hot Lips *taps the* Nurse *on the shoulder. She moves off.*)
Well, that wasn't long, was it?
SOLDIER: Can't live without me, eh?
HOT LIPS: I'm a sucker for a handsome face.
(*The* Soldier *smiles as* Hot Lips *sits and takes his hand.*)
SOLDIER: Say, let me tell you about my girl. We're going to get married when I get back home. We grew up together. She's the prettiest girl I ever saw, next to you, of course.

(During the above, the camera has moved in slowly to a closeup of Hot Lips, *a rigid smile on her face.)*
Cut to:

12. INT. HOT LIPS' TENT. DAY.
(The rain continues. We are on pad and pencil as Hot Lips *is writing. During the following, camera slowly widens to reveal* Hot Lips *near tears as she writes.)*
HOT LIPS: *(Voice over)* Dear Jimmy. Yes, I do get very close to the people we treat. In fact, there are some patients I don't think I'll ever forget. *(Pauses for a beat, then)* So, you had your tonsils out . . .
(She continues writing, as we:)
Fade out

ACT TWO
Fade in

13. INT. "THE SWAMP". DAY.
(It's still raining. Hawkeye *is at his bunk writing, wadded-up paper is all around him.* B.J. *is reading a letter,* Charles *is dictating into his wire recorder.)*
CHARLES: . . . And in conclusion, Peter, I think it's perfectly normal for you to want to dress like a grownup. In fact, I might suggest that you take your father's best suit down to the tailor shop and have it altered to fit your little body to a tee. *(Chuckles evilly)* My, my, isn't it fun to pass on one's wisdom to the younger generation?
B.J.: *(Looks up)* How come you're not using your pen, Charles? Run out of venom?
CHARLES: My dear Hunnicutt, I prefer to record my brilliant insights and then delegate the typing to someone on the same intellectual level as these fourth graders. Suddenly, one Maxwell Klinger springs to mind.
(Hawkeye rips the paper off the pad he's writing on, wads it up and throws it down angrily, as B.J. *looks at him.)*
HAWKEYE: Damn! I'm not responsible for this kid's brother dying.
B.J.: Hawk, you got a toughie. If you need any help, I'm in the book under 'all ears.'
HAWKEYE: *(As he begins to write)* No, no, I'll handle this myself. You just answer your own letter.
*(*B.J. *turns to his letter.* Hawkeye *rips the new page out of his*

pad, wads it up and throws it down.)
Damn!
(As he resumes writing, B.J. looks at Hawkeye, then begins writing his own letter.)
B.J.: *(Voice over)* Dear Louis. Yes, becoming a doctor usually requires a lot of training. But every rule has an exception.
Cut to:

14. EXT. COMPOUND. DAY.
(Bright and sunny. A jeep pulls into the compound, stops and a Captain William Bainbridge *alights. He grabs two bags out of the back of the jeep and waves the driver off as* Klinger *exits his office and approaches.)*
KLINGER: Sir, welcome to Death Valley East. I am M. Klinger, Chief Clerk and bottle washer.
(As he takes the Captain's *bags)*
Please, no tipping for individual favors, sir. Just one lump sum when you leave. By the way, who are you?
BAINBRIDGE: Captain William Bainbridge here on temporary assignment.
KLINGER: Of course you are. I personally requested a replacement for Major Winchester. He's at a four day seminar in Tokyo.
BAINBRIDGE: I was told I'd be here a week.
KLINGER: Well, the Major will need three days to get over his hangover. Hey, there's a couple of your colleagues. They've been anxiously awaiting your arrival.
(Indicates Hawkeye and B.J. who are passing nearby)
Sirs, sirs, I got the pinch-hitter you've been browbeating me for.
(Hawkeye and B.J. approach excitedly.)
This is Captain William Bainbridge.
BAINBRIDGE: Call me Bill.
(Hawkeye pumps his hand.)
HAWKEYE: You're an overdue Bill. I'm Hawkeye, this is B.J.
(B.J. effusively pumps Bainbridge's hand.)
B.J.: Hi. We sure can use a pair of helping hands.
(Bainbridge rubs the hand that has been so rigorously shook.)
BAINBRIDGE: Sorry, I've only got one left. Where can a guy get some food around here?
HAWKEYE: Nowhere. But the Mess Tent's that a way.
B.J.: Come on, we'll take you over. Klinger, sign in Captain Godsend. We'll seal and deliver him.

KLINGER: That's a yo.

(Klinger takes Bainbridge's travel orders as Hawkeye, B.J. and Bainbridge head towards the Mess Tent.)

B.J.: You know, we were betting HQ would lose our request and you'd never get here.

HAWKEYE: But they fouled up and handled everything perfectly. Says a lot for the power of positive incompetence.

BAINBRIDGE: Yeah, well I couldn't believe I was being sent to a MASH unit. Do you really get a lot of cases here?

HAWKEYE: We get cases by the gross, and unfortunately most of them are.

B.J.: Nothing's going on now, but we could get busy tonight.

BAINBRIDGE: Well, I make it a policy to keep regular office hours.

HAWKEYE: Regular hours? Ah, you are a babe in the war.

B.J.: Maybe you can do that at HQ, but here we get wounded around the clock.

(They are now approaching the Mess Tent.)

BAINBRIDGE: Wounded? Wait a minute. I don't go in for chasing ambulances. It's unethical.

B.J.: What?

(Hawkeye and B.J. look at each other.)

Are you afraid of what I'm afraid of?

HAWKEYE: I'm afraid so. *(To Bainbridge)* Uh, Bill, this might sound silly, but just exactly what line of work are you in?

BAINBRIDGE: Same as you. I'm a lawyer.

(Bainbridge enters the Mess Tent as Hawkeye and B.J. stare at each other.)

Cut to:

15. INT. O.R. DAY.

(We pan the length of O.R. It appears empty as we hear B.J.)

B.J.: *(Voice over)* That's right, the Army made a little boo-boo. After sending us a lawyer, we figured the next one would have to be an Indian Chief. So we just decided a little on-the-job training was in order.

(Now, as we get to the last table, we see Hawkeye and B.J. with Bainbridge, all in surgical gowns. Hawkeye is working on a patient. B.J. is showing Bainbridge how to assist.)

B.J.: Okay, Bill, now cut the sutures.

(Bainbridge does.)

BAINBRIDGE: How's that?

B.J.: It's a cut above average.

HAWKEYE: You're great with scissors. You could be a doctor. Or a barber.
(Hot Lips *approaches.*)
HOT LIPS: Doctors, this is most unprofessional. I must object.
B.J.: Objection overruled.
HAWKEYE: Calm down, Margaret, this lawyer is only here on a trial basis.
B.J.: Didn't you ever hear of someone practicing medicine?
(Hawkeye *steps back.*)
HAWKEYE: Anyway, this case is closed and the patient rests.
(B.J. *picks up a reflex mallet and hits it on the instrument table.*)
B.J.: O.R. is now adjourned.
Cut to:

16. INT. "THE SWAMP". DAY (RAIN).
(B.J. *is finishing his letter.*)
B.J.: *(Voice over as he reads)* 'So you see, Jimmy, you can join the Army and be anything you want. No matter what you really are. Sincerely, B.J. Hunnicutt.'
(During the above, B.J. casually reaches towards a full martini glass as if to take a drink. Instead, he merely draws it past his shoulder and deposits what is rain water into a larger pot which is under another leak. As he sets the glass back in its original spot, it catches a drop of rain.)
'P.S. Please excuse the square stationery. I borrowed it from our Company Clerk.' *(Smiles, turns)* Hey, Hawk, do you remember Bill Bainbridge, Doctor at Law?
(Looking at Hawkeye's *bunk, B.J. sees Hawkeye is gone. Only the pad and pencil and wads of paper remain.)*
Cut to:

17. INT. MULCAHY'S TENT. DAY.
(Hawkeye, *dripping, stands before* Mulcahy.)
HAWKEYE: Essentially, he's accusing me of being a very large cog in the war machine, and I'm not sure he's wrong.
MULCAHY: So this letter has triggered a crisis of conscience for you.
HAWKEYE: A crisis of guilty conscience. I'm looking at myself through his eyes. And I don't like what I see. Will you help me out, and answer the letter, Father?
(Mulcahy *thinks for a long beat.*)

MULCAHY: All right, Hawkeye, I'll help you. By *not* writing the letter.
HAWKEYE: Huh?
MULCAHY: Well, you did say no trading.
HAWKEYE: Oh, come on, Father, this is serious.
MULCAHY: I'm quite serious. If this letter has made you aware of deep-rooted feelings, Hawkeye. Then it is *you* who must deal with them. If for no other reason than your own peace of mind.
HAWKEYE: Fine, but how?
MULCAHY: Perhaps in searching your soul for a response to this boy's letter you just might find those answers. Can you see that, Hawkeye?
HAWKEYE: Sure, I can. *(Paces some more)* But that doesn't make it any easier.
MULCAHY: Just remember you're not the only one who has sensitive letters to respond to. Listen to this. *(Picks up a letter, reads)* 'Dear MASH people, I'm writing this only because teacher's making me. Personally I'd rather be playing dodge ball 'cause this is really boring. Your friend, Mary Colonna.'
(Deadpan, Mulcahy *looks at* Hawkeye *who can't help but smile.)*
HAWKEYE: Thanks, Father, I needed that.
*(*Hawkeye *exits.)*
MULCAHY: *(As he writes)* 'Dear Mary, We'd all rather be playing dodge ball.'
Cut to:

18. *INT. POTTER'S TENT. DAY.*
(We see falling water. Pull back to reveal Potter *is pouring hot water into a pan. A box of epsom salts is nearby. With one toe he tests the water. Satisfied, he sits, places his feet in the water. With his other hand he holds a letter and nods as he is reading it.)*
POTTER: Aaah, nothing like toasting the tootsies.
(Having finished the letter, Potter *picks up pen and pad from his desk. He begins to write.)*
POTTER: *(Voice over)* Dear Danny, Hell, yes ... *(Scratches this out)* Heck, yes, sometimes we do get ants in our pants and you'd be surprised what little things will scare up interest. Why, just the other day ...
Cut to:

19. EXT. COMPOUND. TIGHT ON BASKETBALL HOOP. DAY.
(A shot swishes through the net. We pull back to see Potter *is idly taking free throws. He's wearing fatigue pants cut off below the knee, black, high-topped U.S. Keds and socks rolled down to meet the shoe tops. He retrieves the ball, and prepares to take another shot.* NOTE: *He shoots his free throws underhand. People are walking by.* Klinger *approaches, carrying some papers.)*
KLINGER: Good morning, Colonel Setshot, how goes the round ball?
POTTER: *(Turns to* Klinger*)* Aw, this game ain't been the same since they cut the bottom out of the peach basket.
(He takes aim again.)
KLINGER: Well, if I may call time out, these supply forms require your inimitable scrawl.
POTTER: *(Turns to* Klinger*)* See me in the locker room. I got me a run of fourteen straight free throws and I don't want to break my concentration.
(Potter turns and takes aim again.)
KLINGER: *(Shocked)* Do these ears deceive me? Did you say fourteen in a row?
POTTER: *(Turns to* Klinger, *impatient)* Sure, this is 'Hoops' Potter you're talking to. When it comes to basketball, I'm the bees' knees.
KLINGER: But, sir, the camp record's only thirty-one free throws. All you need is . . . *(Thinks)* . . . some more.
(Potter turns back to take his shot as Klinger *calls out to passersby.)*
(Shouting) Hey, hey, everybody, the Colonel's made fourteen free throws in a row.
(The people stop, impressed by this news. Potter *turns to* Klinger, *bugged.)*
POTTER: Klinger, what say we keep this shootin' streak on the Q.T. I'm just getting a little exercise and the last thing I need is a packed house eyeballing my basketballing.
Cut to:

20. TIGHT SHOT. BASKETBALL HOOP.
(The ball swishes through. A loud raucous cheer ensues as the crowd yells in unison: "Twenty-eight!" Pull back to reveal a large crowd has gathered to watch Potter. *In the group are* Hawkeye, B.J., Charles, Hot Lips *and* Mulcahy.*)*
POTTER: *(To* Klinger, *angrily)* Thank you very much.
(Klinger hands Potter *the ball.)*

KLINGER: But, sir, a little hero worship is to be expected. And you're such a cute little hero.

(Hot Lips is leading a cheer with appropriate pom-pom gestures.)

HOT LIPS: Sherman, Sherman, he's our man. If he can't do it, no one can! Yaay, Sherman!

(A loud cheer from everyone.)

POTTER: I feel like a damn fool.

(He takes a shot. Makes it. More cheers and a loud "Twenty-nine!" from the crowd.)

B.J.: You're a BMOC, Colonel. Big Man on Camp.

HAWKEYE: You could be the Army's first draft choice.

MULCAHY: *(To Charles)* My, this is quite exciting, isn't it?

CHARLES: Well, yes, actually it is. *(To Potter)* Come on, Shermy Baby! .. *(Catches himself)* Good Lord, I had no idea I was this desperate for entertainment.

POTTER: *(To Klinger)* I ought to stuff this ball in your big mouth.

KLINGER: Ah, the temperament of the gifted athlete.

(Potter aims.)

MULCAHY: *(Shouts)* Do it for the gipper, Colonel.

CHARLES: *(Shouts)* Yes, yes, for the gipper. *(To Mulcahy)* What in the world is a gipper?

(Potter shoots, makes the shot. The crowd cheers "Thirty!")

B.J.: He's incredible.

HAWKEYE: Steady as a rock.

(Klinger is now massaging Potter's shoulder. Potter is very nervous.)

POTTER: *(Swallows)* I need a drink.

KLINGER: And break training? Never! Just relax, sir. Sir? .. Breathe!

(Potter takes a breath.)

Only one more to tie. But there's no pressure. None at all. Just put it out of your mind that you're carrying the hopes and dreams of all these desperate people who have so little to cheer about.

POTTER: *(Pulling away)* Get away from me.

(He gets the ball, takes aim. Suddenly all is silent. Potter is sweating. He concentrates intensely, shoots ... and misses. An audible sigh of dejection from the crowd. Potter looks around as all begin to silently disperse. Klinger approaches Potter, having retrieved the ball.)

KLINGER: You disappointed a lot of people, sir. *(Bitterly)* I hope you're happy.

(He hands Potter *the ball and walks away. As the camera slowly pulls back,* Potter *is left alone, a forlorn figure holding a basketball, and we hear:)*
POTTER: *(Voice over)* So, son, take a word of advice from a retired bucketeer. If you take up a sport, make it horseshoes, where you don't have to be perfect.
(During the above we:)
Cut to:

21. INT. POTTER'S TENT.
(Potter is still writing.)
POTTER: *(Voice over)* Sincerely, Sherman T., formerly, 'Hoops', Potter.
(Potter looks up, spots a wadded piece of paper on his desk. He picks it up, takes aim and shoots it into the wastebasket.)
One.
Cut to:

22. INT. "THE SWAMP". DAY.
(B.J. and Charles *are reading letters.* Hawkeye *enters, shakes off rain, and in doing so, gets water on* Charles.)
CHARLES: You mildewed moron, you're soaking me.
HAWKEYE: No harm done, you've been all wet for years.
(With a silent curse, Charles *returns to his letter.* B.J. *looks at* Hawkeye, *who hangs up his coat and crosses to his bunk.)*
B.J.: Have a nice walk, Captain Nemo?
HAWKEYE: I went to see Mulcahy. I wanted to pawn my letter off on him.
B.J.: And?
HAWKEYE: And he said, in essence, physician heal thyself.
B.J.: What's to heal? Hawk, you've done nothing wrong.
HAWKEYE: *(Sits on his bunk)* I wish I could be that sure.
B.J.: What's with all this guilt? Ronnie Hawkins might not appreciate it, but you *save* lives, remember?
HAWKEYE: But I'm also in weapons repair. I fix people up to be killed or to kill others. I can't deny that. And I can't live with it, either. What the hell am I doing here?
B.J.: *(Wryly)* What the hell are any of us doing here?
HAWKEYE: What good has it done? I mean, really what good has it done? *(Sighs)* I'm gonna try to sleep. And fail.
(Hawkeye lies down. B.J. *looks to* Charles *who shrugs. Then they both turn to their letters. We stay on* Charles.)

YOUNG GIRL: *(Voice over)* 'Dear Doctor or Nurse, right now it is Autumn in Maine. Everything seems very beautiful. I don't know if you have Autumn in Korea, so I am sending you a leaf from a birch tree. I hope you like it.'
(As she reads, Charles *removes a leaf from the envelope. It is wrapped in wax paper. It's a lovely rust-colored leaf. He holds it gently and stares at it, very moved.)*
CHARLES: *(Quietly)* Autumn in New England.
B.J.: *(Turns)* What's that, Charles?
CHARLES: *(Holds up letter)* Ah . . . nothing. Just more childishness.
(B.J. turns back to his letter. Charles *reaches for his recorder, then decides against it and picks up pad and pen, begins writing.)*
CHARLES: *(Voice over)* 'Dear . . . ' *(Checks letter)* 'Virginia, it is with indescribable joy that I accept your gift. It is indeed testimony to the beauty that exists in all creation, but perhaps nowhere more than in a Young Girl's heart . . . '
(He continues writing as Hot Lips *rushes in, accompanied by a middle-aged man. This is* Dr. Breuer. *Both are wearing raincoats, and* Dr. Breuer *is very wet.)*
HOT LIPS: Doctors, we have an emergency.
(B.J. pulls on his boots, Hawkeye *goes for his coat.)*
(Indicates Breuer*)* This is Dr. Breuer. He runs the missionary school.
BREUER: One of our little girls slipped in the mud and hit her head against a rock. She's unconscious. I'm an M.D., but I'm afraid she needs a surgeon.
CHARLES: *(To* Hawkeye *and* B.J.*)* Need any help?
HAWKEYE: No, we can handle it. Let's go.
(B.J., Hawkeye, Breuer and Hot Lips rush out.)
Cut to:

23. INT. O.R. DAY.
(The rain continues. Hot Lips *is anesthetizing* Kwan Li, *a pretty Korean girl of about eight.* Hawkeye, B.J. *and* Dr. Breuer, *in surgical gowns, stand nearby looking at X-rays.)*
HAWKEYE: *(To* Breuer*)* You were right, Doctor, subdural hematoma.
B.J.: All right, let's drill, then try to evacuate the clot.
HOT LIPS: She's ready, Doctors.
(Hawkeye and B.J. prepare to operate. Breuer *steps forward.)*

BREUER: Please, before you start . . .
(Breuer *makes the sign of the cross over* Kwan Li, *clasps his hands together.*)
Dear God. I thank you for providing these skilled surgeons. To have them here, in this place at this time is truly a sign of your providence. Please bless their work.
(Breuer *steps back.* Hawkeye *and* B.J. *exchange a look. Then begin to work.*)
Cut to:

24. INT. POST-OP. DAY.
(Hawkeye *is seated next to the unconscious* Kwan Li. *He's writing a letter.*)
HAWKEYE: *(Voice over)* '. . . . And believe me, Ronnie, I hate being a part of this war. But today I saved a little girl's life. Her injury had nothing to do with the war. I just happened to be here when a surgeon was needed. A fortunate coincidence, I suppose. Saving one life could never make up for all the incredible ugliness, it can't compensate for the loss of your brother, but it's something. It's something good, and I'm going to remember it.'
(*During the above, camera has slowly panned from* Hawkeye's *face down to his hand as he writes, across to the bed of the unconscious* Kwan Li, *her head bandaged, tilts up as* B.J. *enters, approaches the bedside and gently takes* Kwan Li's *pulse. As* Hawkeye *finishes the letter, he looks up at* B.J.*)*
B.J.: She's doing okay.
HAWKEYE: Yeah, I think she's gonna be fine.
B.J.: *(Looking at* Hawkeye*)* And you?
HAWKEYE: Better.
(B.J. *nods, then:*)
B.J.: The rain stopped.
(Hawkeye *rises, looks outside.*)
HAWKEYE: Hey, whatta you know. A break in the gloom.
(Hawkeye *yawns, stretches and smiles a little. He motions to a* Nurse *to attend* Kwan Li *as he and* B.J. *slowly depart.*)
Fade out

TAG
Fade in

25. INT. "THE SWAMP". DAY.
(Flaps are up. It's a sunny day. Hawkeye, B.J., Charles *and* Klinger *are gathered near the door seated around an open mail-bag. There are envelopes everywhere.)*
HAWKEYE: I don't believe it. At least five hundred more letters . . . and there's only four hundred people in Crabapple Cove.
KLINGER: *(Irritably)* Sure, they must have notified the whole state. And I'm the one who's got to lug 'em in here.
(B.J., who's been looking at a postcard, hands it to Klinger.)
B.J.: Here, lug, this'll brighten your day.
KLINGER: What's this? *(Reads aloud)* 'An order for ten reams of official MASH square stationery.' *(Brightening)* I love these kids.
CHARLES: From the wallets of babes oft times come pearls.
(Suddenly their attention is drawn to a single loud cheer.)
POTTER: *(OS)* Ya-hoo!!!
(As they look at each other quizzically, the door bursts open and there stands a gleefully sweaty Potter *in full basketball regalia with the basketball crooked in his arm. With a look of triumph, he exclaims:)*
Hot sausage! THIRTY-TWO!!!
(Freeze frame.)

Fade out

A F T E R W O R D

1. Draw a cartoon or a comic strip based on any of the humorous scenes in *Letters*. Create a classroom display of the cartoons.

2. a) Hot Lips is the only character who doesn't tell her story in her letter. Why do you think she decides not to tell about the dying soldier?

b) What was your first impression of Charles? What was your final impression of him?

c) With a partner, improvise a scene between Charles and Hot Lips in which they discuss how they felt about writing their letters. Share your improvisation with another group, and prepare to give feedback on their improvisation.

3. You are the director of this episode of M*A*S*H, and it is up to you to decide how many "jolts per minute" (JPMs) will occur in each scene. "Jolt" is TV jargon for an exciting moment. A jolt can be created by rapid movement, a quick cut of a shot, a loud noise, a laugh on the laugh track, or a violent or humorous action. Read Scenes 14–16 to time roughly how long they would take to perform. Identify the places in the script that could become jolts, and calculate the number of jolts per minute. Present your notes to classmates, explaining how you would achieve each jolt.

4. Hawkeye finally finds a way to answer his letter after he saves the life of Kwan Li. Were you satisfied with what he said? With a group, think of a different way in which he might have resolved his uncertainties about his role in the war. Each group could present its ideas to the class. Which solution do you like best? Why?

5. What five words or phrases would you use to describe Father Mulcahy? Is his behaviour what you would expect from a priest? What qualities do you believe a member of the clergy should demonstrate? Write a paragraph to explain whether you agree or disagree with the way Father Mulcahy is portrayed. Compare your paragraph with one that takes the opposite point of view.

6. In a group, evaluate the merits of *Letters*. The script combines comedy and serious drama. Do you think it would be more effective as straight comedy? straight drama? Or did you like

the mix of the two? What kinds of humour do you notice in *Letters?* Look for one-liners, slapstick comedy, puns, insults, visual jokes, and double-entendres.

Imagine that you have been hired by a television network to discover the "secret formula" of two current sitcoms (you might choose your favourite or least favourite program). Try to watch at least two episodes of each sitcom. Record
- the kinds of humour used,
- how frequently the humour occurs, and
- how much, if any, serious drama is mixed in with the comedy.

Your report to the network should summarize your findings, perhaps including charts and graphs, as well as state your views about which show has the most effective humour, in your opinion, and why. Present your report to the class.

7. In a group, decide on a scene from *Letters* to present to the class. Have each group member choose a role and prepare an actor's notebook of the scene, making notes about movement, props, characterization, and how particular lines should be read. Practise the scene until all of you are comfortable with it, then present it to the class, either live or on videotape. Ask your classmates to tell you whether the characters are easy to identify, if the lines make sense, and what changes would improve the presentation.

8. Find the letter from Mary Colonna that Father Mulcahy reads to Hawkeye in Scene 17. As Father Mulcahy, or as any other character in the script, write a reply to Mary. Try to capture the language and personality of your character in your letter.

▼ ▼ ▼ *INTRODUCTION TO:*

Doors

Suzan L. Zeder

"I am profoundly interested in children as protagonists who find themselves in crises, who struggle against overpowering forces, and conduct themselves as heroes. I respect the efforts of parents and children facing troubled times with dignity and depth. I find these efforts to be legitimate and compelling dramatic history."
Suzan L. Zeder

nternationally acclaimed in her writing of dramas for family audiences, Suzan L. Zeder teaches playwriting at a university in Texas. Her work often focuses on the issues and stresses of family life. Her plays have been produced all over the United States, Australia, West Germany, Great Britain, and Japan.

Doors is a play that dramatizes, in Zeder's words, "the journey of three individual survivors through a particularly difficult day." Here is Zeder's description of the experience that inspired *Doors*:

"This play began for me with a real child and a real divorce. A friend, whose marriage had recently exploded, shared a story about her ten-year-old son reaching out from his own pain and sadness to comfort her. It was an act of two human beings meeting in a moment of healing that went beyond the boundaries of a 'social problem' into the realm of art. The story haunted me for years until I gave it a second life in the final lines of this play."

GETTING STARTED

1. Everyone gets angry occasionally. In your group, brainstorm a list of ways in which people show their anger. What are some ways you find effective for handling anger?

2. In a journal entry, describe your idea of a "perfect" family.

3. What are some of the things parents argue about? How do you think children feel when they hear their parents arguing? Discuss these questions with a partner; then draw a cartoon of a wife and husband in the middle of a dispute.

4. Imagine that someone you know is going through a difficult time and needs your support. Think of a personal experience that, although difficult at the time, turned out to have a positive effect on you. Summarize your story and share it with a friend.

▼   ▼   ▼   STAGE PLAY

Doors
Suzan L. Zeder

CHARACTERS
. . . .

JEFF — *an eleven-year-old boy who is upset by his parents'*
arguments
HELEN — *his mother*
BEN — *his father*
SANDY — *his best friend*

*(A fragmentary set suggesting Jeff's bedroom. At first glance it
seems to be the rather ordinary room of an eleven-year-old boy;
but there are odd angles, slanting doorways, and joints that do
not quite connect. The whole room is slightly off-kilter.*

*The room is dominated by a large closed door, center stage. It
is the door to Jeff's parents' bedroom. Down left is a smaller
door to the rest of the house. The walls of the room are defined
by large scrimmed panels. The panels are decorated with posters
of movies, mostly science fiction adventure films currently popular at the time of the production. The posters are oversized
and made of a scrim material; they are also hinged so that actors can pass through them.*

*Also in the room are a small bed, a couple of chairs, a desk or
work area, a T.V. set, a stereo, and an over-flowing laundry
basket.*

*At rise, Jeff is alone on stage, seated at the desk. He is work-
ing intently on a large, complicated model of a spaceship. The
model is almost finished. Jeff works with great concentration
with the directions and a tube of glue.*

*The first sounds we hear are muffled Voices coming from Jeff's
parents' room. They are arguing. This argument will be ongoing
during most of the play; at times, specific voices and words will
be heard, at other times, muffled sound, sometimes, nothing.
Care should be taken to preserve the illusion that the argument*

is continuous without detracting from the primary focus, which is to be on stage with Jeff *and his actions.* [See Production Notes at the end of the script.]

Jeff *tries to concentrate on his task of building the model, but he is obviously distracted and upset by the sounds coming from behind the door. He reads from the directions.)*

JEFF: "When the glue is partially set, insert cockpit window flaps G and H into the main body of the craft."

(The sounds of the argument grow louder and Jeff *tries to concentrate harder.)*

"Hold firmly in place for a few seconds until the glue sets . . ."

(There is another sound from behind the door. Jeff *looks up, the part slips. He tries again.)*

"When the glue is partially set, insert cockpit window flaps G and H into the main body of the craft."

(As Jeff *lines up the parts, a series of angry bursts are heard, they register on his face, but he does not move.)*

. . . "until the glue sets" . . .

*(Jeff *rises, turns on the stereo set, and returns to the model.)*

"Insert wheel hub N into wheel rim O and affix wheel assembly to landing gear C."

(He looks all over the model.)

Where's the landing gear? Where's the landing gear? Where's that . . .

(Sounds from behind the door increase. Jeff *picks up the model, looking for the landing gear and the cockpit falls off. The phone rings.* Jeff *looks at the door. The phone rings again.* Jeff *tries to return to the model, the phone rings again.)*

"Insert wheel hub" . . . yeah . . . yeah . . . yeah . . . "Affix to landing GEAR!"

(The phone continues to ring. Finally, Jeff *rises and answers. The stereo is very loud.)*

Hello? Just a second.

*(Jeff *puts down the phone, crosses to the stereo and turns it off. He returns to the phone.)*

Sorry. Hello, Gramma. Yeah, this is Jeff. Yeah, we got out of school last week. . . No, I'm not going to camp this year. . . Gramma, they don't have camps for Grandmothers.

(Sounds behind the door increase.)

Yeah, they're both here, but they can't come to the phone right now. They're in their room with the door closed and I

don't think I'd better . . . I'll tell them you called. I'm sure
Mom will call you back later . . . Yeah, you too, Gramma.
Bye.
*(Jeff hangs up the phone, and crosses back to the desk, on the
way he turns on the stereo and the T.V. very loud.)*
Stop it. Stop it! STOP IT!
*(Jeff sits and buries his face in his hands; the sound is tremen-
dous. After a beat, the large door bursts open and* Ben *enters
angrily.)*
BEN: Jeff! Turn it down!
(Jeff does not move.)
Damnation, Jeff!
(Ben crosses to T.V. and stereo and turns them off.)
We can't even hear ourselves think in there. Why does it have
to be so loud?
JEFF: I like it loud.
BEN: Well, you're blasting us out of the house.
JEFF: Sorry.
BEN: Your Mother and I are trying to . . . talk and that doesn't
help.
JEFF: Sorry.
BEN: If you're sorry, then keep it down. You can listen, but keep
it reasonable, okay?
*(Ben turns the stereo back on much lower and starts to exit
back through the door. Jeff rises and stops him.)*
JEFF: Hey, Dad?
BEN: *(Turning back to him)* Yeah?
(Jeff turns the stereo off.)
JEFF: Gramma called.
BEN: Oh . . . What did she want?
JEFF: I don't know, just to talk I guess.
BEN: *(Under his breath, with frustration)* Oh, brother . . .
JEFF: What?
BEN: Nothing.
(Ben notices that Jeff *is really "down.")*
Jeff?
(Jeff does not respond; Ben, *not sure of what to do, assumes a
wrestling stance.)*
Hey, Jeff?
JEFF: Oh, no, Dad!
*(After a beat, Jeff responds with a wrestling stance, this is some-
thing they have done frequently. For a brief moment, they mock*

wrestle, or tickle, resulting in a much needed laugh for both of them. Helen's *voice is heard offstage.)*
HELEN: Ben?
(Ben starts to go, Jeff *stops him.)*
JEFF: Dad, can you have a look at this?
BEN: What?
(Jeff holds up the model.)
JEFF: The cockpit keeps falling off.
BEN: That's really coming along.
JEFF: Mom painted the flag and the wing trim.
BEN: I was going to help you with that. I'm sorry, Jeff.
JEFF: Mom helped me with the body and the engine.
BEN: But things kind of got away from me.
JEFF: I can't get the cockpit to stay on.
BEN: Let me see it. *(Ben inspects the model.)* Well, the flag is in the wrong place and wing trim's crooked. But you put it together just fine.
JEFF: Really?
BEN: Oh, yeah. Have you got a razor blade?
(Jeff hands him a razor blade and watches as Ben *scrapes the glue.)*
The surface has to be clean for it to seal. Now, the glue.
(Ben applies the glue and positions the cockpit.)
JEFF: You've got to keep holding until the glue sets.
HELEN: *(Off)* Ben?
BEN: In a minute!
JEFF: Look out, Dad, it's slipping.
BEN: I've got it.
JEFF: Your hands are shaking.
BEN: They are not!
JEFF: You've got to hold it still.
BEN: I know!
(There is a pause. Ben *looks toward the door, back at* Jeff, *and toward the door again.* Jeff *notices.)*
JEFF: Have a look at this.
(Jeff shows him an old photograph.)
BEN: Where did you get that?
JEFF: I found it.
BEN: That's our old house on Beachcroft. What are you doing with that?
JEFF: I just like to look at it sometimes.
BEN: You remember that place?

JEFF: I remember.

BEN: But that was years ago.

JEFF: I remember.

(Ben *takes the photo in one hand and holds the model in the other.*)

BEN: I built every inch of that house. Built it and rebuilt it.

JEFF: I remember my bedroom; it had clouds and stars on the ceiling.

BEN: We painted them for you when you said that you wanted to sleep in the sky.

JEFF: When I turned out the lights, the stars glowed.

BEN: That was a good house, Jeff, a good house. Solid foundations, thick walls, none of that stucco, pre-fab garbage. I can't build 'em like that anymore.

JEFF: How come?

BEN: I haven't got the time, and who's got the money, and nobody cares.

JEFF: I miss that house.

BEN: Yeah, so do I.

(Ben *puts down the photo and looks at* Jeff.)

Jeff, there's something going on here, something we all have to talk about . . .

JEFF: *(Interrupting quickly)* Dad, you've got to hold on to it!

BEN: Huh?

JEFF: The cockpit, it's slipping again. You've got to hold it in place or it won't work.

BEN: I've got it.

JEFF: You've got to hold it steady.

BEN: I am holding it steady.

(Helen *enters and stands in the doorway.*)

HELEN: What are you doing?

BEN: I'll be right there.

JEFF: Dad's helping me with my model.

HELEN: But, Ben . . .

BEN: I said, I'll be right there!

HELEN: Jeff, honey, you spend so much time inside these days, and it's a beautiful day out there. Why don't you go on over to Sandy's . . .

JEFF: I don't want to go to Sandy's.

HELEN: But, I thought you two were going to work on the movie.

JEFF: He's coming over here later.

HELEN: It's a beautiful day and here you are all cooped up . . .

BEN: He said, he didn't want to go.

HELEN: It was just a suggestion.

BEN: You know, you could have waited.

HELEN: Ben, I have been waiting . . .

BEN: I'm talking about this model.

HELEN: The model?

BEN: I was going to help him with it, just as soon as I got a little ahead on the Carlson development.

JEFF: It's okay, Dad.

HELEN: He needed help and he asked me.

BEN: You could have waited.

HELEN: Sure, I could have waited, but he couldn't.

JEFF: It's almost done now.

BEN: Just as soon as I finished the bids and worked out the contracts, and . . .

HELEN: And when would that have been, Ben? Next week? Next month? Next year?

BEN: I was looking forward to it!

(The tension in their tone rises.)

JEFF: *(Suddenly)* I don't feel well.

HELEN: *(Concerned)* What's the matter?

JEFF: I just don't feel so hot.

HELEN: Do you have a headache?

JEFF: I guess so.

BEN: He's all right.

(Helen crosses to Jeff.)

HELEN: Do you have a temperature?

JEFF: I don't think so.

BEN: He's all right.

HELEN: *(To Ben)* How do you know he's all right?

BEN: *(To Jeff)* You're all right, aren't you?

JEFF: I'm all right.

HELEN: But you just said . . .

BEN: He just said he was all right!

JEFF: Dad, the cockpit's all screwed up again.

BEN: Helen, will you let me finish this?

HELEN: I was just . . .

JEFF: The glue's all over the place.

(Jeff takes the model from Ben and returns to the desk with it.)

HELEN: I'll be in our room when you're finished!

(Helen exits through the large door and slams it as she goes.)

BEN: I'll be right there!

(Ben *paces in anger as* Jeff *returns dejectedly to the model.*)
JEFF: Hand me the razor blade?
(Ben, *distracted, does not answer.*)
Dad, can you hand me the blade?
BEN: Oh, yeah, sure; just kind of scrape it there . . . it'll be all right.
JEFF: Yeah.
BEN: Just hold it firm until the glue sets.
JEFF: Yeah.
BEN: You're all right aren't you?
JEFF: Yeah.
(Ben *crosses to the large door, hesitates for a beat, then exits.* Jeff *holds the model perfectly still during the next few lines, which we hear through the door.*)
HELEN: *(Off)* When we discuss this with Jeff, will you at least do me the courtesy of allowing me to be there?
BEN: *(Off)* We were talking about the model.
HELEN: *(Off)* When we do talk to him, we can't be emotional and upset.
BEN: *(Off)* I am NOT EMOTIONAL!
HELEN: *(Off)* Then why are you shouting?
BEN: *(Off)* I wasn't emotional then, now I'm emotional!
(Jeff *slowly and deliberately pulls off the cockpit.*)
HELEN: Stop shouting!
BEN: Stop picking! You always have to pick at me, at Jeff!
(Jeff *breaks off one wing.* Ben *and* Helen *continue offstage.*)
HELEN: He said he didn't feel well.
BEN: He's all right.
HELEN: Just because you say he's all right, doesn't mean . . .
BEN: He said he was all right!
(Jeff *snaps off the other wing.*)
HELEN: I was just concerned!
BEN: Can't you leave anything alone?
(Jeff *suddenly hurls the model at the door. It smashes onto the floor and breaks into pieces.* Jeff *rises and turns both the stereo and the T.V. on full blast. He returns to his desk and cradles his head in his hands. After a beat or so,* Sandy *is heard pounding on the smaller door.*)
SANDY: *(Off)* Jeff, you in there? Jeff?
(Sandy *enters through the small door. He is a bit put out and he lugs a life-sized dummy with him.*)
Jeeze, Jeff, doesn't anyone around here answer the door? I've

been out there about a half an hour ringing the bell and yelling. Hey, do you know the T.V. is on?

(Jeff *pulls himself together, but avoids looking at* Sandy.)

JEFF: Yeah.

SANDY: And the stereo, too?

(Sandy *turns off the T.V.*)

This much noise will rot your brain, at least that's what my Mom says.

(Sandy *starts to turn off stereo.*)

JEFF: Don't.

SANDY: Can I at least turn it down?

(Jeff *looks toward the large door.* Sandy *turns it down but not off.*)

JEFF: What are you doing in here?

SANDY: I knew you were home and the front door was unlocked so I . . .

JEFF: What do you want?

SANDY: We've got to finish the script, remember?

JEFF: Look, Sandy, this isn't a good time.

SANDY: Don't you even want to see what I brought?

JEFF: What's that?

(Sandy *holds up the dummy proudly.*)

SANDY: It's a body for the crash scene! I figure we could put ketchup all over it for blood and maybe some dog food for brains.

JEFF: That's gross.

SANDY: Wait until you hear how I got it.

JEFF: Sandy . . .

(Sandy *acts this out as he goes along.*)

SANDY: I was downtown in this alley behind Nordstroms and I saw this arm sticking out of a dumpster . . . OH MY! I thought some bum had crawled in there and died, but then I figured out that it was a dummy. So, I asked this big goon by the loading dock, if I could have it. And he said, "It'll cost you a dollar." So I grabbed it and ran down Fifth like I was kidnapping it or something. Then this number fourteen bus came along, and I hopped on. The driver said, "You can't bring that thing on this bus!" So, I said, "How dare you insult my younger brother!" And I paid two fares, sat it next to me, and talked to it all the way over here. Man, everyone on that bus really thought I was weird.

JEFF: You are weird. (Jeff *turns away.*)

SANDY: You're the weird one. I thought that would really crack you up. All the way over here, I just kept thinking, "this will really crack Jeff up!" *(No response)* What's the matter?

JEFF: Nothing.

SANDY: Your report card! Your parents hit the ceiling about that F in science.

JEFF: I never showed it to them.

SANDY: The dog! You finally asked them if you could have a dog, and they said no, and . . .

JEFF: I haven't asked them about that yet.

SANDY: Then what's wrong?

(Sounds can be heard from behind the door.)

JEFF: Sandy, I'll come over to your house later and . . .

SANDY: Did you get the video camera from your dad?

JEFF: Uhhhh, he's been out of town.

SANDY: You mean you haven't even asked him yet?

JEFF: I'll ask him.

SANDY: We've got to start shooting tomorrow!

JEFF: I'll ask him later.

SANDY: All right! How's the starship coming along?

JEFF: *(Pointing towards the door)* It's over there.

(Sandy crosses to the door and picks up the wrecked model.)

SANDY: What happened to the starship?

JEFF: It got hit by a meteor shower!

SANDY: It got hit by something! Jeff, the wings are all broken and the frame is cracked! These things cost a lot of money!

JEFF: I'll pay you back! I'll buy you another one! What more do you want?

SANDY: Jeff, we are supposed to be doing this together and all you're doing is screwing up!

(More sounds are heard)

JEFF: I don't want to do this today! Go home, Sandy. I'll call you later.

SANDY: I'm not leaving until we finish the script! And I'm turning that thing off!

(Sandy switches off the stereo; for a second the sounds of the argument can be heard, Sandy hears it and chooses to ignore it. Jeff turns away. Sandy pulls some pages out of his pocket.) Okay, we start with a long shot of the ship hurtling toward the death asteroid. Then we show the crash . . . This will work great!

(He sarcastically holds the model up.)

Then we show the crew, those who haven't been burned alive
or had their heads split open . . .
(He indicates the dummy.)
. . . . struggling out of the wreck.
*(Sandy acts this out as he goes along; Jeff watches, becoming
more and more involved.)*
Colonel McCabe is the first one out; that's me. Then comes
Rocco, the navigator; that's Paul; and then the ship's doctor,
old blood and guts; that's Rick; and finally comes the ship's
robot computer, C.B. 430; that's you . . .
(Jeff suddenly joins in.)
JEFF: Suddenly, the robot computer starts acting strangely. His
lights flash and smoke comes out of his ears. He walks toward
the ship's doctor and grabs him . . .
(Jeff grabs the dummy.)
He punches him in the stomach, hits him in the head, crushes
him in his steel grip and throws his lifeless body to the ground.
(Jeff beats the dummy and throws it.)
SANDY: *(Laughing)* Rick's not going to like that.
JEFF: Then he whirls around and walks toward Rocco.
(Jeff turns in a circle and grabs the dummy again.)
He grabs him by the arms and twists them out of their sock-
ets! He throws him on the ground, time after time, after time,
after time.
(Jeff beats the dummy on the floor.)
SANDY: Jeff?
JEFF: *(Totally carried away)* He kicks him in the stomach, in the
back, in the head, in the guts!
SANDY: Jeff, that's not in the script.
JEFF: Finally, he turns on Colonel McCabe.
(Jeff turns on him and stalks him.)
SANDY: Cut it out, Jeff.
JEFF: Comes at him, slowly, slowly . . .
SANDY: I said, cut it out.
JEFF: Closer and closer.
(Jeff moves in and Sandy grows alarmed.)
SANDY: Stop it!
JEFF: He raises his arm . . .
SANDY: Jeff!
(Jeff backs him up until he is next to the bed.)
JEFF: And zap! The death ray! Colonel McCabe collapses in
agony.

(Sandy is forced down on the bed. He is angry and confused.)

SANDY: He does not.

JEFF: He does too.

SANDY: Colonel McCabe does not die! It says in the script, I don't die!

JEFF: You will if I want you to.

SANDY: I will not!

JEFF: Who's got the camera?

SANDY: I don't know, Jeff. Who does?

(Jeff turns away.)

You're such a jerk! I'm going home!

JEFF: Get out of here!

SANDY: I am!

JEFF: And take this piece of junk with you!

(Jeff throws the dummy at Sandy.)

Go home to your Mommy and your Daddy, clear out of here and leave me alone!

SANDY: You're a stupid jerk, Jeff. You've been acting like a stupid jerk ever since your parents first started . . .

JEFF: You shut up about my parents! You don't know anything about my parents!

SANDY: I know that they're yelling again. Jeff, I've heard them ever since I've been here. I could even hear them down on the street.

JEFF: Get out of here, Sandy!

SANDY: I know all about it.

(Jeff turns away.)

My Mom told me. Your Mom talks to my Mom; they gab all the time.

JEFF: *(Without turning to him)* What did she say?

SANDY: She said that there was trouble over here and I should keep my big nose out of it.

(Jeff sits, upset. Sandy hesitates and approaches cautiously.)

You want to talk about it in the pact?

JEFF: The pact?

SANDY: You remember the pact, Jeff?

JEFF: We were just little kids.

SANDY: You remember how we both pissed on that dead frog and buried it? How we both cut our fingers and spit and swore with our blood that we would always tell each other everything?

JEFF: We were just little kids.

SANDY: Yeah.

JEFF: *(After a pause)* I don't care anymore, Sandy. They can scream at each other until they're hoarse, I don't care. They can slap each other around all day, I don't care. I just want it to stop.

SANDY: Do they really hit each other?

JEFF: I don't know. I don't care!

SANDY: Jeeze, I don't know what I'd do if my parents ever hit each other.

JEFF: I didn't say they did. I just said, I didn't care.

SANDY: Do you ever see them?

JEFF: I never see anything, it's always behind the door.

SANDY: Do they ever come down for breakfast in the morning, you know, with black eyes or bruises?

JEFF: Blow it out your ear, Sandy.

SANDY: Do you know what it's about?

JEFF: Nobody tells me anything.

SANDY: Do you know when it started?

JEFF: I knew something was up when they started having all these appointments. When I'd ask Mom where she was going, she'd say, "Your Father and I have an appointment."

(Lights change and the posters are lit so the scrim becomes transparent. Behind each poster we see Ben and Helen. The following is played as though they are each speaking to an offstage counselor. The boys continue with their dialogue, seemingly oblivious to the words of Ben and Helen. Underneath this scene there is sound which is not really music, but sets it apart from reality. [See Production Notes at the end of the script.]

BEN: It all started about two years ago, Doctor. She went back to college for her Master's degree.

HELEN: It all started about four years ago. He stopped building houses and started building condominiums.

JEFF: *(To Sandy)* But it really started last Tuesday. Dad left and was gone for two days. Mom told me he was on a business trip, but he wasn't.

HELEN: "Condominiums," he said, "that's where the money is!" But the time? Time for electricians, carpenters, and clients; no time for us. So, I went back to school.

BEN: A Master's degree in Psychology? Why didn't she study something useful? What kind of work is psychology?

JEFF: When he came back, they tried to pretend everything was all right. But it wasn't. Everything had changed.

HELEN: I changed into someone neither of us had anticipated. I discovered I have my own ideas, feelings, needs . . .

BEN: I need her to be with me while I'm building something, something for all of us.

JEFF: Now, everything's different.

SANDY: But do you know why?

BEN: I don't know why. She talks to me now, I don't understand what she's saying. She tells me I'm not giving her enough. Enough of what?

HELEN: When Ben gives, he gives things. When I give, I give things up.

JEFF: Something's happened, Sandy, I'm afraid it's something big.

HELEN: I won't give this up! It's my one chance to make something of my own.

BEN: I can't! I can't start all over again from scratch! This isn't just a job, it's my life!

JEFF: They hardly ever look at each other.

SANDY: Yeah?

BEN: We're tearing each other apart.

JEFF: They almost never talk to each other.

SANDY: Yeah?

HELEN: I want to put it back together again, with all the same pieces, but I want them to fit together differently.

JEFF: And they never ever smile at each other.

BEN: I want out.

(Lights out behind the posters. They appear to be solid again.)

SANDY: Jeeze.

JEFF: Every night, when they think I'm asleep, Dad gets in his car and leaves. By morning he's back at the breakfast table. Every morning we eat breakfast in silence.

(Lights change, sound comes in. The walls become transparent and then swing open. Ben and Helen enter in fantasy. Helen carries a tray of utensils which transforms Jeff's desk into a breakfast table. [See Production Notes at the end of the script.]
   The scene is played with great tension and contrapuntal rhythms of the various utensils. Jeff sits at the middle of the table. Helen stirs a pot of hot cereal. As Ben enters she stops, they glare at each other. Helen continues to stir as Ben pours coffee, sits, and opens a newspaper. Helen stirs the pot in an ever increasing rhythm. Ben is bothered by the sound but ignores her. Finally she crosses to him, stirs faster and faster until

*she dumps a spoonful into his bowl. Ben looks at her and then
at the bowl and half sighs, half grunts in response. Jeff is aware
of the tension, but doggedly eats his cereal, scraping the bowl
loudly with every bite. Helen pours herself some coffee, and
stirs it with her spoon clinking on the cup. The sound annoys
Ben, and he shoots her a look and retreats to his paper. Jeff,
aware of the cross currents, eats quietly and retreats to a comic
book. Helen speaks to Jeff but looks at Ben.)*

HELEN: Don't read at the table, Jeff! It's rude.

*(Ben crumples his paper. Jeff stops reading and begins to tap his
foot in a habitual nervous gesture. After a beat Helen taps her
foot in a similar rhythm. Ben speaks to Jeff, but looks at
Helen.)*

BEN: Don't tap your foot, son. It's very annoying.

*(Helen glares at Ben, he picks up a piece of toast and scrapes
it into his cereal bowl. Jeff eats, noticing everything, but pretending to see nothing.)*
(Meaning the opposite) Don't you just LOVE cream of wheat,
Jeff?

*(Helen rises and clears the table. She clears all the dishes, in-
cluding Ben's coffee, leaving him with the spoon twirling in the
air. Ben rises and leaves the table. There is a moment of word-
less confrontation before they both exit through their posters.
Jeff beats his hand down on the table as the lights return to
normal.)*

JEFF: I hate breakfast.

SANDY: Maybe you shouldn't have read at the table.

JEFF: It wouldn't have made any difference.

SANDY: My parents do that kind of thing all the time. It's like
they have a secret code or something; they don't even have to
talk, they read each other's minds.

JEFF: It used to be that way with my folks too, but now it's like
they are screaming at each other, but their voices are so high
pitched that only dogs can hear them.

SANDY: Jeeze.

*(There is a pause and voices can be heard from behind the
door. Jeff turns away. Sandy is a bit curious.)*
Jeff, do you ever, you know, listen?

JEFF: Huh?

SANDY: I mean, when they fight, do you, you know, try to hear
what they're saying?

JEFF: Sandy, I spend most of my time trying not to hear.

SANDY: Well, sometimes my folks argue, they don't really fight or anything; but when they argue, part of me tries to shut it out and part of me really wants to know what's going on.

JEFF: *(Not unkindly)* You little creep!

SANDY: No, but the weird thing is, the really weird thing is, whenever I listen, it all sounds so stupid! Like last year, you know, we all went down to Puyallup, to the fair. We go every year, and every year the same thing happens.

(Sandy uses a couple of chairs to set up a "car" and he plays out the following.)

My Dad always drives and my Mom sits next to him and does needlepoint. Julie, Carrie, and I sit in the back seat and argue over who has to sit on the hump. After we have been driving for about a half an hour, my Mom looks up and says, "We always go this way and we always get lost."

Then my Dad says, "You got a better route?"

And my Mom says, "Back there at the service station, I told you to turn left."

"But that's the way all the traffic goes."

"That's because it's the right way."

"There's less traffic this way."

"THAT'S because we're going to Auburn."

Then, Julie says, "But I thought we were going to the fair!"

And they both say, "Be quiet, Julie."

And my Mom says, "Daddy's trying to drive."

And Dad says, "What's that supposed to mean?"

So, my Mom says, "It's not supposed to mean anything. I am just trying to get us to the fair. If you'd listen instead of charging ahead, we wouldn't be lost."

Then, Dad says, "Who's lost? I know exactly where we are."

And Mom says, "Okay, where are we?"

And we all say, "WE'RE LOST!" Then they both turn around and yell at US.

JEFF: Did you get to the fair?

SANDY: Yeah.

JEFF: How was it?

SANDY: It was great.

JEFF: With my folks we'd never get there.

(Jeff takes Sandy's place and acts out the following.)

JEFF: My Mom would say, "The reason you're driving this way is because you really don't want to go to the fair."

And my Dad would say, "What?"

"You didn't want to go last night when I suggested it and you didn't want to go this morning, while I was packing the picnic. That's why you didn't help."
"You said, you didn't need any help."
"Still, it would have been nice."
"Nice? I'm being nice. I'm taking you to the fair aren't I?"
"Only because you feel guilty."
"Guilty?"
"Because you didn't take us last year."
"But I'm taking you this year! I am taking you to the god-damned fair when I should be at the office."
"See, I knew you didn't want to go."
Then we'd turn around and all the way back to Seattle all you'd hear would be the sound of ice melting in the cooler.

SANDY: Did that really happen?
JEFF: No, but that's what would have happened.
SANDY: How do you know?
JEFF: I know, believe me, I know.
SANDY: What do you know?
JEFF: I know that's what would have happened.
SANDY: That's not what I mean. What do you know about what's happening?
JEFF: I don't know.
SANDY: You don't know what you know?
JEFF: No! What are you talking about?
SANDY: Look Jeff, if you can figure out what's going on, then maybe you can do something about it.
JEFF: I've tried.
SANDY: Well, try again! What are the facts?
JEFF: You sound like something out of *Magnum, P.I.*
[Update to any popular police or detective show and have Sandy imitate the lead characters in his inquisition.]
SANDY: I'm just trying to help.
(Sandy *leaps to his feet and becomes a detective.*)
Come on, man, what do you know?
JEFF: I know my Dad's not sleeping at home at night.
SANDY: Okay, where does he go?
JEFF: I don't know.
SANDY: Well, if he's not sleeping at home, he has to be sleeping somewhere else.
JEFF: Brilliant.
SANDY: Have you asked him?

JEFF: No.

SANDY: Why not?

JEFF: I can really see me going up to my father and saying, "Where you been sleeping these days, Dad?" Get real.

SANDY: We may have to tail him.

JEFF: I'm not going to do that!

SANDY: It was just a suggestion. Say, Jeff, do you think he's got a . . . girlfriend.

JEFF: No.

SANDY: Why not?

JEFF: He just wouldn't!

SANDY: Okay, scratch that. What else do you know?

JEFF: I know they fight a lot.

SANDY: What about?

JEFF: Everything . . . Anything.

SANDY: You must have heard something in particular.

JEFF: This afternoon, I heard my Mom say, "I'm not giving up."

SANDY: Giving up what?

JEFF: I couldn't hear.

SANDY: Smoking! Your Dad wants her to give up smoking!

JEFF: She doesn't smoke.

SANDY: When my Mom tried to give up smoking, she threw a whole plate of spaghetti at my Dad. She said it slipped, but I knew she threw it.

JEFF: I said, she doesn't smoke.

SANDY: You sure?

JEFF: She's my Mother!

SANDY: What else did you hear?

JEFF: I heard my Mom say something about a job.

SANDY: YOUR DAD LOST HIS JOB!

JEFF: I don't think . . .

SANDY: That's it! Jeff, I saw this thing on *Sixty Minutes*, about how all these people are losing jobs. First they lose the job, then they go on welfare, then everybody starts fighting with everybody and . . .

JEFF: My Dad works for himself, he's a contractor.

SANDY: Oh no, Jeff! That's the worst.

JEFF: But he just started a new project over in Bellevue . . .

SANDY: Don't take my word, ask Mike Wallace!

JEFF: Do you really think . . .

SANDY: Here, I'll show you.

(Sandy *grabs the dummy and mimes the characters with it.*)

Here is your Father, sitting around reading his paper. And your Mother comes in and says, "Well, I certainly hope that you're looking for a job." And he says, "Job, I have a job." And she says, "I mean a job with some money!" "Maybe if you wouldn't spend so much on cigarettes and panty hose . . ."

JEFF: I told you, she doesn't . . .

SANDY: And she says, "Me spend so much? You're such a cheapskate. . ."

JEFF: Sandy . . .

SANDY: And that really makes him mad so he hauls off and . . . Bam! SLAP! POW! THWACK!

(Sandy makes the dummy punch the air. Jeff grabs it from him.)

JEFF: I never said they hit each other!

SANDY: I was just trying to . . .

JEFF: I've never seen them hit each other. They're not like that at all!

(There is a pause.)

SANDY: Hey, Jeff, why don't you just ask them what's going on?

(Jeff tenderly carries the dummy over to the bed.)

Ask your Mom, she'll tell you something. My Mother always tells me something.

JEFF: I just want it to stop, Sandy. That's all I really want. Every night when I hear them in there, I put the pillow over my head, so I can't hear them and I try to imagine what it would be like if they would just stop fighting. I try to make myself dream about it. If they would just stop fighting, everything would be perfect.

(Jeff covers the dummy's head with a pillow during this speech. Lights change and there is music as we move in to his fantasy.)

It would be morning; and the first thing I hear would be Mom, in the kitchen making breakfast. The first thing I smell would be bacon frying. The first thing I feel would be sunlight on my face.

(Lights come up on the poster to the right of the door. Helen appears behind it.)

HELEN: Jeff, time to get up! Time for breakfast!

JEFF: So, I'd get up, and I'd come downstairs.

(Jeff manipulates the dummy out of bed, and brings it to the desk which will serve once again as a breakfast table. The poster swings open and Helen enters with utensils. Jeff enters the

scene with the dummy. He manipulates the dummy and all relate to it as though it were him.)
HELEN: Morning.
JEFF: Morning.
HELEN: Sleep well?
JEFF: Very.
(Jeff seats the dummy at his place.)
HELEN: Ben, breakfast is ready.
BEN: I'll be right there.
(Poster swings open and Ben enters the scene. He takes his place at the table. In this scene there is no tension initially, everything is warm and loving, unreal and exaggerated.)
HELEN: Morning.
BEN: Morning.
HELEN: Sleep well?
BEN: Very.
(Helen hands Ben a plate with obvious pleasure.)
BEN: *(Delighted)* Eggs over easy, hash browns, bacon, toast, coffee with cream and two sugars. Thank you, dear.
HELEN: You're welcome, darling.
BEN: *(To the dummy)* Morning, son.
JEFF: *(Nodding the dummy toward Ben)* Morning.
BEN: Sleep well?
JEFF: Very.
(Helen sits at table and all mime eating.)
(To Sandy) In this family everyone eats breakfast.
HELEN: This afternoon, I thought we'd all go to the circus. I've called for the tickets. They're at the box office.
BEN: This afternoon, I thought we'd all go to the Sonics game. I've called for the tickets. They're at the box office.
HELEN: But, Dearest, the circus . . .
BEN: But, Darling, the Sonics . . .
HELEN: Circus.
BEN: Sonics. *(Tension begins to build.)*
HELEN: CIRCUS!
BEN: SONICS!
JEFF: In this family there is NEVER any arguing.
HELEN: We'll go to the Sonics!
BEN: We'll go to the Circus!
JEFF: In this family there is ALWAYS a solution.
SANDY: In this family there is a dog!
(Sandy enters the scene as a boisterous slobbering dog.

He bounds around the room.)
HELEN: Who let the dog in?
BEN: He's all right! Here, Boy! Atta Boy! Good Dog. Good Boy!
HELEN: *(Pleasantly)* Ben, that's a hunting dog; don't you think he should really be outside?
(Sandy bounds playfully over to Ben, jumps on him and they tussle.)
BEN: Hey, Jeff, have a look at this. Fetch, boy.
(Ben throws an imaginary object and Sandy bounces after it.)
HELEN: Please, Ben, not in the house.
JEFF: Sandy!
BEN: Good Dog! Bring it here. Good Boy!
(Sandy fetches it and knocks into the table.)
HELEN: Ben, he's knocking over the table.
BEN: Oh, he's just a puppy.
JEFF: Sandy . . .
(Ben throws the object again.)
BEN: After it, boy!
(Sandy leaps onto the bed and kicks up the covers.)
HELEN: He's tearing up the house. Stop it, Ben.
JEFF: Stop it, Sandy.
(Sandy knocks over the hamper, scattering the contents.)
HELEN: *(Very angry)* Ben, that dog just made a mess on the living room carpet!
BEN: Don't yell at me, I didn't do it!
JEFF: Stop it, Sandy!
HELEN: He's tearing up my house.
BEN: Your house? I thought this was my house, too!
HELEN: Well, if it's your house, then you can clean it up!
(Helen exits behind her poster.)
BEN: I'll have MY dog in MY house any damn time I want!
(Ben exits behind his poster. The lights return to normal.)
JEFF: You spoiled everything! There aren't any dogs in this house!
(Jeff kicks Sandy, who yelps like a dog and dives under the bed.)
SANDY: You kicked me!
JEFF: Why did you do that?
SANDY: I was just fooling around and you kicked me.
JEFF: Come out of there.
SANDY: Not until you say you're sorry.
JEFF: I'm sorry.
SANDY: You don't really mean it.

JEFF: I said I was sorry.

SANDY: Get down on your knees and say it.

(Jeff gets down on his knees, reluctantly.)

JEFF: I'm sorry, I'm sorry, I'm sorry! Now, come on out!

(Just as Sandy starts out, the large door opens and Helen enters in reality. Sandy ducks back under the bed.)

HELEN: Jeff!

JEFF: *(Startled)* Huh?

HELEN: What are you doing?

JEFF: Nothing.

HELEN: What happened to your room?

JEFF: I'll clean it up.

HELEN: Never mind about that now, I didn't come in to talk about your room. Your Dad and I need to talk to you.

JEFF: What about?

HELEN: About all of us.

JEFF: Why?

HELEN: Just come on in. I think we'll be more comfortable in there.

(Helen indicates their room, Jeff pulls away.)

JEFF: I'm cleaning my room.

HELEN: That can wait.

JEFF: I'm busy.

HELEN: Jeff, we need to talk to you now.

JEFF: I just want you to leave me alone.

HELEN: We've left you alone too much, but now we need to talk. Daddy's waiting . . .

(Jeff pulls away and kicks the remains of the model, which has wound up on the floor.)

Your model? What happened to your model?

(Helen picks up the smashed model.)

JEFF: I broke it.

HELEN: How?

JEFF: I just did. I smashed it.

HELEN: But you were so careful.

JEFF: I made it and I can smash it if I want!

(Jeff lunges for it and Helen holds it out of his grasp.)

HELEN: Not after we worked so hard on it.

JEFF: What do you care?

HELEN: I care.

JEFF: *(Explodes)* Oh yeah, you care a lot, a whole damn lot!

(Helen, exhausted, sits on his bed.)

HELEN: I am so tired of fighting, Jeff. I don't want to fight with you.

JEFF: Then don't. Just go away and leave me alone!

HELEN: Jeff, do me a favor. Just sit here with me for one minute and let's not talk, let's not even think.

JEFF: Why?

HELEN: Please.

(Jeff *sits, sullen at first;* Helen *sighs. After a few seconds,* Helen *starts to say something;* Jeff *catches her eye and looks at his watch; she is silent.* Helen *reaches out to him and he slides closer to her. They relax in a moment of mutual comfort. In the silence,* Jeff's *anger is defused, for the moment.* Helen *holds him and her face betrays her sorrow, pain, and concern. After a beat,* Jeff *speaks.)*

JEFF: Are we on welfare?

HELEN: What?

JEFF: Did Dad lose his job?

HELEN: No. What ever gave you that idea?

JEFF: Just something I heard.

HELEN: Heard? Heard where?

JEFF: *(Nods toward the large door)* I heard you guys yelling something about a job.

HELEN: Oh, Jeff, I'm sorry; I didn't want you to hear about it like that. I wanted to tell you myself as soon as I was sure.

JEFF: Tell me what?

HELEN: I've been offered a job with a Community Mental Health Center in Portland.

JEFF: Portland?

HELEN: It's a good job, a very good job, and it could be important to both of us.

JEFF: You aren't going to take it, are you?

HELEN: I haven't decided yet.

JEFF: So that's what it's all about, I mean with you and Dad.

HELEN: What's happening with us has very little to do with this job. There are other things, much more serious things.

JEFF: You have to tell them no. Tell them you have to stay here with Dad and me.

HELEN: If I thought that would solve anything, I would. I'd turn it down in a second if I thought it would change things with us. Your Dad and I have problems, serious ones. They don't need to be your problems, but they do affect you, so we need to talk.

JEFF: I don't want to talk, anymore.

HELEN: If you would rather talk here, I'll go get your Dad and we'll talk right here in your room. (Helen *starts out.*)

JEFF: Why don't you get a job here?

HELEN: That wouldn't help.

JEFF: You could find a job here!

HELEN: That wouldn't change anything.

JEFF: There must be all sorts of jobs here that you could . . .

HELEN: IT'S NOT THE JOB!

JEFF: I don't want to talk to you.

HELEN: Jeff . . .

(Jeff *turns away.*)

JEFF: I won't listen to anything you say!

HELEN: Stop it!

(Jeff *claps his hands over his ears.*)

JEFF: I can't hear you.

HELEN: I want you to stop this right now!

(Sandy *sneaks out from under the bed and tries to slip out the door.* Helen *catches sight of him.*)

Sandy!

SANDY: *(Embarrassed)* Excuse me.

HELEN: I didn't know anyone was here.

JEFF: I said I was busy.

SANDY: I uhhhhhhh, gotta be going.

HELEN: *(To Jeff)* Why didn't you tell me?

SANDY: I'm sorry, Mrs. Stuart.

HELEN: Sandy, Jeff's Dad and I need to talk to him.

SANDY: Yeah, I know.

HELEN: I think you had better . . .

SANDY: I'm going right now, Mrs. Stuart.

JEFF: Can I at least say good-bye to him?

HELEN: Yes.

JEFF: Alone?

HELEN: Come into our room when you're done. Good-bye, Sandy.

SANDY: Bye, Mrs. Stuart. Uhhhh, Mrs. Stuart?

HELEN: Yes?

SANDY: I didn't mean to listen. I didn't hear much.

HELEN: Good-bye, Sandy. Say hello to your Mother for me. We'll be waiting, Jeff.

JEFF: I'll come when I'm ready.

(Helen *exits through the large door.* Sandy *picks up the dummy*

and starts toward the small door.)
SANDY: Bye, Jeff. See you tomorrow.
JEFF: Don't go.
SANDY: You heard what she said.
JEFF: Don't go!
SANDY: But, Jeff . . .
JEFF: Please, Sandy, just for a little while.
SANDY: They're waiting for you.
JEFF: I know.
SANDY: I feel weird.
JEFF: I'll go in there when I'm ready, not right now.
(Sandy sits and looks at Jeff. There is an awkward moment between them. Sandy looks at the door and then at his watch.)
SANDY: When do you think you'll be ready, Jeff?
JEFF: Something's got to happen. Something big, something so she won't take that job.
SANDY: Didn't you listen? She said it wasn't the job.
JEFF: Something to make them stop fighting.
SANDY: Like what?
JEFF: Like if something happened to me. Like if I got hit by a truck or something.
(Jeff jumps up, makes a wailing sound, grabs the dummy, and runs around the room. He dumps the dummy face down on the desk and lights begin a gradual change as he moves into fantasy. Sandy does not join the fantasy as quickly.)
SANDY: Jeff?
JEFF: Doctor, we have a very serious case here, a very serious case.
SANDY: Jeff . . .
JEFF: I said, Doctor we have a serious case here, a very serious case.
SANDY: I gotta go home.
JEFF: Please, Sandy! We have a serious case here.
(Sandy reluctantly crosses to the desk, which has become an operating table, and joins in.)
SANDY: Name?
JEFF: Jeff Stuart.
SANDY: Age?
JEFF: Eleven.
SANDY: Pulse?
JEFF: Weak!
SANDY: Heartbeat?

(Jeff *listens at the dummy's chest.*)
JEFF: Going, going, GONE!
SANDY: EMERGENCY!
 (*Both boys pound frantically on the dummy's chest.*)
 Hold it!
JEFF: What is it?
SANDY: It's started again. He's better now.
(Sandy *tries to leave the fantasy,* Jeff *pulls him back.*)
JEFF: No, we have to operate!
SANDY: Operate?
JEFF: OPERATE! Knife!
(Jeff *holds up an imaginary knife.* Sandy *assumes the role of the Doctor.* Jeff *slaps the knife into his hand.*)
SANDY: Knife!
 (Sandy *mimes the operation,* Jeff *makes sound effects.* Sandy *opens the "patient."*)
 Oh, gross!
JEFF: Look at his guts.
SANDY: All twisted up.
JEFF: Look at his liver.
SANDY: That's disgusting.
JEFF: He's losing a lot of blood!
SANDY: TRANSFUSION!
 (Sandy *stands with one arm raised and his hand cupped, like a plasma bottle.* Jeff *jabs* Sandy's *other arm at the dummy's arm.*)
 Glub, glub, glub . . .
 (Sandy *slowly closes his hand as though the bottle were emptying.*)
 We saved him again; he's better now!
(Sandy *tries again to leave the fantasy;* Jeff *won't let him.*)
JEFF: No! The parents have to be notified.
SANDY: (*Dropping the fantasy*) Jeff, this isn't going to help.
JEFF: Sandy, we have got to call the parents!
 (Jeff *crosses to the phone, picks up the receiver and hands it to* Sandy.)
 Tell them to come right away!
 (Jeff *makes* Sandy *take it.*)
 Ring! Ring!
(*Lights come up on posters;* Ben *and* Helen *are seen each holding a phone receiver.*)
BEN and HELEN: Hello.

JEFF: *(To* Sandy*)* Tell them!

SANDY: This is the hospital! We have your son here. You'd better come right away.

BEN and HELEN: Oh, my God!

(Posters swing open and Ben *and* Helen *enter the scene. They each take a chair and establish a waiting room.* Jeff *crosses to them,* Sandy *hangs back and watches.)*

JEFF: Mr. and Mrs. Stuart?

HELEN: Is he going to be all right?

JEFF: Too soon to tell.

BEN: Is he going to make it?

JEFF: That all depends.

BEN and HELEN: On what?

JEFF: On what you do now. We've done everything that medical science can do for him. Now, you take him home and take good care of him. He needs rest and peace and QUIET!

(Jeff crosses to dummy and picks it up, he gives one end to Sandy *and both boys race around the room like an ambulance. They dump the dummy on the bed.)*

SANDY: *(Out of the fantasy)* Jeff, I'm going now.

JEFF: You can't; this is the best part!

(Ben and Helen *rise and cross to the bed. They kneel on either side of it.* Jeff *takes the two chairs and places them near the bed.* Jeff *and* Sandy *sit on the backs of the chairs with their feet on the seat, overlooking the scene. In this scene, everyone treats the dummy as* Jeff.*)*

HELEN: Jeff, Jeff, this is your Mother.

BEN: Son, we're right here.

SANDY: He seems to be in a coma.

JEFF: But he can still hear you.

BEN: You've got to get well, son.

SANDY: So, he gets well and everybody lives happily ever . . .

(Sandy starts off the chair, Jeff *pulls him back.)*

JEFF: Not yet.

BEN: How do you feel son?

HELEN: Where does it hurt?

BEN: Can you hear us?

SANDY: No, he can't! His ears are filled with wax!

JEFF: Yes, he can! Go on!

HELEN: We promise things will change.

BEN: We'll do anything.

SANDY: Get him some soup! Get him a comic book!

JEFF: No, don't. Keep talking.

BEN: From now on, we'll be a family again.

JEFF: He's starting to come 'round.

SANDY: Still looks out of it to me.

HELEN: We'll all stay together, right here, we promise.

JEFF: He's definitely beginning to come 'round.

HELEN: If only we'd listened to each other.

BEN: If only we'd taken more time. If only your Mother had paid more attention.

HELEN: If only your Father had been home more.

SANDY: There they go again.

JEFF: Hey, he's back in a coma!

BEN: *(To* Helen*)* This is all your fault, you know.

HELEN: My fault? Why is it always my fault?

JEFF: Will you look at your son?

HELEN: At least I tried, I helped him with his model and that's more than I can say for you.

BEN: Oh yeah, well, I would have helped him, if you'd just given me a chance!

JEFF: He's dying!

HELEN: I can't talk to you, you're impossible!

BEN: I'm impossible? You're impossible!

(They both storm off and exit through their posters. Jeff and Sandy sit, looking at the patient for a long beat. Sandy jumps down and begins to march around the bed singing the "Funeral March.")

SANDY: Dum dum dee dum, Dum dee dum dee dum dum dum.

JEFF: Cut it out, Sandy.

(The phone rings. Sandy continues. The phone rings again. Jeff makes no move to answer it. The phone rings again.)

SANDY: Jeeze, Jeff, doesn't anyone around here ever answer the phone?

(Sandy answers the phone.)

Hello? Stuarts' residence . . . Oh, hi, Mom . . . Yeah, this is me . . . Obviously, I'm still here if I answered the phone . . . No, what time is it? . . . Aw, do I have to? . . . Yeah, I know . . . Yeah, I know . . . Yeah, I know . . . Okay, right away . . . Yeah, I know! Bye.

(Sandy hangs up and turns to Jeff.)

I gotta go. I have an appointment with the orthodontist.

JEFF: Orthodontist?

SANDY: I hate it when my Mom makes me dentist appointments during vacations. I don't even get to get out of school.

JEFF: Do you have to go?

SANDY: Yeah.

JEFF: Can't you tell her you're sick or something?

SANDY: Then she'd just make me come home and go to bed.

JEFF: Can't you tell her I'm sick?

SANDY: She'd be afraid I'd catch it, she'd still make me come home.

JEFF: Can I come with you?

SANDY: To the orthodontist?

JEFF: Sandy, I need you to stay with me, just five more minutes.

SANDY: What good would it do? Jeff, you can't change anything by not talking to them.

(Jeff *turns away.*)

Things will be better when it's over.

JEFF: When what's over?

SANDY: After you've talked to them.

JEFF: Are you sure?

SANDY: No. Bye, Jeff. See you tomorrow.

JEFF: Yeah.

SANDY: *(On his way out)* Hey, take it easy.

JEFF: Okay.

(Sandy *exits,* Jeff *turns away.* Jeff *sees the dummy and runs after him.*)

Hey, Sandy, just a minute, you forgot . . .

(Jeff *exits through the small door, but he returns immediately dragging the dummy behind him.*)

Damn!

(Jeff *dumps the dummy on the floor and looks at the large door, he paces back and forth across the room. On each pass, he kicks the dummy out of the way.*)

Can't feel that, can you?

(He *continues to kick the dummy.*)

Or that! Or that! You can't feel anything!

(After one last savage kick, Jeff *picks the dummy up in his arms and hugs it tightly. He places it tenderly on the bed.* Jeff *crosses to the large door. It is the longest walk he has ever made. He opens the door but stands in the doorway and looks into the next room.*)

What are you doing?

BEN'S VOICE: Packing.

JEFF: Another business trip?

BEN'S VOICE: Not this time, son.

(Jeff *turns away and steps back into his room.*)

BEN'S VOICE: Jeff, come back in here.

JEFF: I don't want to!

BEN'S VOICE: I'll get your Mother. She's making coffee. You wait right there.

(Jeff *stands near the door for a moment and then bolts into his parents' room. He returns to his room immediately with a suitcase.*)

Hey, what are you doing?

(Ben *enters and faces* Jeff. Jeff *holds the suitcase defiantly.*)

Why are you packing?

BEN: I've got to get out of here and let things settle down for a while.

(Jeff *drops the case on the floor, falls to his knees and begins pulling articles of clothing out of the case.*)

JEFF: You can't take these, they're dirty. I'll wash them for you!

(Jeff *throws a handful of clothing on the floor.*)

BEN: Hey!

JEFF: Can't take these, they've got holes in them.

BEN: What are you doing?

JEFF: Can't take these, they're too old. Just rags! Can't take rags!

BEN: Easy, Jeff.

(Jeff *rises with the case and dumps the rest on the floor.*)

JEFF: You can't take them! They belong here!

(Jeff *hurls the empty suitcase to the ground.*)

BEN: For God's sake, Jeff!

JEFF: You can't leave! We've got to all stay here, together!

(Ben *reaches out to* Jeff.)

BEN: Let me talk to you!

(Jeff *pulls away viciously.*)

JEFF: Don't touch me!

BEN: Oh, God, Jeff!

JEFF: And don't you DARE cry!

BEN: Please, try to understand.

JEFF: Understand what?

BEN: Your Mother and I fight all the time, you must have heard us!

JEFF: I just turn up the T.V. and I don't hear anything.

BEN: That doesn't mean it isn't happening.

JEFF: I don't have to hear this!

(Jeff *starts to try to leave.* Ben *stops him.*)

BEN: Yes, you do! Now, sit down.

(Ben *sits him on the bed.*)

It's happening and it has been happening for years, and you know it!

JEFF: No, I don't!

BEN: Yes, you do! There hasn't been peace or quiet or comfort in this house for a long time, and you know that, too.

JEFF: How do you know what I know?

(Helen *enters and stands in the doorway with two coffee cups.*)

BEN: We can't go on like this, any of us. It has to stop sometime. Now, I know how you feel but . . .

JEFF: You don't know what I feel!

HELEN: Jeff, honey, please listen to us.

JEFF: Mom, ask him not to go!

(Ben *and* Helen *look at each other. She can't do this and they both know it.*)

BEN: Jeff, about a week ago, I moved into a hotel, just temporarily, until I could find an apartment.

JEFF: Is that where you've been sleeping?

BEN: Yes.

HELEN: *(Astonished)* You knew?

JEFF: I've seen you go every night.

BEN: *(To* Helen*)* I knew we shouldn't have done it this way, we should have told him when I first left.

HELEN: Ben . . .

JEFF: But every morning you'd be back for breakfast.

BEN: *(To* Helen*)* I told you this wouldn't work.

HELEN: All right, Ben! *(To* Jeff*)* Why didn't you say something?

JEFF: Why didn't you?

HELEN: I still hoped that we could work things out. We were seeing a counselor and I thought if we could just solve some of the . . .

BEN: It was a dumb thing for us to do and we're sorry.

HELEN: *(Angrily to* Ben*)* I thought it was best, Ben!

JEFF: I can help!

HELEN: No, Jeff there's nothing you can do.

JEFF: I can help around the house more. I can be quieter. I can stay out of the way more.

HELEN: You are not responsible for this in any way.

JEFF: From now on, I'll clean up my room. I won't play the T.V. loud or the stereo . . .

HELEN: Jeff . . .

JEFF: Just tell me what I did wrong and I'll fix it; I will!

BEN: Jeff, you are the one really good thing in our lives. You were never the problem.

HELEN: That's right, honey.

BEN: What's happening here is between your Mother and me. It's not your fault.

JEFF: So, why are you doing this?

HELEN: It's complicated . . . there are so many reasons.

JEFF: Like what?

HELEN: Things we thought we wanted when we got married, just don't seem to be the things we want now.

JEFF: What things?

BEN: Jeff, I need . . . want, your Mother to be the kind of wife she just can't be to me anymore. And she wants . . . needs, things from me that I just can't give her.

JEFF: I don't understand.

BEN: Sometimes, adults have to make decisions all their own. Now, they might not sound like good reasons to you but . . .

JEFF: You are changing everything in my whole life and you can't even give me one good reason why?

BEN: We can't keep living this way, Jeff!

JEFF: Because you fight? So what?

HELEN: It isn't only the fighting, Jeff.

JEFF: So, just stop! Stop fighting! Everything would be okay if you'd just . . .

BEN: It's why we fight.

JEFF: *(Very belligerent)* Oh, yeah? Why?

BEN: *(Blurts it out)* We just don't love each other anymore.

(Helen *is shaken by this.*)

HELEN: Ben.

BEN: *(Realizing it himself for the first time)* That's it, isn't it, Helen?

HELEN: I have never heard you say that before.

BEN: That's what's really wrong, isn't it?

HELEN: I don't know.

(Helen *crosses away from him.*)

BEN: Don't you?

HELEN: If we could just solve some of the problems.

BEN: *(Simply)* Helen, do you love me?

HELEN: I don't think we should talk about that here.

BEN: I do.

HELEN: But Jeff . . .

BEN: That's why we have to. Do you love me?

HELEN: There are things I love about you.

BEN: That's not what I . . .

HELEN: I know what you asked me.

BEN: And?

HELEN: *(Inaudible)* No.

BEN: Helen?

JEFF: Mom?

HELEN: No.

(There is a long pause.)

JEFF: Will you get a divorce?

HELEN: *(After a beat)* Probably.

JEFF: And what I think doesn't matter?

HELEN: It matters very much.

JEFF: And if I don't want you to?

BEN: I'm sorry, Jeff.

JEFF: You don't care.

BEN: That's the hard part, we do care, maybe not enough, maybe not about the same things, but we do care.

JEFF: But you're getting a divorce.

BEN: Not from you.

(Ben tries to touch Jeff, who pulls away.)

This day, Jeff, this day is the hardest. Things will be better for all of us when this day is over.

JEFF: And then what happens to me?

HELEN: You'll stay here with me for now and then we'll . . .

JEFF: I mean, who do I live with? Will I have to go to Portland? What if I don't want to go? Will I have to leave all my friends?

BEN: We'll settle all that later.

JEFF: Who decides what happens to me?

HELEN: We all will, together.

JEFF: How do I know you aren't lying to me again?

HELEN: Lying?

JEFF: What do you think all that sneaking around was?

BEN: *(Very firmly)* Just a minute, sport, we may not have told you everything that was going on, but we never meant to lie to you.

HELEN: And when I tried to talk to you, you wouldn't listen. You just turned away and tuned me out.

BEN: This is a hard time for all of us. All of us, Jeff.

JEFF: From now on, will you tell me things?

BEN: Yes.

HELEN: From now on, will you listen?

JEFF: *(Softly)* I'll try.

HELEN: And so will we.

BEN: We've got two whole months to figure this Portland thing out, so let's just take it a step at a time. Okay?

JEFF: Do I have a choice?

BEN: Come on, Jeff. I think you'll like my apartment. It has a room for you, and an elevator, and a pool . . .

JEFF: Can I have a dog?

(Both Ben and Helen laugh.)

BEN: We'll see.

JEFF: Will you ever decide to get back together again?

(They are caught off-guard and hesitate.)

BEN: I don't think so.

JEFF: Mom?

HELEN: No.

(There is an awkward pause.)

BEN: Well, if I'm going to get moved in, I'd better get with it. I still have to check out of the hotel and take my things from there . . . *(He checks his watch.)* I'd better get with it. I'll come back for this stuff, Helen, okay?

(Helen nods. Ben takes a card out of his pocket and writes on it.)

Jeff, let me write down the address of the apartment for you. Come see me anytime. I've got a phone, so just call and I'll come for you.

JEFF: *(Turns away from him)* I can take the bus.

BEN: Anytime, Jeff, I'll come for you anytime . . .

(No response from Jeff)

I'll call you.

(He stands there for a moment, uncertain.)

Jeff?

(He holds out his arms, Jeff crosses to him and hugs him. Before the hug is really completed, Jeff pulls away.)

JEFF: See ya.

(Jeff turns away. Ben looks at Helen, she is looking away.)

BEN: Helen? . . . Take care. *(He starts out.)*

HELEN: You too.

(Ben exits through the small door. Both Jeff and Helen look toward the door as we hear Ben's footsteps disappearing. A final door shuts offstage and the sound shudders through Helen's body.)

HELEN: *(After a beat to compose herself)* You okay?

JEFF: *(Shrugs)* You?

HELEN: Lousy.

JEFF: Me, too.

HELEN: Well, at least we're lousy together.

JEFF: Yeah. *(After a beat)* I hate this.

HELEN: I know. I hate it with you.

(Jeff turns to her and looks away. Helen moves toward him slightly and speaks from her own need for comfort as much as his.)

Jeff, what do you do when you feel rotten? What do you do when you're really depressed?

JEFF: I don't know . . . Nothing . . . Sometimes I take a walk and just look around for something I like. Something like a leaf or a piece of glass or something, and I just look at it for a while.

HELEN: *(This is a risky question for her.)* Want to take a walk?

JEFF: *(His voice says "yes," his body says "no.")* Okay.

HELEN: I'll get the house key.

(Helen exits to her room. Jeff crosses to the desk and picks up the card, he looks at it and then at the small door. He puts the card in his pocket. Finding release in activity, he gathers up Ben's clothes and puts them in the suitcase. Helen enters and stands in the doorway.)

JEFF: After we get back, I'll take these over to Dad's.

(Jeff indicates the dummy.)

And then I'll take this over to Sandy's.

HELEN: Okay.

(Jeff starts out the door, Helen waits, unsure. Jeff turns and really sees her for the first time since Ben's exit.)

JEFF: Let's go, Mom.

(He holds out his hand to her. She takes it and they exit out the small door. There is music. Lights dim to black.)

(Curtain)

Production Notes

• *Off-stage Argument*

I have deliberately not written specific dialogue for the off-stage argument. In an earlier draft I did try to sketch it out, but I felt it tended to limit and constrain the actors, and sounded artificial.

It is my intention that the argument should be created improvisationally by the actors and the director, and that the improvisational quality be maintained in production.

Some guidelines might be helpful:

It should be a real argument, and not random words or sounds. The actors should decide what specific circumstances and previous action have led Ben and Helen to this particular moment and each should have specific and conflicting motivations and objectives.

The dynamics of the argument must be modulated to work with the primary action on stage. Off-stage sounds must never overwhelm what is happening on stage, but should underscore action, and provoke reactions from Jeff and Sandy. At the same time, there must be variety, build, and flow to the off-stage sounds.

When Ben and Helen enter a scene on stage in "reality" they must bring some of their previous off-stage actions with them. When they enter a scene in "fantasy" they are primarily projections of Jeff's thoughts, fears, hopes, and feelings.

• *Treatment of the Fantasies*

Perhaps the most important direction for my intention concerning the fantasies is to keep in mind that they are grounded in Jeff's needs in real life. It is this relevance to reality, rather than a departure from the real world, that gives these scenes their power.

Every director will interpret this in a different way, and will make his or her own stylistic choices. This is as it should be. I feel that light and sound can be important elements in introducing and underscoring these scenes. It must be clear that they are somehow different visually, rhythmically, and emotionally from the scenes "in reality," but they must move the dramatic action of the play forward, rather than divert it.

If Jeff's motivations and objectives are the springboards for fantasy, then the best stylistic choices can be made.

• *A Final Note*

The words and actions of this play provide all the essentials for production; but much of the depth and intensity of this script must be found between the lines, in subtext, and in silence.

The story yields only the uppermost layer and there is much to be discovered and created by actors and directors. I urge you to be bold in your emotional choices, to be clear and specific with the development of all relationships, and to bring the same emotional intensity to both the words of the text and the thoughts and feelings which remain unspoken.

AFTERWORD

1. As an older friend, what advice might you give to Jeff about his parents' decision to divorce? Write, tape, or roleplay a short monologue that would help Jeff cope with the changes in his life.

2. After reading the stage directions at the beginning of the play and the production notes at the end, develop the sound effects for the opening of *Doors*, up until Ben makes his first entrance. Tape your sound effects, and play the tape for the class.

3. In groups, prepare a dramatization of the first breakfast scene (page 352). Discuss the tone of voice, physical gestures, and facial expressions each actor should use. Rehearse the scene until you are comfortable with the dialogue and timing; then present it to your class. What made each group's presentation different? Which presentation was most effective? Why?

4. a) There are times during the play when Jeff seems to lose control. Choose two such moments from the play. Present your examples to a classmate and explain why you chose them. After you have compared examples and answered each other's questions, discuss why Jeff might be having difficulty maintaining control. Share your ideas with the class.

   b) Imagine a situation (or recall one from experience) in which someone loses control in a family setting. Write a story about it. When you have finished a draft of your story, you might ask a classmate to read it and give you suggestions about its strengths and weaknesses.

5. In a group, assign parts and read aloud the scene in which Jeff's parents describe their problems to a marriage counsellor. Taking the role of the counsellor, decide what Helen and Ben seem to want for themselves, how they see each other, and why their marriage isn't working. Present your findings to the class in a chart or report.

6. Sandy describes how his parents argue every year during the trip to the fair. With a classmate discuss what, if anything, you think Sandy's description adds to the play.

7. Imagine that you are a newspaper editor. You have just seen the play *Doors* and have decided that you will write about

FRESH PERSPECTIVE MARCH 1990 4

EDITORIAL

Task Force Set to Include Youth

It seemed that at 12:01am on January 1, 1990 I didn't feel much different. I suppose through the 80's the talk of the new decade was something that was an excuse or reason or whatever to not get anything done at that particular moment. You know what its like avoiding something. We've all done it.

Avoiding things because the net decade was on the horizon may have been a cop out but it was widely used. The world collectively just sort of took it easy. Perhaps the turbulent 60's and the "Me" hedonism of the 70's had tired everyone out for awhile: especially the ever aging Yuppie Generation now older than ever.

But as the 80's came to a close there seemed to be a new feeling around the globe. Young people stood up and spoke out in Beijing. They stood up, these young people, in Eastern Europe and showed their discontent. They stood up on dance floors across the world to a new musical eruption from the heart of the yearning of young people unsatisfied with what had been left them and how they were treated.

But back to the original point and the feeling of indifference on that Holiday. I think that I came to the realization that it could not be a new decade or a new time that would change the ills of the world. It would have to be me, and you and everyone else that have the need to stand up and voice the concerns of our increasingly polluted and volitile world.

The steps that our global brothers and sisters took, toward change, was historic. But it takes only a moment to realize that those students in China were gunned down after their brave revolution; that the unrest continues in Eastern Europe over the pace that the new democratic regimes are taking on change; that the racial discrim ination in North America is still prevalent in what we feel is a liberal society.

Change may have begun but it is a mere spark. Only you and I can be the fuel for the necessary fire.

By James Cudmore

Within the past couple of years, chances are that you've heard of the YOUTH TASK FORCE. Hearing of it is one thing, but knowing what it is, is something completely different.

The YOUTH TASK FORCE (Y.T.F.) is an organization completely dedicated to youth and is the representative of youth at the municipal legislative level.

It is comprised of different people from all different districts and business sectors of Metro Toronto.

One of the Y.T.F.'s major goals is to further youth's image in Metro and deal with any problems youth face in any way they can. Metro Councilor Brian Ashton is chairman of the Y.T.F. "We thought it important to emphasize and portray youth in a positive way, in a way youth feel comfortable with."Says Ashton."we want to raise the issues of youth in a positive way."

But why?

"You see, society defines what youth issues should be, we want to see what youth perceive their issues to be. We want to change legislation and social issues to focus on youth."

Councilor Ashton also sees the youth gang problem to still be a major issue in Metro. He feels there are reasons for this gang problem that should be explored. "We're studying why we have gang problems and also what causes youth problems. Is it poor parenting, the school system or something else."

One way of accomplishing this study would be to go where youth congregate. "I want to gain gang confidence, so they can tell us privately and individually what the problems are and why they are doing the things that they're doing," he continued. "We are looking at conducting mall sessions with youth. There is a radio station interested in broadcasting a two hour mall session."

The Y.T.F was first conceived two years ago when the youth gang problem first started making news. So if the Y.T.F. has been in operation for two years, why haven't we seen the results that would and are expected?

Councillor Brian Ashton: Head of Metro's Youth Task Force

"We're working hard. We've fallen behind schedule because we want to do it properly,"says Ashton. "It has been slow but we are studying the kaleidoscope of problems facing youth today and also trying to develop a means that would encourage youth to take part in the Y.T.F."

The means by which the Y.T.F. hopes to entice youth to participate is by a series of 12 consultation sessions with one Y.T.F member talking with youth about the problems of today. Issues like drugs, sex, family, gangs and criminal activities will be discussed.

"When we start discussing issues, youth might want to attend these sessions and participate," says Ashton.

But again why is it taking so long to organize these sessions?

"This is the first committee of it's kind in Metro's history," Ashton replies. "It's like jumping into a pool when you don't know how deep it is. We need and want to feel this out."

The major problem facing the Y.T.F. is getting youth to realize that there are organizations out there which want to hear what youth has to say. "We're looking for a celebrity who feels positively about youth, and who is also a celebrity because of youth, to be a spokesperson for the Y.T.F. in an information/advertising campaign."

"Who wants to see a broken down hippie like me!" he adds "We don't want to patronize youth."

It is safe to say that the youth of Toronto does not want to patronized. "We want youth to know that we are accessible. We want an open door policy."

It seems that the Y.T.F. is truly concerned with youth, but is this a singular phenomenon among Canada's governments? Well, not to discourage you, but, it is.

"To the federal government," says Ashton, "youth is not an issue, they've cut spending on youth programs and we want to change this. We hope to go national and then onto the U.N."

As uninvolved as the provincial and federal governments are, the Y.T.F. is attempting to help youth along with a host of social workers, teachers,and guidance counsellors. It is these programs and avenues of help as well as your parents that the Task Force wishes you to remember when you need to talk to someone about problems.

(James Cudmore is a Grade 12 Student at the A.I.S.P. School in North York)

Letter to the Editor

Hey, you!"

So, you think you got what it takes to be a big time journalist. Well here is your chance. Just call us at Youth Communication and we'll give training, computer time and all the enlightenment you could ever ask for. 592|9003. Or, don't be shy and just com'on down after school some time. We're open until 5:00pm 312 Adelaide St. West.

Don't want to be a journalist. Well that's okay with us. There's tons o' stuff you can get involved with like Youth 2000 or our Youth Arts Directory. We are here to help you hear and be heard. So just come on down or call. Its up to you to take charge of your future.

Dear Fresh Perspective,
I'd like to respond to your editorial or letters. I've had my share of experiences with a lethargic audience and know how valuable feedback can be. So...

The articles I love in your paper are those that tackle social concern specific to Toronto's youth. ie. violence in the schools, condom machines in the schools, street kids, etc. The experience of youth growing up today in Toronto seems so alien to my experience (which wasn't long ago) that I'm intrigued by how they cope with such a rapidly changing world. As well, I'm always curious as to the reality of the situation. Is violence in the really a concern or is that just media hype?

As well, I'd like to see more on the changes happening in education. Toronto schools are making some great inovative changes in the traditional system. Tell me more! What do the students think? How do the universities feel about the students such changes produce?

What about a look into the future for today's youth what sort of jobs are they hoping for? What sort of world are they hoping for?

I think your doing a great job and at the risk of sounding like a cliche, keep up the good work.

Leslie Garret
Kids Toronto Associate Editor

(IF YOU HAVE ANY SUGGESTION, GRIPES OR ANY OTHER IDEAS THAT YOU'D LIKE TO TALK ABOUT, LET US KNOW. THE LETTER TO THE EDITOR IS NOT JUST A FORUM TO TELL US ABOUT THE PAPER BUT IT IS ALSO A WAY TO EXPRESS YOUR IDEAS TO AN EVER CHANGING WORLD)

divorce in your next editorial. Remember that divorce is a broad subject, but an editorial is short and to the point. Narrow your focus to a manageable topic, and be sure to present your own views on the subject.

Ask a classmate to read your editorial and comment on it. Does it present your views clearly? Are your points well supported? Would changes make the editorial more persuasive? Circulate your editorial to some of your classmates, and ask them to reply in the form of a "letter to the editor."

8. In a group, brainstorm some reasons why Zeder called her play *Doors*. Can you think of other titles for the play? Share your ideas with your class.

Glossary

Theatre, Television, Film, and Radio Terms

Act: One of the main divisions of a play.

Actor's notebook: A book an actor uses to help him or her to develop a particular role. The notebook contains the actor's lines and his or her ideas about how the lines should be spoken and what gestures and facial expressions should be used. See example page 274.

Adaptation: A literary work, such as a play, poem, short story, screenplay, or novel, rewritten in a different literary form.

Background (BG): In theatre, the very back of the set, which sometimes is painted to create the illusion of distance. In television and film, the area behind the actors that is farthest away from the camera lens but still clearly visible. In radio, background is created by reducing the volume of sound effects or dialogue to give an impression of distance.

Beat: A short pause in speech or action.

Camera angle: The height from which the camera photographs the action. A STRAIGHT or NORMAL SHOT, taken from eye level (a little more than one metre), is the camera height for most shots. A LOW ANGLE SHOT is taken from well below eye level. A HIGH ANGLE SHOT is taken from well above eye level.

Camera cues: In a television or film script, information that explains how the camera should be manipulated. See **camera angle, camera distance, camera movement, film transitions.**

Camera distance: The distance between the camera and the subject being photographed. See **closeup, medium shot, long shot.** The length of time the shot is held, extended (**E**) or medium length (**M**), may also be included in a script indicating the camera cues.

Camera movement: The way in which the camera is moved as the action is being photographed. See **dolly, pan, pull back to reveal, tilt.**

Centre stage: See **stage.**

Choral reading: An oral reading performed so that a group of people read the same lines at the same time in a chorus. It helps to develop a feeling for the flow of language and voice intonation. It can be developed as a two-part reading or a multi-part performance, with parts for solo speakers and parts for small groups.

Closeup (CU): The shot seems to have been taken a short distance from the subject. For example, the head and shoulders of an actor might be photographed so that they fill the frame. An EXTREME CLOSEUP is a detailed shot of a very small area. For example, just the eyes of an actor might fill the frame.

Credits, or opening and closing titles: The names of the writers, artists, and technicians listed at the beginning or end of a television program or a film.

Cue: A signal to indicate when some dialogue, action, lighting change, or sound effect is to take place.

Curtain: In stage productions, the curtain hides the stage from the audience's view. The play begins with the curtain's RISE and ends with its FALL. Sometimes the curtain is used to hide the stage between scenes or acts so that the set can be changed. The use of the curtain is less prevalent today than it once was.

Cut to: A transition in which one shot is immediately succeeded by the next shot without a break or blackout. It is the most common transition used in film and television.

Dissolve: In film or television, a transition created by overlapping two shots. As one shot fades out, the next shot fades in. At the midpoint of the dissolve, the two shots are on the screen at the same time.

Docudrama: A play that presents a fictionalized version of an actual event.

Dolly: A camera, mounted on a mobile platform, moves toward a subject (DOLLY IN) or away from it (DOLLY OUT).

Downstage: See stage.

Echo chamber: In radio, a room with sound-reflecting walls used to produce echo effects. Today this effect is generated electronically, not in a special room.

Establishing shot: A shot that indicates to the viewer what the setting is for the shots that follow it.

Exterior (EXT): A notation at the beginning of a scene indicating that the action takes place outside.

Fade: In radio, to decrease the volume of the sound gradually until it disappears.

Fade in: In television and film, a technique in which a dark screen slowly brightens and an image appears.

Fade out: In television and film, a technique in which a bright screen slowly darkens and the image disappears.

Fade up: In radio, to increase the volume of the sound gradually.

Feature, or full-length film: Any film with a running time of seventy-five minutes or more.

Film transitions: The techniques used to link shots together. See **cut to, dissolve, fade in, fade out.**

Flashback: The drama shifts back in time to show an episode that occurred in the past.

Frame: Each of the images on a strip of film. Motion pictures are typically projected at a rate of twenty-four frames per second. Frame also refers to everything that can be seen inside the "frame" created by the camera lens.

Freeze frame: All the action is stopped or "frozen" onscreen. A freeze frame is often used at the end of a movie or television program when the credits are being shown.

Houselights: The lights that illuminate all of the theatre (the house), including the audience, before and after the play and during intermissions.

Interior (INT): A notation at the beginning of a scene indicating that the action takes place indoors.

Long shot (LS): A shot in which the camera is placed far away from the subject.

Medium shot (MS): The camera distance midway between short and long shots. Filming normally uses medium shots.

Montage: A film editing technique. A sequence of quick shots conveys a particular idea or feeling. For example, an editor might blend shots of a tree in summer, fall, and winter to suggest the passing of time.

Narration: See **voice over.**

Off, offstage, off the set (OS): In theatre, the areas immediately behind or to the sides of the stage, out of the audience's sight. In film and television, the area immediately beyond what is shown by the camera. In radio, a similar effect is created by reducing the volume of voices and sound effects so that they seem to come from a distance.

Over: See **voice over.**

Pan shot: The camera in a fixed position pivots to one side and/or to the other side. If you turn your head to one side to see something and then slowly move it across to the other side, you'll know what a pan shot looks like.

Pantomime, or mime: Drama without words. The actors convey meaning through facial expression, gesture, and movement.

Photomontage: By combining parts of different photographs, or by superimposing parts of photos, a single photographic image is created. In film, the juxtaposition or superimposition of several shots can form a single image. See also **montage.**

Point of view (POV): The scene is filmed as if it were seen through one character's eyes.

Properties, or props: Objects that help to create a belief in the drama; they are symbols of things that are important in the drama. A prop helps build the power of a dramatic moment.

Pull back to reveal: The camera is moved away from the subject to show some new element.

Reader's theatre: A staged reading of a script in which words and voices are given prominence over movement and action. The performers sit on stools facing the audience and are allowed to read directly from a script. They also use a few facial expressions and gestures to enhance the spoken words.

Scene: In a stage play, a subdivision of an act that presents a single action, setting, or dramatic situation. When scenes are not marked formally, the scene changes whenever a character enters or exits the stage. In film and television, a short series of shots taking place in one location and presenting a single action, setting, or dramatic situation. In radio, a single unified action, often separated from other scenes by sound effects.

Screenplay: A film or television script that includes descriptions of settings and actions as well as dialogue.

Scrim: In stage productions, a large, loose-woven piece of cloth that is hung to divide up the stage without using solid walls. When the scrim is lit from in front, it is opaque and resembles a wall. When lit from behind, it becomes transparent.

Script: The written form of a play. A script usually begins with a list of all the characters. It contains all the lines spoken by the actors, in order, and usually stage directions. A film or television script may include some or all of the camera cues.

Scripting: Writing the dialogue and stage directions that describe what the stage should look like, what special effects should be used, and how the actors should speak and move in a play.

Sequence: In film and television, a group of related shots.

Series: A number of radio or television programs or movies that usually feature a basic set of characters and situations, but different plots or stories.

Set: In television, film, and stage productions, the specially constructed area in which the drama takes place. The set may include real or imitation buildings, walls, rooms, furniture, or even outdoor scenery such as rocks and plant life.

Shot: A single piece of film exposed continuously without cuts. Shots may be as short as a second or as long as several minutes.

Shooting script: The written form of a play, divided into audio and visual parts, in which the audio part and the visual part support each other.

Slow motion: A technique in which the action is slowed down by filming at a faster rate than normal and then projecting the film at a normal rate.

Sound collage: A tape recording of a series of different sounds used to suggest a mood or theme.

Spotlight: An intense light with a narrow beam that can be used to illuminate a small part of the stage or set, leaving the rest in darkness.

Stage: The part of the theatre on which the drama is enacted. People who work in theatre use special terms to refer to different areas of the stage. DOWNSTAGE or DOWN refers to the front part of the stage, the part closest to the audience. UPSTAGE or UP refers to the back of the stage. STAGE RIGHT is the right-hand part of the stage from the actor's point of view, or the left-hand side if you're in the audience. STAGE LEFT is the side on the audience's right. The central portion of the stage is called CENTRE STAGE.

Stage directions: Information written into the script about how the actors should speak and move, and about what lighting and sound effects are required. See also **stage**.

Stage left: See **stage**.

Stage right: See **stage**.

Stock shot: Film taken from film archives or newsreel footage and inserted into a movie or television program.

Storyboard: A series of drawings that look like a comic strip without words, used to plan the scenes in a movie or television show.

Subtext: The attitudes and emotions that provide the reasons for the words and actions of the character. The subtext must be discovered by the actor; it is not part of the text.

Tableau: A short interval during a scene in which the actors freeze, and then resume action.

Tag: A short scene at the end of a teleplay, after the main plot has ended. Its purpose is to tie up any loose ends in the plot.

Teaser: A short scene at the beginning of a teleplay dramatizing a striking incident or action. Its purpose is to grab the audience's interest.

Telephoto lens: A lens that magnifies the image of a subject in the far distance.

Teleplay: A drama written for television.

Tight shot: A technique in which the camera moves in close to the subject. See **closeup.**

Tilt: A technique in which the camera is held in one place and tilted either up or down.

Upstage: See **stage.**

Videotaping: To create a videotape of a scene the following preparation is recommended:
- prepare a written or sketched series of visuals, or a "shot list ";
- prepare a shooting script that links the audio (text, music, sound effects) with the visual;
- edit the shooting script to ensure that each shot is completely described, the directions to the camera director are clear, and that the audio script supports and balances the visual script.

The technical team for this activity could include the camera operator(s), director, sound and lighting consultants, and set and prop designers.

Voice over (VO): In film or television, the narrator or a character speaks off-camera and describes the events or actions that are presented onscreen.

Wing: The areas to either side of a theatre stage, out of sight of the audience. The actors wait in the wings to hear the lines that cue them to come onstage.

Zoom: A shot in which a special camera lens is adjusted to make the subject appear larger (ZOOM IN) or smaller (ZOOM OUT).

Permission Credits